TEACHER'S MANUAL

Integrated Mathematics: Course I
Second Edition

(textbook by Isidore Dressler and Edward P. Keenan;
  revised by Ann Xavier Gantert and Marilyn Occhiogrosso)

AMSCO

When ordering this manual, please specify: *either* **N 481 T** or
TEACHER'S MANUAL / INTEGRATED MATHEMATICS: COURSE I, SECOND EDITION

AMSCO SCHOOL PUBLICATIONS, INC.
315 Hudson Street/New York, N.Y. 10013

AUTHORS OF THE TEACHER'S MANUAL (SECOND EDITION)

Edward P. Keenan
Curriculum Associate, Mathematics
East Williston Union Free School District
East Williston, New York

Ann Xavier Gantert
Department of Mathematics
Nazareth Academy
Rochester, New York

Marilyn Occhiogrosso
Former Assistant Principal, Mathematics
Erasmus Hall High School, New York City

CONSULTANT

SAT Preparation Exercises

Peter Duffy
Chairman of Mathematics
White Plains High School
White Plains, New York

ISBN 0–87720–267–2

About the Teacher's Manual

This manual, paralleling the organization of the text, provides:

- a suggested time frame for teaching the course.

- aims for each chapter.

- commentary on each instructional section of the text.

- leading questions to stimulate classroom discussion.

- suggestions to maximize the effectiveness of specific model problems and exercises.

- a variety of approaches to promote flexibility in problem solving.

- techniques for dealing with difficulties that students often encounter.

- more challenging aspects of topics in the text.

- supplementary material that reflects current thinking in mathematics education.

- suggestions for promoting dimensional analysis.

- computer activities for both original programming and tutorial practice.

- a set of SAT preparation exercises for each chapter.

- questions to form the basis for chapter tests.

- an answer key for the text, the SAT preparation, and the suggested test items.

Contents

SUGGESTED TIME OUTLINES

Since teaching from a new text can create time problems during the first year, a timetable is offered to assist you in planning your work. In order to focus effectively on material that is unique to this course, time considerations may require reducing coverage of topics that are largely review material, or topics that are optional at this level. Thus, as noted, certain sections may be dealt with quickly, and others omitted.

In addition to the time outline for Course I, an outline for Course II is provided for reference, so that coverage of topics may be seen in the context of the ongoing program.

Course I

CHAPTER	TOPIC	TIME (in days)
1	**Numbers, Sets, and Operations** Discuss operations in general; skip Sections 1–9 and 1–10; review the other sections quickly, or pretest and skip them.	5–6
2	**Problem Solving** Present the strategies; use the exercises throughout the course.	6–7
3	**Algebraic Expressions and Open Sentences** Pretest, but cover this material.	6–7
4	**Simple Equations and Problems** Pretest, but cover this material.	5–6
5	**Introducing Logic** Cover the entire chapter.	5–6
6	**Using Logic** Cover the entire chapter.	10–12
7	**Signed Numbers** Pretest; possibly skip this chapter.	2–4
8	**Operations With Monomials** Skip Sections 8–8 and 8–9 (review).	6–7
9	**Operations With Polynomials** Skip Section 9–7 (optional).	6–8
10	**First-Degree Equations and Inequalities in One Variable** Cover the entire chapter.	10–12
11	**Geometry** Cover the entire chapter.	15–17
12	**Ratio and Proportion** Cover the entire chapter.	7–8
13	**Special Products and Factoring** Cover the entire chapter.	8–10
14	**Fractions, and First-Degree Equations and Inequalities Involving Fractions** Limit work to monomial denominators.	10–12
15	**Probability** Cover the entire chapter.	12–14
16	**Statistics** Skip Section 16–3 (review).	8–10
17	**The Coordinate Plane** Skip Section 17–13 (optional).	12–14
18	**Systems of Open Sentences in Two Variables** Cover the entire chapter.	7–8
19	**The Real Numbers** Cover the entire chapter.	5–6
20	**Quadratic Equations** Skip Sections 20–4 and 20–7 (optional).	5–6

TOTAL DAYS   150–180

Course II

CHAPTER	TOPIC	TIME (in days)
1	**Introducing Geometry** Cover the entire chapter. Familiar material can be reviewed quickly, but students should be aware from the start that Course II requires precision in definitions, notation, etc.	8–10
2	**Logic** If necessary, skip Section 2–12 and all exercises in Section 2–13 that make use of the Laws of Simplification, Conjunction and Addition.	12–14
3	**Proving Statements in Geometry** Spend no more than three days on Sections 3–1 to 3–4.	10–12
4	**Triangle Congruence and Inequalities** Cover the entire chapter.	14–16
5	**Perpendicular and Parallel Lines, Angle Sums, and More Congruences** Cover the entire chapter.	12–14
6	**Quadrilaterals** Cover the entire chapter.	8–10
7	**Similarity; Special Triangles** Cover the entire chapter.	10–12
8	**Trigonometry of the Right Triangle** Cover the entire chapter.	4–6
9	**Coordinate Geometry** Cover the entire chapter.	10–12
10	**Quadratic Equations** Review Sections 10–1 to 10–3 briefly. Spend only as much time on Section 10–4 as is necessary for students to understand the derivation of the quadratic formula. Sections 10–9 and 10–10 are optional.	15–17
11	**Locus With and Without Coordinate Geometry** Cover the entire chapter. Present locus proof in Section 11–3 and locus derivation of parabola equations in Section 11–7 to more able students if time allows. With average students, derive only the simplest parabola equations.	8–10
12	**Transformation Geometry and Coordinates** Section 12–6 is enrichment, to be covered as time allows. Cover the rest of the chapter.	8–10
13	**Probability** Review Sections 13–1 to 13–3 quickly and cover the rest of the sections carefully.	13–14
14	**Mathematical Systems** Cover Sections 14–1 to 14–3 carefully. Sections 14–4 to 14–7 are optional; cover as time allows.	5–8
15	**Operations With Fractions** Cover the entire chapter.	6–10
16	**Constructions** Constructions may be taught as they relate to the other chapters. Allow a few days to present some challenging problems.	3–5

TOTAL DAYS 146–180

Course III

CHAPTER	TOPIC	TIME (in Days)

Note: Sections recommended for review may treat topics in greater depth than in earlier courses.

1 **The Rational Numbers** — 3–8
Review Sections 1–1 and 1–6 through 1–10. Sections 1–2 and 1–3 cover the notation ∀ and ∃, which is required; further discussion of quantification is enrichment. Section 1–4 is largely enrichment, but serves to clarify the required topic of Fields in Section 1–5.

2 **Rational Expressions** — 5–8
Review Sections 2–1 through 2–5 and 2–7. Section 2–6 is new work.

3 **Geometry of the Circle** — 9–11
Omit common tangents in Section 3–4. Constructions are optional. Emphasize applications rather than proofs of theorems.

4 **The Irrational Numbers and the Real Numbers** — 11–13
Cover Sections 4–1 through 4–5 quickly. Omit Section 4–6 entirely, teach only one method (the square-root algorithm or divide-and-average), or delay this topic until logarithms are taught. Note that the quadratic equation is covered more fully in Chapter 14.

5 **Transformation Geometry and Coordinates** — 2–5
Pretest this chapter and review only as needed.

6 **Relations and Functions** — 6–9
In Section 6–5, students must recognize a conic section, given its equation or its graph. The rest of Section 6–5 is enrichment.

7 **Functions and Transformation Geometry** — 7–9
Cover the entire chapter. In Section 7–5, mention the types of compositions but demonstrate only the Three-Line Reflection Theorem. Cover Section 7–6 quickly.

8 **Trigonometric Functions** — 15–19
Cover the entire chapter. The right triangle may be omitted in Sections 8–1 and 8–3 if functions are to be introduced from the unit circle only. Omit Section 8–8. In Section 8–14, teach one method only.

9 **Trigonometric Graphs** — 9–11
Omit Section 9–8. In Section 9–10, omit the functions $y = \text{Arc sec } x$, $y = \text{Arc csc } x$, and $y = \text{Arc cot } x$.

10 **Exponential Functions** — 7–8
Cover the entire chapter.

11 **Logarithmic Functions** — 10–12
Omit Section 11–9. Emphasize the function concept and the laws, rather than the solution of complicated arithmetic problems by logarithms.

12 **Trigonometric Applications** — 11–14
Cover the entire chapter.

13 **Trigonometric Equations and Identities** — 14–18
Cover the entire chapter. Note that students are given a list of formulas on the Regents examination (see page 747).

14 **The Complex Numbers** — 10–12
Cover the entire chapter. The vector approach to complex numbers may be omitted from Sections 14–2, 14–3, and 14–4. Cover Section 14–6 quickly.

15 **Statistics** — 9–11
Cover the entire chapter. Section 15–2 is review material, and should be done quickly.

16 **Probability and the Binomial Theorem** — 8–10
Cover the entire chapter. Sections 16–1 and 16–2 are review, and should be done quickly.

TOTAL DAYS: 136–178

CHAPTER 1

Numbers, Sets, and Operations

Aims

- To review the basic operations in arithmetic and to introduce new operations with familiar sets of numbers.

- To show that operations exist in geometry and in sets as well as in arithmetic.

As the definition of binary operation is formalized and applied to arithmetic, geometry, and sets, the stage is set for integration of topics throughout the text.

1-1 THE BASIC OPERATIONS

How would you reply if a very young child asked "What is two"? A question such as this can be used to stimulate discussion at the beginning of this section. Students will find this a difficult question and answers will probably involve a display of two objects or some way of considering the idea of "how many" in a set of two objects. Discuss with students the use of numbers for counting as the first use of numbers in the history of humankind as well as in the lives of most individuals.

The familiar operations of addition, subtraction, multiplication, and division are reexamined in the light of the formal definition of a binary operation. This definition requires that we consider the important ideas of *order* and *uniqueness.*

Beginning with this definition, students see how letters are used in general statements. Some use of letters is made throughout this introductory work, preceding the definition of variable in Chapter 3, where the formal study of algebra begins.

1-2 THE NUMBERS OF ARITHMETIC

While fractions and decimals are used in this section, we do not present the formal development of rational numbers and their properties until Chapter 19. We introduce additional arithmetic operations such as the average of two numbers and the maximum of two numbers to show that there are more binary operations than just addition, subtraction, multiplication, and division. You may give problems such as $\frac{3}{8}$ avg $\frac{3}{4}$ and $\frac{7}{4}$ max 1.8 to reinforce computational skills with fractions, mixed numbers, and decimals. Note that the binary operation called avg is the average of *two* numbers and cannot be extended to define the average of a larger set of numbers, the way addition of two numbers can be extended to define the addition of more than two numbers.

You may wish to encourage some creativity, either through a classroom discussion or through a homework assignment, by having students invent their own binary operations

1

for numbers in arithmetic. In some cases, the examples provided by students will not fit the definition of a binary operation, leading to further discussion and eventual clarification.

Exercises 87 and 88 are problems that require the use of division in which only the integral part of the quotient is used in the solution. If students are familiar with a computer language, ask them to compare the binary operation that could be defined to give the solution of Exercise 88 with DIV in Pascal, and INT(A/B) in BASIC and in LOGO. Note that it may be necessary to define the required binary operation in words. For example, the binary operation for Exercise 87 may be defined as $a * b =$ the smallest integer that is greater than or equal to $a \div b$. The binary operation for Exercise 88 may be defined as the greatest integer that is less than or equal to $a \div b$.

1-3 BASES, EXPONENTS, AND POWERS

Make sure the students are familiar with the terms *base, exponent,* and *power*. Once they realize that the exponent tells how many times the base is to be used as a factor, incorrect answers such as $2^3 = 6$ will no longer be so commonplace. You will find additional reference to base, exponent, and power in Section 3-3, when we consider the vocabulary used in algebraic terms and expressions, and in Chapter 8, when we develop monomial operations.

In this manual, when we suggest computer or hand calculator exercises, we will use ^ exclusively to indicate raising to a power. However, students should be told to use only the symbol appropriate for the available hardware. Thus, it would be wise to mention the different symbols used by computers and calculators when raising numbers to a power, such as:

$$2 \uparrow 3 = 8, \quad 2 ** 3 = 8, \quad \text{or } 2 \wedge 3 = 8$$

1-4 ORDER OF OPERATIONS

In the definition of a binary operation, students are introduced to the concept of an ordered pair; 2^3 and 3^2 do not name the same number. Similarly, when numerical expressions contain two or more operations, a need for an agreed order of operations becomes apparent.

Grouping symbols such as parentheses are used to change the order of operations. Once students feel comfortable with the procedures for order of operations, they should be introduced to sentences written in words. In order to translate these verbal sentences into numerical symbols, parentheses are needed to establish the correct order. For example:

Ask students to compare "the sum of 8 and 5, times the product of 2 and 3," written $(8 + 5)(2 \times 3) = 78$, with "the sum of 8 and 5 times the product of 2 and 3," written $8 + 5(2 \times 3) = 38$. Discuss ways of rewording these expressions to clarify their meanings.

Computer Activity (1-4) After students have evaluated expressions in the exercises, answers may be checked by using simple PRINT statements on a computer. The symbols for multiplication and division in standard BASIC are * and /, respectively. For example, to check $28 + 0 \div 4 - 10 \times .2$, students should enter on the computer:

```
PRINT 28 + 0 / 4 - 10 * .2
```

The answer, 26, should appear after a RETURN or ENTER key is hit. Mention that the order of operations is built into the internal workings of the computer.

Calculator Activity (1-4) The solution to $3 \times 4 - 1$ (namely, 11) can be checked on a hand calculator by entering the following keys:

$$\boxed{3} \boxed{\times} \boxed{4} \boxed{-} \boxed{1} \boxed{=}$$

However, the solution to $5 + 3 \times 7$ (namely, 26) does not appear on a calculator when the keys are pressed as follows:

$$\boxed{5} \boxed{+} \boxed{3} \boxed{\times} \boxed{7} \boxed{=}$$

The order of operations is not built into most hand calculators. You may wish to demonstrate the use of parentheses with a scientific calculator that features the ( ) symbols for grouping. If a hand calculator does not contain any grouping keys, however, ask students how to enter problems such as: 4[5 + (10 ÷ 2)]

Answer: The keys must be pressed in the sequence of the order of operations:

1-5 PROPERTIES OF OPERATIONS

When numbers behave in a certain way for an operation, this behavior is described as a *property*. The most important of these properties involve addition and multiplication, since they will help us in every branch of mathematics studied in this course.

Most students are already aware of the commutative property of addition and the commutative property of multiplication as described for those familiar operations they have performed on the numbers of arithmetic. Let the class test the binary operations of maximum and average for commutativity. Conclude that the commutative property does hold for many binary operations.

There are, however, binary operations for which the commutative property does not hold. For example, if ⊕ is defined as $2a + b$, then the operation ⊕ does not have the commutative property, since $5 ⊕ 3 \neq 3 ⊕ 5$.

To conclude that the commutative property does not hold for a given operation, it is sufficient to show one counterexample. At this level, if a counterexample for a given operation cannot be found, it would appear that the commutative property holds for that given operation.

Addition and multiplication are operations that are associative as well as commutative. Subtraction and division are operations that are not commutative and not associative. Students may think that commutative operations are also associative. The binary operation of averaging will show that this is not the case. Averaging is commutative but not associative.

Later, students will use the distributive property of multiplication over addition when performing algebraic operations such as adding like monomials and finding the product of two binomials. For now, they are introduced to the idea that this property can be used to change the form of an expression.

Keep in mind that students may mistake $2(x + 4)$ as $2x + 4$. Such incorrect applications of the distributive property are dealt with in the exercises provided.

The substitution principle is introduced to assist in computations.

After students recognize that zero is the identity element for addition and one is the identity element for multiplication, ask them if there is an identity element for subtraction. Some will answer 0, since $5 - 0 = 5$ or $a - 0 = a$. Remember, if 0 is the identity element for subtraction then $a - 0 = 0 - a = a$, which is not true.

Establish that, in general, an identity element for a given operation allows every element in the set to remain unchanged under that operation.

Computer Activity (1-5) A program may be written to illustrate the distributive property. For example, show that $5(a + b) = 5a + 5b$ when $a = 3$ and $b = 4$.

```
10    REM    THIS PROGRAM WILL TEST THE
20    REM    DISTRIBUTIVE PROPERTY FOR
30    REM    ONE CASE.
40    LET A = 3
50    LET B = 4
60    PRINT "5(A + B) = ";5 * (A + B)
70    PRINT "5A + 5B = ";5 * A + 5 * B
80    END
```

The computer will display:

```
5(A + B) = 35
5A + 5B = 35
```

1-6 COMPARING NUMBERS

Students should have no problem understanding that when two numerical expressions are compared, they will either be equal or not equal to each other. For example, $8 - 2 = 3 \cdot 2$ and $3 + 7 \neq 7 - 5$. The inequality symbols $>$, representing "is greater than," and $<$, representing "is less than," are introduced at this point. As compared with $3 + 7 \neq 7 - 5$, the symbols $3 + 7 > 7 - 5$ are more specific. Some students need to be reminded that the symbols $>$ and $<$ point to the smaller of two numbers when the inequality is written.

You may wish to mention the Trichotomy Property at this point, namely, "for any two real numbers a and b, one and only one of the following statements is true: $a > b$ or $a < b$ or $a = b$."

This property appears in Chapter 10 during a discussion of inequalities.

It is interesting to note that to write the statement $x \neq 5$ on the computer, it is necessary to write $x < > 5$, that is, x is less than 5 or x is greater than 5.

1-7 NUMBER LINES

Examples of number lines used in our daily lives, such as rulers, speedometers, and thermometers, may enhance the students' appreciation of this topic and serve as motivation in this section. Point out that a radio dial does not satisfy the definition of a number line since the units are not evenly spaced.

Since a number line is described as a collection or set of points to which all the numbers of arithmetic can be assigned, the branches of arithmetic and geometry are brought together. Once 0 and 1 are assigned to two points on a number line, the unit measure and the direction of the line are determined.

The extension of the number line to include negative numbers will be introduced in Chapter 7 (Signed Numbers). Ordered pairs and coordinate axes will be dealt with extensively in Chapter 17 (The Coordinate Plane). For now, the number line should include positive fractions, decimals, and mixed numbers, along with the whole numbers. You should also stress the concept of an order relation to integrate this work with the inequalities studied in Section 1-6.

1-8 OPERATIONS IN GEOMETRY

It is important for students to realize that operations exist in geometry as well as in arithmetic. Certain binary operations in geometry that depend upon operations in arithmetic, such as finding the distance between two points on a number line, the midpoint of a line segment, and the measure of an angle, are introduced in this section.

By relating distance to subtraction or midpoint of a line segment to averaging, students will see relatively simple examples of the integration of geometry and arithmetic.

The difference between segment AB ($\overline{AB}$) and distance AB (AB) should be clarified at this point and will be reviewed in Chapter 11 (Geometry).

1-9 SETS

This section contains a condensed review of sets. You should be aware that set-builder notation is probably a new concept for most students at this grade level. Set-builder notation will be used throughout the Integrated Mathematics sequence.

As an extension of Exercises 38–47, you may lead students to discover that a set containing n elements has 2^n subsets.

1-10 OPERATIONS WITH SETS

Operations such as the intersection of sets, the union of sets, and the complement of a set are three more examples of binary operations. Point out again that operations are a common thread running through the various branches of mathematics.

Since this course does not require an in-depth study of set theory, it is recommended that you do not go beyond the scope of the material presented in this section. You may wish to use simple Venn diagrams to illustrate some concepts. For example:

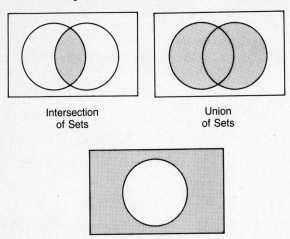

Intersection of Sets

Union of Sets

The Complement of a Set

In Chapter 2, one of the problem-solving strategies students will study involves the use of pictures and diagrams. Following here are examples of problems for which Venn diagrams are useful in the solution. You might discuss these problems with your class now or you might save them for later discussion.

Problem 1: At a birthday party, of the 11 children who ate cake and 10 who ate ice cream, 8 ate both cake and ice cream. One child had neither cake nor ice cream. How many children were at the party?

Solution:

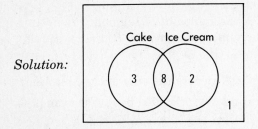

To find the total number in the universe, add. Thus, there were 3 + 8 + 2 + 1 or 14 children at the party.

Problem 2: Of the first 29 persons who ordered breakfast at a restaurant, 20 had eggs, 22 had toast, and 18 had both eggs and toast. How many had neither eggs nor toast?

Solution:

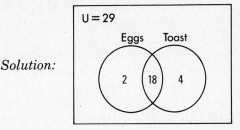

To find the number outside both sets, subtract the sum of the numbers in the sets from the number in the universe. Thus, there were 29 − (2 + 18 + 4) or 5 persons who had neither eggs nor toast.

SAT PREPARATION EXERCISES

College-intending students should be given experience that will promote ease in dealing with unusual problems presented in a variety of ways, thus increasing their chances for success in standardized testing. This experience should be made available throughout the students' mathematics education. In keeping with the philosophy that the classroom teacher is uniquely qualified to offer such training on an ongoing basis, this Manual provides a set of SAT Preparation Exercises for each of the 20 chapters of the Manual.

These exercises, which are of the type and level of difficulty students will encounter in actual SATs, include both quantitative comparisons and multiple-choice items. Each set of problems reflects the basic concepts of the chapter, but many of these problems are quite challenging. Students may be asked to attempt individually to solve two or three problems each night or the students may work in groups. No matter how these problems are assigned, students should not be discouraged if they find them to be difficult. In time, students will begin to learn how to approach these questions and how to find correct solutions.

SAT PREPARATION EXERCISES (Chapter 1)

Questions 1–9 each consist of two quantities, one in Column A and one in Column B. You are to compare the two quantities and choose:

  A if the quantity in Column A is greater;
  B if the quantity in Column B is greater;
  C if the two quantities are equal;
  D if the relationship cannot be determined from the information given.

Notes

1. In certain questions, information concerning one or both of the quantities to be compared is centered above the two columns.
2. In a given question, a symbol that appears in both columns represents the same thing in Column A as it does in Column B.
3. Letters such as x, n, and k stand for real numbers.

Column A	Column B
1. $\left(1\frac{1}{2}\right)^2$	$2\left(1\frac{1}{2}\right)$
2. $\left(\frac{1}{2}\right)^3$	$\left(\frac{1}{3}\right)^2$
3. The multiplicative identity	The additive identity
4. $x > 0$ 3 avg x	5 avg x
5. $x > 0$ 3 max x	5 max x
6. $\frac{9}{10}$ of $1\frac{1}{10}$	$\frac{9}{10}$ avg $1\frac{1}{10}$
7. $(2\cdot3^2)$ max $(2\cdot3)^2$	$3+6\cdot4$ max $3\cdot6+4$
8. $\left(2 + \frac{1}{10}\right)^2$	$(2)^2 + \left(\frac{1}{10}\right)^2$
9. The number of steps forward, if 2 & 1 means "take 2 steps forward and one step back."	
(5 & 3) & 1	5 & (3 & 1)

In 10–17, select the letter of the correct answer.

10. If W is the set of whole numbers less than 10, what is the sum of the least even number in W and the greatest odd number in W?
  (A) 11 (B) 10 (C) 9 (D) 8

11. What is the product of the numerators of $\frac{4}{8}$ and $\frac{8}{10}$ when these fractions are written in lowest terms?
  (A) 2 (B) 4 (C) 16 (D) 32

12. What is the difference between $\frac{3}{4}$ of 500 and $\frac{1}{2}$ of 300?
  (A) 50 (B) 125 (C) 225 (D) 250

13. Which of the following is greater than 1?
  (A) $(0.99)^2$ (B) $3\frac{1}{4} \div 3\frac{1}{5}$
  (C) $5 - 2\cdot2 - 1$ (D) 0.8 avg 1.2

14. The product of x and y is 40, and the average of x and y is an odd number. How many possible values are there for x, if x is a whole number?
  (A) 1 (B) 2 (C) 3 (D) 4

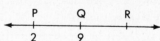

15. Q is the midpoint of segment $\overline{PR}$. If $2x$ is the number assigned to R, then x equals
  (A) 8 (B) 12 (C) 16 (D) 24

16. Let $\boxed{n\!\!\diagup}$ denote the sum of the first n natural numbers divided by n. For example,

$$\boxed{7\!\!\diagup} = \frac{1 + 2 + 3 + 4 + 5 + 6 + 7}{7}$$

Then, the average of 1 and 4 equals
  (A) $\boxed{2\!\!\diagup}$ (B) $\boxed{3\!\!\diagup}$ (C) $\boxed{4\!\!\diagup}$ (D) $\boxed{5\!\!\diagup}$

17. If set H contains 3 elements and set G contains 2 elements, what is the least number of elements in $H \cup G$?
  (A) 2 (B) 3 (C) 4 (D) 5

SUGGESTED TEST ITEMS (Chapter 1)

1. Which of the following is not a binary operation using the whole numbers but is a binary operation using the numbers of arithmetic?
   (1) addition   (2) subtraction   (3) multiplication   (4) division

2. Which of the following is not a binary operation using the numbers of arithmetic?
   (1) addition   (2) subtraction   (3) multiplication   (4) division

3. If $a * b = 2(a + b)$, what is the value of $5 * 3$?

4. Each row contains five numbers. Which number is not equivalent to the other four?

   a. $.25$ $\frac{1}{4}$ 25% $\frac{1}{2}$ avg $\frac{1}{6}$ $\frac{25}{100}$

   b. $\frac{1}{20}$ $.5$ 5% $.05$ $\frac{5}{100}$

   c. $.2$ $.20$ 2% 20% $\frac{1}{5}$

   d. $\frac{1}{8}$ $.125$ 12.5% $\frac{1}{8}$ max $\frac{1}{10}$ 8%

5. Simplify each numerical expression.

   a. $3 + 7 - 2^2$ **b.** $\frac{12 + 2^2}{4}$ **c.** $8 \div (20 - 4) + \frac{1}{2}$ **d.** $.3[2 - (1.4 - 0.6)]$

6. In each of the following, state whether the sentence is true or false. If it is true, name the property illustrated.
   a. $6(4 + 2) = 6(4) + 6(2)$ **b.** $5(3 + 7) = 5(7 + 3)$ **c.** $10 + 0 = 10$
   d. $5 \times (2 \times 18) = (5 \times 2) \times 18$ **e.** $14 - (7 + 2) = (14 - 7) + 2$

7. In each of the following, evaluate the expressions and replace $\neq$ by $<$ or $>$ in order to make the resulting statement true.
   a. $3 \times 5 - 2 \neq 3(5 - 2)$ **b.** $3(4)^2 \neq (3 \times 4)^2$ **c.** $5.2 - (3 - 0.8) \neq (5.2 - 3) - 0.8$

8. Use the number line to answer the following questions.
   a. If B is the midpoint of $\overline{AC}$, what number should be assigned to B?
   b. If d is the number assigned to D, what is the value of d max 9?
   c. Find CE.

9. In the figure, B is on $\overleftrightarrow{AC}$.
   a. Name three rays.
   b. Name a straight angle.
   c. Find $m\angle ABD$.

10. $A = \{1, 2, 3, 4, 5, 6, 7, 8, 9, 10\}$
    $B = \{3, 6, 9, 12\}$
    $U = \{1, 2, 3, 4, . . . , 20\}$

    List the elements in each of the following sets.
    a. $A \cup B$ **b.** $A \cap B$ **c.** $\overline{A}$ **d.** $\overline{A} \cup A$ **e.** $\overline{A} \cap A$

BONUS: A salesperson is offered a job which pays $250 a week or a commission of $3.50 on each sale. Which is the better wage if the salesperson averages 75 sales per week?

BONUS: Place parentheses to make the following statement true: $3 + 3 \div 3 - 3 \times 3 = 3$

CHAPTER **2**

Problem Solving

Aims

- To review the general technique for problem solving.

- To review some of the strategies that are useful in finding the solution of a nonroutine problem.

In the study of mathematics and in the use of mathematics in applications outside of the classroom, it is useful to be able to perform routine calculations either mentally or by using some type of electronic or mechanical device. But before calculations can be performed, it is necessary to be able to determine which calculations are appropriate by understanding and relating the concepts involved. This ability to find relationships is the essence of problem solving.

Students vary greatly in their ability to solve problems, and this ability does not always accompany computational skill. However, it is a skill that can be developed and that must be taught and encouraged in the mathematics classroom in a variety of ways.

This chapter on problem solving is intended to be a review and extension of problem-solving techniques that students should have encountered in previous mathematics courses. The inclusion of these strategies in a chapter by themselves at the beginning of the text is not intended to imply that they should be taught in isolation from the mathematical concepts and computational principles to

which they are related. Rather, some strategies of problem solving are illustrated here in order that they may be a useful resource to students as they encounter problem solving throughout the text. The relationships that are developed in the solution of these problems will provide insights that will be helpful in writing equations, when algebraic skills are acquired and an algebraic strategy employed.

Teachers are encouraged to make use of the material in this chapter in any or all of the ways listed here, according to the needs and abilities of their students.

1. Spend five to eight days reviewing the general problem-solving technique illustrated in this chapter. Continue to use the problems given in this chapter throughout the course, returning to problems previously solved when the development of algebraic skills makes new methods of solution possible.
2. Set aside one day a week to discuss nonroutine problems in the classroom. Allow students to work in small groups, sharing insights and skills. Encourage students to find more than one method of solution.
3. As often as possible, begin the class with a problem. A relatively simple one might be solved by the class in a few minutes. A more difficult problem could be left unsolved for students to work on for the next day. Some problems might require several

days or weeks before a solution is found.

4. Use more difficult problems as a weekly challenge. Encourage a variety of methods of solution. Allow students to explain their solutions to the rest of the class.

5. Put a nonroutine problem at the end of each test. A really challenging problem will present useful activity for those students who complete the test quickly while other students who work more slowly are still finishing the test. Offer extra credit or some other reward, such as a shorter homework assignment, for the solution. Base your reward on the quality of the effort as well as on the correctness of the solution.

The strategies illustrated in this chapter are intended to give the students a way to begin thinking about a problem. Many students do nothing if they cannot immediately identify a sequence of computations that will provide the answer. In classroom discussion, create an atmosphere in which any suggestion is welcome even if it does not lead to a solution. Show students how, by evaluating why a suggested strategy fails, a successful strategy might be developed.

Many of the problems that are solved in this chapter by working backward or by trial and error are problems that can be solved later in the course by using equations. As students develop algebraic skills, they will recognize that these skills enable them to solve problems more efficiently. The ability to use reasoning skills in the solution of routine and nonroutine problems is an ongoing goal of mathematics instruction. Do not expect mastery at this level. The development and use of an algebraic strategy in the solution of a problem is a specific goal of this course and, as such, is emphasized throughout this text. On final examinations, students should be expected to demonstrate mastery of an algebraic technique.

The four steps listed here as a general technique for the solution of a problem will be particularly helpful for those students who, when faced with a nonroutine problem, don't know where to start. Students whose insights and experience enable them to go directly to the solution should not be asked to work through each step. Not all suggested parts of the planning step are applicable to all problems. Esti-

mating an answer is often not possible and should be used only when appropriate. Notice that, in many of the problems that are solved in this chapter, no estimate is given.

The strategies listed are ones commonly accepted as useful approaches. Teachers may add other strategies to the ones given or may wish to combine two or more of these strategies. The problems solved as examples of these strategies presuppose a knowledge of the numbers, operations, and symbolism that were reviewed in Chapter 1.

2-1 GUESSING AND CHECKING

While even wild guesses are acceptable since they can be gradually refined to arrive at the answer, suggest that students try to start with an "educated guess," based on the largest and smallest possible values. Encourage students to make orderly lists of the numbers that they try in order that trials will not be repeated.

A number near the middle of the range of possible values is sometimes a good starting point. This is shown in Model Problem 1 and is applicable to several of the exercises in this first set. Exercises 1 and 2 are essentially the same as Model Problem 1. After students have solved a problem, discuss the numbers that they tried before they arrived at the answer. Encourage students to observe that, when two numbers have a given sum, as one number is increased, the other is decreased. Ask students by how much the difference between two numbers with a given sum will change when the larger is increased by 1. (The difference will increase by 2.)

Exercises 3 through 5 are similar to Model Problem 2. Reasonable first guesses might be half the number of coins, half the number of stools, and half the number of corsages of each kind.

After Exercise 3 has been solved, ask the students to determine the largest and the smallest values for 24 nickels and dimes. Could the value of the 24 nickels and dimes have been $2.50? Could it have been $1.00? Could it have been $2.12? Ask similar questions about the number of legs in Exercise 4 and the number of flowers in Exercise 5. Encourage students to ask themselves, "Is a solution possible?"

In Exercise 6, be sure that students recognize the distinction in meaning between digit and number, by showing an example such as the digits 1 and 5 forming the numbers 15 and 51. After the problem has been solved, ask the students to write several pairs of numbers that use the same two digits. What is always true of the difference of such a pair? (It is always a multiple of 9.) Could you find a pair of numbers that use the same two digits and have a difference of 21? (No, it is not a multiple of 9.)

2-2 USING A SIMPLER RELATED PROBLEM

Using a simpler related problem is less familiar to students than guessing and checking, and may require more practice. Thus, although the exercises in this section can be done using a variety of approaches, encourage students to work with this strategy to reinforce their understanding.

Exercise 7 offers a good motivation for using problem-solving strategies. Although students may at first think that there is not enough information to solve this problem, they will appreciate how perseverance in trying a succession of numbers can lead to a surprising result.

In Exercise 7, if m families each have 1 child, then these m families have m children. If n families each do not have 1 child, then each of $\frac{1}{2}n$ families has 2 children. Therefore, $\frac{1}{2}n$ families have $2\left(\frac{1}{2}\right)n$ or n children. Since the other $\frac{1}{2}n$ families have no children, the total number of children for the n families is n. Demonstrate this with specific numbers first. If there were 200 families and 80 had 1 child, then 120 would have 2 or 0. If half of the 120 families had 2 children each, then 60 families would have 2 and 60 would have 0. These 120 families would have $2(60) + 0(60)$, or 120 children. Thus, the total number of children is $80 + 120$, or 200. Try this using different numbers of families with 1 child until the pattern is clear. Then use a different total number of families.

2-3 WORKING BACKWARD

In general, working backward requires working from an end result and reversing each step in order to arrive at an initial value. Thus, in Model Problem 1, for example, since the final step of the problem is to go *down* 10 floors, the initial step of the solution is to go *up* 10 floors. Similarly, in Model Problem 2, to work backward, we *subtract* Ms. McCarthy's deposits and *add* her withdrawals, so as to "undo" their effects and arrive back at the original amount.

Many of these problems could be solved by writing and solving an algebraic equation. Students who are already familiar with simple equations may want to use an algebraic strategy. If students do suggest the use of an equation, point out that the solution of an equation is, in fact, an organized way of working backward. Students will find that equations necessary to solve Exercises 4 and 5 are quite complex.

In Exercise 7, one other category is possible—having a cat but not a dog. Remember that the students who have both a dog and a cat must be included in the number of students who have cats. There are two possible approaches. One is to find the number of students who have a cat but not a dog and add that number to the number of students who have both a cat and a dog. The other approach is to subtract from the total number of students, the number who do not have a cat.

Exercise 8 is a similar exercise. The remaining students must study biology but not French. These students, together with those who study French and biology, are the students who study biology.

Exercises 7 and 8 also lend themselves to illustration by Venn diagrams:

Exercise 7

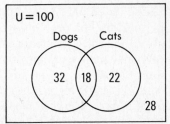

Answer: Of the 100 students, 40 had cats.

Exercise 8

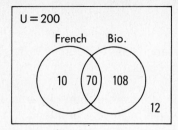

U = 200

French   Bio.

10   (70)   108

12

Answer: Of the 200 students, 178 study biology.

2-4 DISCOVERING PATTERNS

These problems require an investigation of some of the patterns that occur in the set of whole numbers. Students may consider the pattern used to solve Model Problem 2 one that they would never discover by themselves. Reassure them that such patterns are far from obvious and do require searching and ingenuity. However, by studying a variety of examples, they will acquire a familiarity with number patterns.

Present the following sequences to the class:

1, 2, 3, 4, 5, 7, 9, 11, 13, 15, 18, 21, 24, . . .
1, 2, 3, 4, 5, 4, 3, 4, 5, 6, 7, 6, 5, 6, 7, . . .
1, 2, 3, 4, 5, 10, 11, 12, 13, 14, 28, 29, 30, . . .
1, 2, 3, 4, 5, 10, 12, 14, 16, 32, 35, 38, 41, . . .

Each of these sequences begins 1, 2, 3, 4, 5, ... Infinitely many other patterns are possible. However, if we were asked to write the next term of the sequence 1, 2, 3, 4, 5, . . ., we would use the pattern that has already been introduced for which the next term is 6. For each of the other sequences that begin 1, 2, 3, 4, 5, more terms are needed before it is possible to discover the patterns used.

In Exercises 5–7, the next term in the given sequence could be found in several ways. For example, in Exercise 5, each term can be obtained by adding two more than the number added to obtain the previous term.

Position number	1	2	3	4	5	6	7	8
Value of term	1	3	7	13	21	31	43	?
Number added		2	4	6	8	10	12	14

It is also possible to think of each number in terms of its position number.

first number	0(1) + 1
second number	1(2) + 1
third number	2(3) + 1
fourth number	3(4) + 1

. . .

nth number $(n - 1)(n) + 1$

Students may not be ready to think in terms of $(n - 1)(n) + 1$, but they can think in terms of finding the 7th term by using $6(7) + 1$ and finding the 8th term by using $7(8) + 1$. Ask students which of these methods they would use to find the 100th term of the sequence.

Exercises 8 and 9 are more challenging. Allow students time to investigate possibilities on their own. If they have difficulty, suggest that they find sums or products and compare these to the assigned value of the binary operation. For example, in Exercise 8, $4(3) = 12$, $8(2) = 16$, and $1(5) = 5$. Each product is half of the assigned value. Therefore, we might think of this operation as taking twice the product of the numbers $(a * b = 2ab)$. In Exercise 9, $2(3) = 6$, $3(5) = 15$, and $4(5) = 20$. Each product is a factor of the assigned value. In each case, if we divide the assigned value by the product, the quotient is the first number of the pair. Therefore, we might think of $2 * 3$ as $2(2)(3)$, $3 * 5$ as $3(3)(5)$, $4 * 5$ as $4(4)(5)$, and $a * b$ as $a(a)(b)$ or a^2b. Ask students to write similar exercises by thinking of a pattern using two numbers. Have students present these exercises to the class, giving the result of using their patterns in three or four cases, and having the class determine an unknown value.

2-5 DRAWING PICTURES AND DIAGRAMS

Encourage students to draw a diagram whenever possible, even when using other strategies. The solution of any problem that involves a geometric figure should include a diagram.

In Exercise 2, a diagram will help students to remember that there must be one fence post at the beginning of the fence plus one at the end of each 6 feet. Therefore, we need $1 + \frac{30}{6}$ fenceposts.

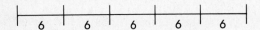

In Exercise 3, first find the smallest number of feet fenced before it is possible to use one less post. When finding the required number of posts, don't forget the beginning post.

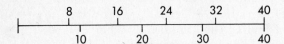

In Exercise 7, there may be 2 bottles or 4 bottles in each row or column. Although there are many possible arrangements, each arrangement must use three rows of 4 and one row of 2.

In Exercise 8, there may be 1, 3, or 5 bottles in each row. An arrangement may have either three rows of 3 and two rows of 1 or one row of 5, one row of 3 and three rows of 1. Ask students if this problem could be done using a crate with four rows of 5. (No, because there would be an even number of rows, each containing an odd number of bottles. This would require an even number of bottles. But at the same time there would also have to be an odd number of columns, each with an odd number of bottles. This would require an odd number of bottles. Therefore, it is impossible to put an odd number of bottles in each row and column of a crate with four rows of 5.)

2-6 MAKING LISTS AND CHARTS

The use of a chart or an organized list is a very useful strategy in problem solving. Often such a chart or list is used in combination with other strategies, including an algebraic strategy. Problems such as Exercises 3–6 require that the numbers of bills or flowers, as well as the values of those bills or flowers, be considered. Note that in Exercises 3–6, several solutions are possible. In Exercises 7 and 8, although many numbers satisfy the given conditions, the smallest number is the required answer.

2-7 CHOOSING AND COMBINING STRATEGIES

The model problems shown here illustrate two important ideas to be kept in mind when solving problems.

1. There is often more than one strategy that can be used to solve a problem.
2. A problem is not always solved by the first strategy that is tried.

The first model shows the same problem solved by two different strategies. The second model shows the use of a strategy that does not give the answer but that provides useful insights that make the solution by a different strategy possible.

The varied set of exercises includes some relatively easy and some very challenging problems. Give the students sufficient time to find their own solutions. Ask questions that may lead students to a strategy if they are having difficulty. Encourage students to formulate their own questions when they are unsure of what strategy to use. Listed below are some questions that might serve as suggestions.

Exercise 1: Can you draw a picture?

Exercise 2: If you combine the weights of the kitten in the bucket and the rabbit in the bucket, what does this represent?

Exercise 3: If you knew the number of benches, would you also know the number of people? Try some numbers.

Exercise 4: What number could you try near the middle of the range of possible numbers of tickets?

Exercise 5: How much money and what part of the car has Greg earned?

Exercise 6: What fractional part of the number of customers ordered salad?

Exercise 7: What is the smallest number of points in which the two squares can intersect if part of one square is inside and part outside the other? What is the greatest number of points of intersection if one square is inside the other?

The problem does not require that the squares be the same size. Ask students to consider the problem again with this condition. Does it make a difference? (It is possible to find a solution for every required number of intersections for squares of the same size and of different sizes. However, some solutions must be different if the squares must be the same size. For example, if 2 or 4 intersections are required, solutions with one square inside the other are possible with squares of different sizes, but not with squares of the same size.)

Exercise 8: Does the number of days in a month determine how many days Rosa works in a month? Does the day of the week on which the month starts determine this?

Exercise 9: Could he buy all gumdrops? Could he buy all chocolate drops?

Exercise 10: Can you count the number of triangles having any one side of the pentagon as a side? Are there triangles that do not use a side of the pentagon as a side of the triangle?

2-8 REVIEW EXERCISES

The following questions may be helpful in solving the review problems.

Exercise 1: Whose places in line are given in the problem?

Exercise 2: How much older than Chris was Carl five years ago?

Exercise 3: If she sets aside 25 cents for each charity, what multiple of 5 cents will she have left if she takes 5 cents from each and only gives 20 cents?

Exercise 4: If Lucy is 1, how old is Ernestine and how long will it take before Ernestine is twice as old as Lucy? What if Lucy is 2?

Exercise 5: How many were in favor of at least one of the issues? If you combine the number of persons in favor of the first issue with the number of persons who were in favor of the second, how many persons were counted twice?

Exercise 6: What is the product of each pair? What is the sum of each pair?

Exercise 7: What number must Q represent? What kind of a number must K represent?

Exercise 8: Can the boxes fit without wasted space? Can more boxes fit if they are not all aligned in the same way?

Exercise 9: Can you make a chart listing Canadians and Americans in categories of boys, girls, men, and women?

SAT PREPARATION EXERCISES (Chapter 2)

SAT questions selected from *5 SATs* and *10 SATs,* College Entrance Examination Board, 1985 and 1983. Reprinted by permission of Educational Testing Service, the copyright owner of the sample questions. Permission to reprint this material does not constitute endorsement by Educational Testing Service or the College Board of this publication as a whole or of any other testing information it may contain.

Questions 1–5 each consist of two quantities, one in Column A and one in Column B. You are to compare the two quantities and choose:

A if the quantity in Column A is greater;
B if the quantity in Column B is greater;
C if the two quantities are equal;
D if the relationship cannot be determined from the information given.

Notes

1. In certain questions, information concerning one or both of the quantities to be compared is centered above the two columns.
2. In a given question, a symbol that appears in both columns represents the same thing in Column A as it does in Column B.
3. Letters such as *x, n,* and *k* stand for real numbers.

Column A	_Column B_

In the last step of an arithmetic problem, John added 15 to the value he had obtained so far, when he should have subtracted 30. He made no other mistakes.

1. The correct answer   John's answer to
to the problem   the problem

There are 26 chairs arranged in rows so that the first row has 5 chairs and each successive row has one more chair than the row immediately preceding it.

2. The number of rows   5
of chairs

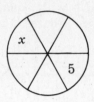

Each of the six sectors in the circle above is assigned a number such that the sum of the numbers in any two sectors adjacent to each other is 9.

3.   *x*   5

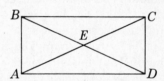

4. The total number of   6
triangles that can
be named in the figure above

In a certain game, there are only four types of moves. These moves advance a playing piece 2, 3, 7, or 9 spaces, respectively, in any order.

5. The minimum number of moves required   4
to advance a piece
exactly 26 spaces

In 6–20, select the letter of the correct answer.

6. The cube above has a number on each of its six faces. If the sum of the numbers on each pair of opposite faces is 10, what is the sum of the numbers on the faces *not* shown?
(A) 8 (B) 10 (C) 12 (D) 14 (E) 16

7. A man has 15 bags of grain in his barn. Given that he can carry at most 2 bags of grain at a time, what is the least number of trips he must make from the barn to the truck in order for him to carry all of the bags of grain to his truck?
(A) 7 (B) 7.5 (C) 8 (D) 8.5 (E) 9

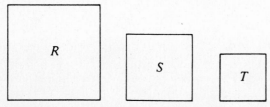

8. Three squares *R, S,* and *T* are shown above. The area of *R* is twice the area of *S,* and the area of *S* is twice the area of *T*. If the area of *S* is 1, what is the sum of the areas of all three squares?

(A) $2\frac{1}{2}$ (B) $3\frac{1}{2}$ (C) 4 (D) $5\frac{1}{4}$ (E) 6

9. A month with 5 Wednesdays could start on a
(A) Sunday (B) Monday (C) Thursday
(D) Friday (E) Saturday

10. A small bus has 3 empty seats, 6 seated passengers, and 2 standing passengers. If 3 passengers get off, 4 get on, and everyone on the bus is seated, how many empty seats would there be?
(A) None (B) One (C) Two
(D) Three (E) Four

11. John had exactly $7 before Bill paid him a $26 debt. After the debt was paid, Bill had $\frac{1}{3}$ the amount that John then had. How much did Bill have before the debt was paid?
(A) $33 (B) $35 (C) $36
(D) $37 (E) $47

12. Several people are standing in a straight line. Starting at one end of the line, Bill is counted as the 5th person and, starting at the other end, he is counted as the 12th person. How many people are in the line?
(A) 15 (B) 16 (C) 17 (D) 18 (E) 19

$$\begin{array}{r} 7X \\ +X1 \\ \hline 1Y7 \end{array}$$

13. The correct addition problem above shows the sum of two 2-digit numbers. If *X* and *Y* represent different nonzero digits, then *Y* =
(A) 1 (B) 3 (C) 6 (D) 7 (E) 8

$$A = \{3,6,9\}$$
$$B = \{5,7,9\}$$
$$C = \{7,8,9\}$$

14. If three *different* numbers are selected, one from each of the sets shown above, what is the greatest sum that these three numbers could have?
(A) 22 (B) 23 (C) 24 (D) 25 (E) 27

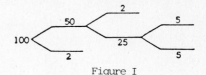

Figure I

15. Figure I is an example of a "factor diagram" of 100. What is the value of *N* if Figure II is a "factor diagram" of *N*?
(A) 70 (B) 120 (C) 150
(D) 240 (E) 300

16. Colored banners are strung on a cord to advertise a carnival. If the colors form a repeating pattern starting with white, red, yellow, blue, green, purple; white, red, yellow, blue, green, purple, and so on, what is the color of the 76th banner?
(A) Red   (B) Yellow (C) Blue
(D) Green   (E) Purple

17. If 25 squares, each painted one of the solid colors red, green, yellow, or blue, are lined up side by side in a single row so that no two adjacent squares are the same color and there is at least one square of each color, what is the maximum possible number of blue squares?
(A) 9   (B) 10   (C) 11   (D) 12   (E) 13

Number of Donuts	Total Price
1	$0.40
Box of 6	$1.89
Box of 12	$3.59

18. What would be the *least* amount of money needed to purchase exactly 21 donuts?
(A) $5.88   (B) $6.68   (C) $7.19
(D) $7.38   (E) $8.40

19. Club A has 10 members and Club B has 15. If a total of 21 people belong to the two clubs, how many people belong to both clubs?
(A) 3   (B) 4   (C) 5   (D) 6   (E) 7

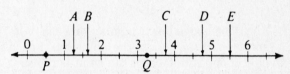

20. If P and Q are numbers on the number line above, which of the points shown best represents $P \times Q$?
(A) A (B) B (C) C (D) D (E) E

ADDITIONAL PROBLEMS (Chapter 2)

Here are some problems that may be used to continue problem solving in the classroom, as bonus questions at the end of a test, or as work for extra credit. It is recommended that they *not* be used as a classroom test.

1. Sylvia has $6 more than Sara. Together the two girls have $24. How much money does each girl have?

2. Chocolate kisses cost 2 cents each and peppermints cost 5 cents each. Robin bought some kisses and some peppermints and spent 20 cents. What did she buy?

3. Judy had 100 math problems to solve. She decided to work some on Monday, and each day after that, work twice as many as she did the day before. Judy kept to this plan and, after working problems on Friday, she still had 7 problems left to complete. How many problems did she work each day?

4. Ann, Beth, and Chris are the daughters of Mrs. Adams, Mrs. Burke, and Mrs. Carroll. Each girl works for the mother of one of the other girls. From the following clues, determine the mother and the employer of each girl.
   1. Ann is not Mrs. Burke's daughter and does not work for Beth's mother.
   2. Chris is Mrs. Adams' daughter.

5. There are fewer than 50 students in a class. The teacher wants to divide the class into discussion groups of equal size. There is 1 extra student when she tries to make 4 groups and there is 1 student too few when she tries to make 5 groups or 6 groups. How many students are in the class?

6. Of 400 students surveyed, 325 liked pizza, 290 liked cheeseburgers, and 12 liked neither pizza nor cheeseburgers. How many of the students surveyed liked both pizza and cheeseburgers?

7. Mr. Winters bought 4 packages of ground beef. The second package weighed three times as much as the first and the third package weighed half as much as the second. The fourth package weighed 15 oz., which was 3 oz. more than the third. How many ounces of ground beef did Mr. Winters buy?

8. What is the largest number of 3-cm by 4-cm rectangles that can be cut from a 12-cm by 10-cm piece of cardboard?

9. At a movie theater, admission for adults was $4.00 and admission for children was $2.00. At the end of the day, the cashier's records showed that $825 had been paid for 250 tickets. What conclusions can you draw?

CHAPTER **3**

Algebraic Expressions and Open Sentences

Aims

- To translate verbal phrases and sentences into algebraic language.

- To evaluate algebraic expressions and formulas, including those related to geometric figures.

- To review formulas for perimeter, area, and volume.

- To determine the solution set of an open sentence by replacing the variable with elements from the domain.

- To lay the foundation for the understanding of an algebraic approach to problem solving.

This chapter uses the students' knowledge of arithmetic to introduce the use of variables to represent related numerical values. Examples are drawn from the common life experiences of students as well as from their knowledge of perimeter, area, and volume. In this way, these geometric formulas are reviewed and new ways of looking at them are explored. Also, preparation is made for the algebraic solution of problems.

3-1 TRANSLATING VERBAL PHRASES INTO ALGEBRAIC LANGUAGE

As verbal phrases are translated into algebraic expressions, compare the process with translation from one language to another. Sometimes a word-by-word change into symbols is possible, but it is often necessary to use a different order, just as different languages use different word orders. For example, the English "white house" is in Spanish "casa blanca," with the adjective after the noun. In algebra, "5 more than x" can be written in the same order, as $5 + x$; but "5 less than x" must be written in a different order, as $x - 5$.

It can prove helpful to students to treat "more than" and "less than" in the same manner. That is, encourage students to write $x + 5$ for "5 more than x," thus cultivating the correct $x - 5$ rather than the incorrect $5 - x$ for "5 less than x."

It is sometimes helpful to insert commas into verbal phrases for clarity. For example, "twice x decreased by 10" could be interpeted as $2(x - 10)$ but "twice x, decreased by 10" clearly means $2x - 10$.

Once students have changed verbal phrases into algebraic expressions, ask them to change the algebraic expressions into verbal phrases that are different from the original ones.

After they have learned to write the algebraic expressions, you may wish to have students translate the verbal phrases in the exercises into computer language. For example:

Verbal Phrase
The quotient of 3a and 2b

Algebraic Language	*Computer Language*
$\dfrac{3a}{2b}$	(3 * A) / (2 * B)

3-2 USING LETTERS TO REPRESENT VARIABLES

In this section, students are encouraged to apply the strategy of using a simpler related problem. They are asked to focus first on an expression using numbers to help them see how to write a corresponding algebraic expression.

As occurs throughout the text, integration of topics is achieved in the exercises at the end of this section. Metric units, geometry, basic operations, and everyday relationships are included in the study of algebraic expressions.

3-3 UNDERSTANDING THE MEANING OF SOME VOCABULARY USED IN ALGEBRA

Just as you, the teacher, use correct terminology in discussing algebraic expressions, students should also begin to use proper terminology, as presented in this section. The terms *base*, *exponent*, and *power*, previously studied in Section 1-3, are now applied to algebraic expressions.

As an interesting exercise, ask the students to list all the factors of the product 2ab. Then, recalling the study of subsets in Section 1-9, compare these factors with the subsets of {2, a, b}. How are they same? How are they different? Observe that the number of factors of 2ab is the same as the number of subsets of {2, a, b}. (The factors of 2ab are 1, 2, a, b, 2a, 2b, ab, and 2ab. The subsets of {2, a, b} are ∅, {2}, {a}, {b}, {2, a}, {2, b}, {a, b}, and {2, a, b}.) Each of the factors closely resembles a subset, with the exception of the factor 1, which must correspond to the subset ∅.

Some mention may be made of computer expressions using exponents. For example,

$$3x^2y^5 = 3 * X \wedge 2 * Y \wedge 5$$

3-4 EVALUATING ALGEBRAIC EXPRESSIONS

The order of operations seen in earlier sections is now applied to evaluating algebraic expressions. Be aware that all replacements for variables in this chapter are restricted to positive rational numbers and zero. In Chapter 7 (Signed Numbers), students will evaluate expressions using negative quantities.

Computer Activities (3-4) To find the numerical value of $\dfrac{3bd}{9}$ when $b = 6$ and $d = 3$, you can show a simple program.

```
10   LET B = 6
20   LET D = 3
30   PRINT 3 * B * D / 9
40   END
```

The computer will display the answer 6.

Exercises such as those on pages 77 and 78 can be evaluated on a computer in calculator mode (that is, using the computer as a calculator without writing a program).
Type:

```
LET A = 8
LET B = 6
LET D = 3
LET X = 4
LET Y = 5
LET Z = 1
PRINT 5 * A
```

The computer will display 40 as soon as the RETURN key is pressed. This is the result of multiplying 5 times 8, the value of *A*. Continue with the rest of the exercises. A computer response will follow each new PRINT statement entered.

```
PRINT A ^ 2
    .
    .
    .
PRINT 3 / 4 * X ^ 3
```

19

In evaluating the exercises, the computer will use the correct order of operations: powers first, then division and multiplication in the order in which they appear in the problem.

After students have completed Exercises 52–72 on page 78, have them check the results on the computer. Some students have used expressions such as 3(5) to indicate multiplication and have associated the parentheses with multiplication. Completing these exercises on the computer requires the use of the multiplication symbol * each time multiplication is indicated for a number and a variable, or for two variables, written with no multiplication symbol between them. Notation is shown below for Exercises 52, 58, and 64.

```
LET W = 10
LET X = 8
LET Y = 5
LET Z = 2
```

`PRINT 2 * (X + 5)`	Note the necessity for both the multiplication symbol and parentheses.
`PRINT 3 * Y - (X - Z)`	Note the necessity for parentheses as a symbol of inclusion but preceded by subtraction rather than multiplication.
`PRINT (Y + Z) ^ 2`	Note the necessity for parentheses used before a symbol for exponentiation.

3-5 TRANSLATING VERBAL SENTENCES INTO FORMULAS

While learning how to translate verbal sentences into formulas, students also review the formulas for area, perimeter, surface area, volume, rate of speed, and Fahrenheit/Celsius conversion, in a broad integration of topics. As students write and evaluate formulas in this section and the next, they should become familiar with most of the formulas and relationships presented.

Computer Activity (3-5)   The following program converts temperatures expressed in Fahrenheit units to Celsius units.

```
10   REM    THIS PROGRAM WILL CONVERT
20   REM    FAHRENHEIT READINGS TO CELSIUS.
30   PRINT "F","C"
40   READ F
50   IF F = 999 THEN 90
60   PRINT F,5 / 9 * (F - 32)
70   DATA  50,77,86,32,212,999
80   GOTO 40
90   END
```

3-6 USING FORMULAS FOR PERIMETER, AREA, AND VOLUME

In this section, formulas for perimeter, area, and volume of various geometric figures are considered. You may find it necessary to review some of the properties of triangles, quadrilaterals, and circles before evaluating the formulas algebraically.

Computer Activity (3-6)   Formulas such as those given in the exercises on page 82 can be evaluated by computer programs. The following program evaluates the formula in Exercise 1. Similar programs can be written for the formulas in Exercises 2-7.

```
100   REM   THIS PROGRAM WILL EVALUATE
110   REM   THE FORMULA FOR THE PERIMETER
120   REM   OF A TRIANGLE.
130   READ A,B,C
140   IF A = 0 THEN 230
150   LET P = A + B + C
160   PRINT "WHEN THE SIDES MEASURE ";A;",";B;",";C
170   PRINT "THE PERIMETER IS ";P
180   PRINT
190   GOTO 130
200   DATA  15,10,7,4.5,1.7
210   DATA  3.8,7.5,5.75,6.5,9,8,1.5
220   DATA  0,0,0
230   END
```

This section provides an opportunity for discussing dimensional analysis, to promote an awareness of unit measures.

Use the model problem on page 87, in which both perimeter and area of the same figure are calculated, to stress the difference between the linear unit that is appled to perimeter and the square unit that is applied to area. Ask students to use a ruler to draw 16.3 centimeters and also 12.2 square centimeters.

```
A                                      B
 └─┴─┴─┴─┴─┴─┴─┴─┴─┴─┴─┴─┴─┴─┴─┴─┘
  1 2 3 4 5 6 7 8 9 10 11 12 13 14 15 16
```

The length of line segment AB is 16.3 units.

```
D                                 C
  │1│2│3│4│5│6│7│8│9│10│11│12│
A                                 B
```

The shaded region $ABCD$ contains 12.2 square units.

When applying the formula for the area of a triangle, some students mistakenly take half of the measure of the base *and* half of the measure of the altitude.

$$\frac{1}{2}(6)(4) \neq (3)(2)$$

If this happens, ask students to interpret the formula verbally and to make the arithmetic correspond to the words.

one-half of the product of base and altitude

$$\frac{1}{2} \quad \times \quad (6)(4)$$

$$= \frac{1}{2} \quad \times \quad (24)$$

$$= 12$$

If students wish to cancel when applying this formula, encourge them to use a cancellation symbol on the numbers that have been used so that they will not be tempted to use them again.

$$\frac{1}{2}(\cancel{6}^{3})(4) = 3(4) = 12$$

Exercises 37–46 provide applications of area and perimeter and the opportunity for students to investigate areas of irregular shapes.

In Exercise 38, some students may choose to find the area of the region to be carpeted by separating the figure into rectangular regions.

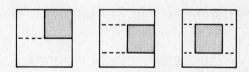

Others may choose to find the area of the entire room and then subtract the area of the uncarpeted region. In each case, call attention to the use of the strategy of using a simpler related problem.

In Exercises 39–43, students will be adding and subtracting areas of basic polygons to calculate the areas of the composite shapes.

In Exercise 44, drawing a diagram will help solve the problem.

(1) Plant 16 seedlings 2 feet apart along each of the 30-foot lengths, thus accounting for 32 seedlings.
(2) Divide the remaining 16 seedlings between the two widths and plant these at 2-foot intervals between the end seedlings.
(3) The diagram shows the number of 2-foot intervals established along the widths, thus leading to the required measure of the width.

In Exercise 45, students may recognize patterns that result from the symmetry or from the relationship between perimeter and area, or they may guess and check.

In Exercise 46, it is useful to work backward to find the dimensions of the pen. From the 26 feet of fence, subtract the number of feet needed for the length parallel to the garage. Then divide the remaining piece into two parts for the two sides of the pen. Trial and error will lead to the maximum area in part **c.** Note that the products 6×14 and 7×12 both give a seemingly maximum area of 84 square feet. The actual maximum area of $84\frac{1}{2}$ square feet is obtained when the length parallel to the garage is 13 feet.

Although a strategy has been suggested here for each of several problems, there is no one correct strategy. Allow students sufficient time to explore strategies in order to develop a familiarity with the applications of these strategies and to build confidence in their own ability to solve problems.

3-7 OPEN SENTENCES AND SOLUTION SETS

Students should recognize that an open sentence in the form of a linear equation will usually have exactly one element or no elements from the given domain as its solution set. Inequalities, however, may have more than one element in the solution set.

The domain presented in each of the exercises here is limited to a finite set.

Computer Activity (3-7) The following program evaluates the solution set of Exercise 44 on page 93:

```
10   REM    THIS PROGRAM WILL DETERMINE
20   REM    THE SOLUTION SET FOR Y - 1 < 8
30   REM    IF Y IS 7, 8, 9, OR 10.
40   DATA   7,8,9,10,-99
50   READ Y
60   IF Y = - 99 THEN 110
70   IF Y - 1 < 8 THEN 90
80   GOTO 50
90   PRINT Y
100   GOTO 50
110   END
```

The computer will display 7 and 8 as the solution set.

This same program can be used to find the solutions sets of other inequalities. Replace 7, 8, 9, 10 in lines 30 and 40 with the elements of the given replacement set. Replace $y - 1 < 8$ in lines 20 and 70 with the inequality to be solved.

Questions 1–9 each consist of two quantities, one in Column A and one in Column B. You are to compare the two quantities and choose:

   A if the quantity in Column A is greater;
   B if the quantity in Column B is greater;
   C if the two quantities are equal;
   D if the relationship cannot be determined from the information given.

Notes

1. In certain questions, information concerning one or both of the quantities to be compared is centered above the two columns.
2. In a given question, a symbol that appears in both columns represents the same thing in Column A as it does in Column B.
3. Letters such as x, n, and k stand for real numbers.

Column A	*Column B*

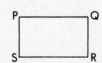

1. The perimeter of triangle PQR | The semi-perimeter of rectangle $PQRS$

2. The number of 10¢ items that can be purchased for ten dollars | The number of cents in ten dimes

$$x = \frac{1}{2}$$

3. $x\left(x + \frac{1}{2}\right)$ | $x^2 + \frac{1}{2}x$

$$x = 10$$

4. $\dfrac{10x + 10}{10}$ | $10 + 10$

5. The area of a triangle whose base and height each equals $1\frac{2}{3}$ inches | The area of a square with each side equal to $1\frac{1}{3}$ inches

6. x^3 if $x = \frac{3}{4}$ | $y \cdot y \cdot y$ if $y = 0.75$

$$F = \frac{9}{5}C + 32$$

7. 25 | C when $F = 75$

$$0 < x < 1$$

8. x^2 | x^3

$$x > 0$$

9. $2x^2$ | $3x^3$

In 10–20, select the letter of the correct answer.

10. A rectangle has a perimeter of $4x + 20$ and a width of $x + 4$. What is the length of the rectangle?
(A) $2x + 12$ (B) $2x + 8$
(C) $x + 6$ (D) $x + 4$

11. If $x - 5 = 3\frac{1}{2}$, then $2x - 5$ is equal to
(A) 7 (B) 12 (C) 17 (D) 10

12. The perimeter of rectangle $PQRS$ is 24. If $x = SP$ and $SP < PQ$, then
(A) $0 < x < 4$ (B) $0 < x < 6$
(C) $0 < x < 8$ (D) $0 < x < 12$

13. If $3x + 5 = 7$ and $3x + 10 = 2 + y$, then y is
(A) 5 (B) 9 (C) 10 (D) 12

14. Luke ate a boiled egg in s seconds. At the same rate, how many can he eat in m minutes?
(A) $\dfrac{60m}{s}$ (B) $\dfrac{ms}{60}$ (C) $\dfrac{60s}{m}$ (D) $\dfrac{s}{60m}$

15. If $w = 1$, $x = 2$, $y = 3$, and $z = 4$, which expression has a value different from the others?
(A) $w + x + y + z$ (B) $w + y^x$
(C) $yz - wx$ (D) $yw^x + w$

16. Ann's age is 80% of Bill's age. If the average of their ages is 2 years more than Ann's age, what is Bill's age?
(A) 12 (B) 16 (C) 20 (D) 24

17. The perimeter of a rectangle is more than 20 but less than 28. If the width is 3, then the length could *not* be a number which is
(A) even   (B) odd
(C) prime   (D) composite

18. If $\frac{2}{3}$ of x is 10, how much is $\frac{1}{10}$ of x?

(A) $\frac{1}{15}$ (B) 15 (C) $\frac{20}{3}$ (D) $\frac{3}{2}$

19. Mary was born when Nancy was 3 and is now half as old as Nancy. A year ago, Mary's age was what percent of Nancy's age?

(A) $33\frac{1}{3}\%$ (B) 40% (C) 50% (D) $66\frac{2}{3}\%$

20. If $\frac{x}{y} = 1$ and $x + y = 10$, then xy equals
(A) 1 (B) 5 (C) 10 (D) 25

SUGGESTED TEST ITEMS (Chapter 3)

1. Using the letter n to represent a number, write the verbal phrase as an algebraic expression.
   a. a number increased by 12   b. 7 less than a number   c. 4 added to twice a number
   d. one-half of a number, decreased by 6   e. the sum of 4 and a number, divided by 3

2. Use the variables in the problem to represent the answer in algebraic language.
   a. Janet spent x dollars. If Jim spent 5 dollars more than Janet, represent the number of dollars Jim spent.
   b. Bus fare is c cents. If Ian rode the bus 10 times this week, represent the amount he spent for bus fare.
   c. Represent the number of minutes in h hours and m minutes.
   d. Represent in cents the value of q quarters and d dimes.
   e. A car rental agency charges $35 a day to rent a car. This charge includes the cost of the first 100 miles or less. The agency charges $.15 per mile for mileage over 100. Represent the cost, in dollars, of renting a car for a day when the car is driven m miles and m is greater than 100.

3. List the factors of $17ab$.

4. What is the base and what is the exponent of the power x^7?

5. Write each expression using exponents.
   a. $3 \cdot a \cdot a$ b. $5 \cdot x \cdot x \cdot x \cdot y \cdot y \cdot y \cdot y \cdot y$ c. $(5a)(5a)(5a)$

6. Find the value of each expression when $a = 3$, $b = 5$, and $c = \frac{1}{3}$.

   a. ac b. $2a - b$ c. $(a + b)^2$ d. $\frac{a + b}{2}$

   e. $27c^2$ f. $4a + b^2$ g. $b^2 - a^2$ h. $a - (b - 2)$

7. Evaluate $\frac{9}{5}C + 32$ when $c = 15$.

8. Write a formula for the cost c of ordering by mail when postage p in cents is added to the price of 4 articles that cost n cents each.

9. The formula for the area of a trapezoid is $A = \frac{1}{2}h(b + c)$. Find the area A when $h = 7$ cm, $b = 12$ cm, and $c = 10$ cm.

10. Use the domain $\{1, 2, 3, 4, 5\}$ to find the solution set of $2x - 1 > 5$.

CHAPTER **4**

Simple Equations
and Problems

Aims

- To explain the meaning of solving an equation.

- To introduce postulates of equality and inverse operations needed to solve equations.

- To provide practice in translating verbal sentences into equations.

- To introduce an algebraic approach to problem solving.

An algebraic solution is one of the most frequently used methods of problem solving. As students acquire algebraic skills, new problems, new approaches to problems solved by other strategies, and more general solutions of problems can be developed. The use of an equation to solve a problem is the most important problem-solving strategy to be developed in this course. This chapter introduces this strategy and lays the foundation for its continued use.

4-1 PREPARING TO SOLVE AN EQUATION

This section uses trial and error to find the solution of an equation from a finite domain. It then introduces the concept of inverse operation in order to prepare to find the solution of an equation by more efficient means.

Before introducing the meaning of solving an equation, review terms such as *variable, open sentence, domain, replacement set,* and *solution set.*

We are again working with linear equations that have only one solution or root. As a challenge, ask students to find a linear equation that has more than one root when the replacement set is the numbers of arithmetic.

Possible responses are equations such as $x + x = 2x$ or $y + 3 = 3 + y$, which are identities. The term "identity" should be introduced and discussed.

This textbook refers to the reflexive, symmetric, and transitive properties of equality as *postulates. Axiom* is an equally acceptable term.

Stress that the statement "if $a = b$, then $b = a$" describes the symmetric property of equality, and *not* the commutative property. Commutativity is a property of operations, not a property of equality.

Show how the substitution principle relates to the transitive property of equality:
If (1) $a = b$ and (2) $b = c$, the transitive property of equality makes it possible to substitute a for b in (2), to obtain $a = c$. Students will use the principle of substitution throughout the program.

Students should realize that addition and subtraction are called *inverse operations*, since one will undo the effect of the other in an expression. Similarly, multiplication and division are inverse operations. The cases of $\frac{ax}{a} = x$ and $a \cdot \frac{x}{a} = x$ are correct uses of inverse operations when $a \neq 0$. Ask why a cannot equal 0; that is, why is division by 0 undefined? You may wish to consider the following:

(1) $\frac{0}{5} = ?$ means $? \times 5 = 0$

Only 0 will make this equality true.

(2) $\frac{5}{0} = ?$ means $? \times 0 = 5$

There is no number that will make this equality true.

(3) $\frac{0}{0} = ?$ means $? \times 0 = 0$

Any number will make this equality true.

From (2) and (3), we establish that there can be no unique result for division by 0.

What would happen if you tried to divide 5 by 0 on a calculator or a computer? (The machine would signal an error.)

4-2 SOLVING SIMPLE EQUATIONS BY USING ADDITION OR SUBTRACTION POSTULATES

Once students understand the concept of equivalent equations, they will see that the addition and subtraction properties of equality are used to form simpler equivalent equations.

Since the set of integers is not formally defined until Section 7-1, refer to the method of solving the equation $x + 2 = 5$ as subtracting 2 from both sides of the equation rather than as adding -2 to both sides.

Note that the check is stressed in all the model problems and exercises. Students should get into the habit of performing a check, whether it is required in the exercise or not.

4-3 SOLVING SIMPLE EQUATIONS BY USING DIVISION OR MULTIPLICATION POSTULATES

Just as simple equations were solved using addition and subtraction in Section 4-2, the division and multiplication properties of equality are now utilized to solve equations. Students should understand that dividing both sides of an equation by 2 is the same as multiplying both sides by $\frac{1}{2}$.

4-4 WRITING VERBAL SENTENCES AS EQUATIONS

If necessary, review the translation of verbal phrases into symbols from Section 3-1. These symbols for verbal phrases will be used in this section together with $=$, which replaces expressions such as *is, the result is,* and *equals,* in writing equations.

As part of the ongoing goal of integrating algebra and geometry, the exercises provide a review of geometric formulas as students translate verbal sentences into equations. Students are not required to solve these equations, since methods of solution are discussed in the next section.

4-5 SOLVING PROBLEMS BY USING VARIABLES AND EQUATIONS

Since this section lays the groundwork for solving verbal problems algebraically, sufficient time must be devoted to understanding the procedures outlined here. Students should identify the variable and what it represents before writing the equation. All too often, they will eliminate this step, write an equation, and then not realize what the equation means.

The check is equally important. The answer should be checked in the words of the problem. Checking a number in the equation written is not sufficient, since such a check verifies that the equation written has been correctly solved but not that a correct equation has been written.

Compare the steps necessary for an algebraic solution of a problem with the general problem-solving steps introduced in Chapter 2. Conclude that the general 4-step framework is still applicable, with attention paid to the algebraic approach. After completing an algebraic solution, students should, wherever applicable, include the unit of measure in the answer.

Understanding of units of measure can be

reinforced in problems such as Exercises 23 and 24 of this section. To show how dividing dollars by dollars can give a result in hours, demonstrate the following "cancellation" for Exercise 23, writing "dollars per hour" as a fraction.

$$132 \text{ dollars} \div \frac{5.50 \text{ dollars}}{1 \text{ hour}}$$

$$= 132 \text{ dollars} \times \frac{1 \text{ hour}}{5.50 \text{ dollars}}$$

$$= \frac{132}{5.50} \times 1 \text{ hour} = 24 \text{ hours}$$

4-6 SOLVING PERCENT PROBLEMS

For some students, a review of the techniques for changing percents to decimals or common fractions may be necessary. *Selling price, dealer cost, discount,* and *taxes* are used to present realistic applications suitable to this level.

4-7 SOLVING EQUATIONS BY USING SEVERAL OPERATIONS

In the equation $2x + 3 = 15$, subtraction and division must be performed to undo the addition and multiplication. The order in which these operations are to be performed does not matter. The text shows the solution in two ways. Ask the students to solve the equation $\frac{2}{3}x + 4 = 8$ in two ways. It should become apparent that it is preferable to perform the subtraction first.

Compare the solution of an equation with the problem-solving strategy of working backward.

Example: A group of friends ordered 4 colas and a pizza. If the pizza cost $8.75 and the total cost without tax was $11.55, what was the cost of one cola?

Some students may suggest that we work backward. If we subtract the cost of the pizza from the total cost, the resulting $2.80 must be the cost of the 4 colas. If we then divide $2.80 by 4, the result, $.70, is the cost of a cola.

These are exactly the steps necessary to solve the equation $4x + 8.75 = 11.55$ that might be written when using an algebraic solution.

Encourage students to use equations to solve problems in these simple cases even though other methods of finding the solution may seem shorter. This will help students to develop their algebraic skills along with their critical thinking skills, thus preparing them for solving more complex problems, when algebraic solutions are the most efficient. Note also that on many formal examinations, an algebraic solution is *required.* Caution students to read directions carefully to see if a particular type of solution is required.

A number of equations in the exercises contain decimals and fractions to maintain skills in these areas.

4-8 MORE PRACTICE IN SOLVING EQUATIONS

No mention is made in this chapter of the term "proportion." It is not until Section 12-4 that a proportion is defined and applied to problem solving. Several examples in this practice section, such as $\frac{x}{14} = \frac{5}{7}$, are not intended to be solved by the method of cross-multiplication. To solve for x, we multiply both members of the equation by 14, resulting in the equivalent equation $\frac{x}{14}(14) = \frac{5}{7}(14)$, or $x = 10$.

Students may be encouraged to use a calculator to solve and check the exercises. Here are two questions that can be posed: Why are some problems difficult to solve using a calculator? Why is the calculator not an effective tool for solving linear equations?

Most calculators only perform operations in the order in which they are entered, not according to the rules for order of operations. Therefore, before entering a calculation such as $3 + 7 \times 8$ into a calculator, it must be rewritten as $7 \times 8 + 3$. Most calculators cannot solve equations. They can only perform the required inverse operations after we have decided what operations are needed. Therefore, to solve the equation $7x + 3 = 38$, we must decide that it is necessary to first subtract 3 and then divide the difference by 7. Thus, we can enter $38 - 3 \div 7$ into the calculator. The calculator will perform the operations in the order in which they are entered, and obtain 5 as the solution. The calculator did not solve the equation. It only performed the necessary computation.

SAT PREPARATION EXERCISES (Chapter 4)

In 1–15, select the letter of the correct answer.

1. If $x + 3 + 1.5 = 6 - 0.9$, then which expression has the smallest value?
   (A) $x + 2$ (B) $\frac{x}{2}$ (C) $2x$ (D) x^2

2. If $\frac{2}{3}x = 5$ and $3y = 7$, then xy equals
   (A) 70 (B) 35 (C) $17\frac{1}{2}$ (D) $10\frac{2}{3}$

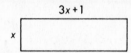
3. If the perimeter of the rectangle is 42, the dimensions of the rectangle are
   (A) 4 and 13 (B) 5 and 16
   (C) 6 and 15 (D) 7 and 15

4. How much is twice a number increased by 5, if half of the same number decreased by 5 is one?
   (A) 29 (B) 21 (C) 12 (D) 6

5. If $x + y = 4$ and $x - y = 7$, then the average of x and y is
   (A) 2 (B) $3\frac{1}{2}$ (C) $5\frac{1}{2}$ (D) $1\frac{1}{2}$

6. If $3x + 1 = 5$, then $1 \cdot 2 \cdot 3 \cdot x$ equals
   (A) 3 (B) 4 (C) 6 (D) 8

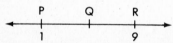
7. Q is the midpoint of segment $\overline{PR}$. If the coordinate assigned to Q is $3x - 7$, then x is
   (A) 0 (B) 3 (C) 4 (D) 6

8. If $3(7) = 7y$ and $y + 3 = z - 3$, then z equals
   (A) 0 (B) 3 (C) 6 (D) 9

9. If $0.1x = 2$ and $2y = 0.1$, then xy is
   (A) 1 (B) 2 (C) 10 (D) 20

10. If x is $\frac{1}{3}$ of y and y is $\frac{3}{5}$ of z and $5x + 3 = 4$, then $z + 5$ is
    (A) 3 (B) 4 (C) 5 (D) 6

11. If $1 \cdot 2 \cdot 3 \cdot x = 1 + 2 + 3 + x$, then how much is $(1 + 2 + 3 + 4) x$?
    (A) 6 (B) 10 (C) 12 (D) 24

12. If n is an odd number, then the average of n and five times n is
    (A) twice n (B) six times n
    (C) odd   (D) even

13. If one number is half of another and their average is 15, then the smaller number increased by 2 is
    (A) 8 (B) 10 (C) 12 (D) 20

14. The product of 4 and a number is 4 more than 12. What is half of the number?
    (A) 2 (B) 3 (C) 6 (D) 8

15. The original price of a coat was discounted 20% and put on sale at $100. The coat was later marked up 50% from this sale price. The difference between the original price and the final price was
    (A) $20 (B) $25 (C) $30 (D) $33.33

SUGGESTED TEST ITEMS (Chapter 4)

1. Using the domain {1, 2, 3, 4, 5}, tell whether the equation is a conditional equation or an identity.

    a. $2x - 1 = 5$ **b.** $4x + 1 = 1 + 4x$ **c.** $2x - 2 = 2(x - 1)$ **d.** $\frac{1}{2}x + 4 = 6$

2. Solve and check each equation.

    a. $a + 7 = 12$ **b.** $3b = 18$ **c.** $y - 1.4 = 3.6$ **d.** $\frac{x}{7} = 2$

    e. $2n - \frac{1}{3} = 7\frac{2}{3}$ **f.** $\frac{1}{4}x + 1 = 10$ **g.** $.7a - 3.2 = 1.7$ **h.** $8 + 5c = 13$

    i. $\frac{1}{3}y - 7 = 11$ **j.** $6d + 5 = 7$

3. If $4x - 3 = 21$, find the value of $\frac{2}{3}x$.

    In 4-7: **a.** Write the sentence as an equation, using n to represent the number. **b.** Solve for n.

4. Five less than three times a number is 28.
5. Seven more than one-half of a number is 19.
6. Three times a number, decreased by 7, is 23.
7. The sum of 6 and twice a number is 18.
8. Use an algebraic equation to solve the following problem.
    The larger of two numbers is 8 more than three times the smaller. The larger number is 35. Find the smaller.

    Use any strategy to solve the following problems.

BONUS: Eleanor needs the correct change to pay the bus fare of $.80. She has only quarters and dimes. What coins can she use?

BONUS: A carpenter wants to cut a board that is 400 cm long into pieces that are 17 cm long. What is the largest number of pieces possible? How long is the piece that is left over?

CHAPTER **5**

Introducing Logic

Aims

- To introduce the vocabulary and notation of mathematical logic.
- To introduce the basic connectives of logic and their truth tables.
- To examine the truth values of sentences using the basic connectives.

Since reasoning is based on the ways we put sentences together, the topic may initially resemble lessons in English grammar. However, its application to mathematics is soon apparent.

Only sentences that can be judged to be true or false (statements) are discussed in each section. The negation of a statement and the truth values of the conjunction, disjunction, and conditional are dealt with extensively. Truth tables are inserted where applicable, both to verify truth values and to strengthen powers of reasoning.

Computer activities are added in this commentary to demonstrate the logic of the computer as it relates to the various logical connectives.

5-1 SENTENCES, STATEMENTS, AND TRUTH VALUES

Some students may believe that sentences and statements in the English language have no place in a mathematics classroom. It is not uncommon to hear students say, "This isn't math." The examples and exercises of this chapter and the next will show that mathematical logic is not restricted to mathematical settings.

Recall the work done with open sentences and solution sets in Section 3-7. These concepts are now expanded to include open sentences in logic, that is, sentences with truth values that depend upon the replacement of the pronoun. The solution set for the open sentence "$x - 3 = 5$" is {8}. The solution set for the open sentence "He was the first black major league baseball player" is {Jackie Robinson}. Notice that pronouns are now added to the list of acceptable variables, allowing us to extend the concept of an open sentence beyond that of an equation or an inequality. From this point on, any sentence that can be judged to be true or false is called a *statement*.

Computer Activity (5-1) If a variable such as P represents a statement in arithmetic, a simple program can be written to determine the truth value of the arithmetic statement. When the program is entered on the computer, the variable P is not typed; rather, the arithmetic statement is entered in place of the variable.

```
10  REM    THIS PROGRAM WILL TEST THE
20  REM    TRUTH VALUE OF AN ARITHMETIC
30  REM    STATEMENT OF EQUALITY.
40  IF P THEN 70
50  PRINT "THIS STATEMENT IS FALSE."
60  GOTO 80
70  PRINT "THIS STATEMENT IS TRUE."
80  END
```

In general, if P is a true statement, the computer will move from line 40 to line 70. If P is not a true statement, the computer will not move from line 40 to line 70, but will follow the numerical sequence from line 40 to line 50. For example, let P represent "3 + 2 = 5." Enter the line:

```
40  IF 3 + 2 = 5 THEN 70
```

Enter the other lines of the program as shown above. The output will be:

```
THIS STATEMENT IS TRUE.
```

Suppose we let P represent "5 + 8 = 58." Enter the line:

```
40  IF 5 + 8 = 58 THEN 70
```

Enter the other lines of the program as shown above. The output will be:

```
THIS STATEMENT IS FALSE.
```

5-2 NEGATIONS AND SYMBOLS

Students should readily see that a statement and its negation have opposite truth values. At times, some students will refer to the symbolic statement $\sim p$ as a false statement, since it carries the negation symbol. Dispel this erroneous thought by illustrations: if p represents "2 + 2 = 5," then $\sim p$ represents "2 + 2 ≠ 5," a true statement.

A statement may contain more than one negation symbol. The truth value of $\sim(\sim(\sim p))$ can be determined by a truth table. The similarities that exist between $\sim(\sim(\sim p))$ and $-(-(-3))$ may help to promote understanding (although work with operations of signed numbers is not considered until Chapter 7).

5-3 CONJUNCTIONS

Once you define the compound sentence called *conjunction*, students are confronted with the problem of considering a truth table that takes into account every possible combination of true and false statements.

A tree diagram is provided in this section as a means of explaining the four possible cases. The idea of a tree diagram reappears in Section 15-7 (The Counting Principle and Sample Spaces) of the probability chapter.

Make a statement: "Jeff is going to the store *and* to the movies." Then, ask students to tell the conditions they think are required for this conjunction to be true. Students will probably give the correct response, "When Jeff does both." If Jeff did not go to the store, or go to the movies, or go to either, the claim is false. Stress the fact that a conjunction is true only when both conjuncts are true.

Since logic is the formal study of reasoning, it is desirable to have students draw conclusions from the truth table. For example: If $p \wedge q$ is a false statement and it is known that p is true, it can be determined from the truth table that q must be false. If this method is employed throughout the study of logic in

Course I, the transition from an informal treatment of logic in Course I to the formal treatment in Course II will be a smooth one.

The number of rows in a truth table is determined by the formula 2^n, where n is the number of variables in the logical sentence. For example: since $p \wedge q$ contains two variables, a truth table for $p \wedge q$ must contain 2^2 or 4 rows. If a third variable, r, is introduced, 2^3 or 8 rows are needed to display the truth table.

To demonstrate the eight possible arrangements of truth values for the parts of a statement composed of three variables, add a third branch to the tree.

A truth table for a statement with two variables can be expanded to a three-variable table. Write each row of truth values twice, and add T to one row and F to the other. The resulting entries are as shown in the table at the right.

p	q	r
T	T	T
T	T	F
T	F	T
T	F	F
F	T	T
F	T	F
F	F	T
F	F	F

Tree Diagram   *Truth Table*

Computer Activity (5-3)   When the variables P and Q in the following program are replaced by simple arithmetic statements, the truth value of the conjunction can be determined by the computer.

```
10   REM    THIS PROGRAM WILL TEST THE
20   REM    TRUTH VALUE OF A CONJUNCTION.
30   IF P AND Q THEN 60
40   PRINT "THIS STATEMENT IS FALSE."
50   GOTO 70
60   PRINT "THIS STATEMENT IS TRUE."
70   END
```

For example, enter the program as shown but enter line 30 as follows:

```
30   IF 7 + 2 = 9 AND 8 / 4 = 2 THEN 60
```

The output will be:

```
THIS STATEMENT IS TRUE.
```

If P, or Q, or both are replaced by false statements in arithmetic, the output will indicate that the statement is false.

5-4 DISJUNCTIONS

Use the compound sentence "Jeff is going to the store *or* to the movies," and ask the students to determine the conditions under which this disjunction will be false. Students will probably give the correct response, "When Jeff does not do either one."

The difference between the *inclusive or* and the *exclusive or* should be discussed at this point. In our study of logic, we define *or* to be the *inclusive or*. Therefore, the disjunction is false only in the case when both disjuncts are false.

Mention is made in this section of the similarities that exist between negation, conjunction, and disjunction in logic and the complement, intersection, and union in set theory. This transfer of thought, or integration of topics, should also serve as a review of sets seen in Section 1-10.

You may wish to challenge good students to use a truth table for a statement with three variables to prove that disjunction is distributive over conjunction and that conjunction is distributive over disjunction.

$$p \vee (q \wedge r) \leftrightarrow (p \vee q) \wedge (p \vee r)$$
$$p \wedge (q \vee r) \leftrightarrow (p \wedge q) \vee (p \wedge r)$$

Computer Activity (5-4) When the variables P and Q in the following program are replaced by simple arithmetic statements, the truth value of the disjunction can be determined by the computer.

```
10   REM    THIS PROGRAM WILL TEST
20   REM    THE TRUTH VALUE OF A DISJUNCTION.
30   IF P THEN 70
40   IF Q THEN 70
50   PRINT "THE DISJUNCTION IS FALSE."
60   GOTO 80
70   PRINT "THE DISJUNCTION IS TRUE."
80   END
```

For example, enter:

```
30   IF 2 * 5 = 10 THEN 70
40   IF 2 + 5 = 8 THEN 70
```

The output will be:

```
THE DISJUNCTION IS TRUE.
```

An alternate program may also be used on some computers:

```
10   IF P OR Q THEN 40
20   PRINT "THIS STATEMENT IS FALSE."
30   GOTO 50
40   PRINT "THIS STATEMENT IS TRUE."
50   END
```

5-5 CONDITIONALS

The truth table for the conditional is not so obvious to students as are the truth tables for other kinds of statements. You may present a conditional statement to the class, such as: "If it is raining, then I'll carry an umbrella." If it rains and I carry an umbrella, or $T \rightarrow T$, the statement is true. If it rains and I do not carry an umbrella, or $T \rightarrow F$, then this claim is false. In other words, I have told a lie.

Students will see the truth values of these first rows easily. The next two rows, however, will pose problems. If it does not rain, whether I carry an umbrella or not, the original statement cannot be judged to be a lie. Since the statement or claim is not a lie, the conditional statement is deemed to be true in these cases. In other words, the *only* time that a conditional statement is false is when a deliberate lie has been told, namely, when $T \rightarrow F$.

It may be necessary to give many more examples at this stage. In addition to the conditional statements given in the text, provide the class with some statements of your own: "If you do the extra report, then you'll get an A on the next report card." "If you talk one more time, then I'll call your parents." Encourage students to think of similar examples.

You may wish to present a hidden conditional without first explaining the concept: "Boat rides make me sick."

The students may say this is not a conditional statement. Simply say that this is a hidden conditional, and ask them to restate the sentence in the *if . . . then* form: If I go on a boat ride, then I'll get sick. Elicit from students other examples of hidden conditionals based, perhaps, on newspaper advertisements or TV commercials.

Order is important when symbolizing the conditional statement. For example, $p \to q$ and $q \to p$ do not necessarily have the same truth values, as did $p \land q$ and $q \land p$. Plan a lesson that involves identifying the antecedent and the conclusion. For example, "I will go to the beach if it is not cloudy" is *not* symbolized by $B \to \sim C$. Since "it is not cloudy" follows the word *if*, $\sim C$ is the antecedent. Hence, the sentence can be rewritten as "If it is not cloudy, then I will go to the beach," or $\sim C \to B$.

Computer Activity (5-5) When the variables P and Q in the following program are replaced by simple arithmetic statements, the truth value of the conditional $P \to Q$ can be determined by the computer.

```
10   REM   THIS PROGRAM WILL TEST THE
20   REM   TRUTH VALUE OF A CONDITIONAL.
30   IF P THEN 60
40   PRINT "THE CONDITIONAL IS TRUE."
50   GOTO 80
60   IF Q THEN 40
70   PRINT "THE CONDITIONAL IS FALSE."
80   END
```

Consider an example where P is true and Q is false, such as "If $12 + 8 = 20$, then $2 + 2 = 6$." Enter:

```
30   IF 12 + 8 = 20 THEN 60
60   IF 2 + 2 = 6 THEN 40
```

The output tells us:

```
THE CONDITIONAL IS FALSE.
```

All other True-False combinations will result in true conditional statements.

SAT PREPARATION EXERCISES (Chapter 5)

In 1–13, select the letter of the correct answer.

1. p: x is even.
  q: x is a multiple of 3.
How many whole numbers less than 20 make $\sim p \wedge q$ true?
(A) 3 (B) 4 (C) 6 (D) 10

2. p: x is divisible by 3.
  q: x is divisible by 6.
Which of the following is true for $x = 27$?
(A) $p \wedge q$ (B) $\sim p \wedge q$
(C) $p \wedge \sim q$ (D) $\sim p \wedge \sim q$

3. p: $x < 2$
  q: $x^2 < 2x$
The statement $p \rightarrow q$ is false when x is
(A) 3 (B) 2 (C) 1 (D) 0

4. p: $x < (1 + 2)(3) + 4$
  q: $x < 1 + (2)(3 + 4)$
Which of the following is true for all values of x?
(A) $p \wedge q$ (B) $p \vee q$
(C) $p \rightarrow q$ (D) $q \rightarrow p$

5. p: X is between Y and Z.
  q: Y is between X and Z.
If X, Y, and Z are points on a line with $XY = 1$ and $XZ = 2$, which of the following statements must be true?
(A) p (B) q (C) $p \vee q$ (D) $p \wedge q$

6. p: The area is 4π.
  q: The circumference is 4π.
Which of the following is *not* true for a circle with a diameter of 4?
(A) $p \wedge q$ (B) $p \vee q$
(C) $\sim p \wedge q$ (D) $\sim p \vee q$

7. Let x represent a number.
  p: Twice x exceeds 10.
  q: x increased by 5 exceeds 12.
How many counting numbers less than 10 make $p \rightarrow q$ true?
(A) 4 (B) 5 (C) 6 (D) 7

8. p: N divided by 3 gives a remainder 1.
  q: N divided by 5 gives a remainder 1.
What is the largest whole number less than 20 for which $p \vee q$ is true?
(A) 19 (B) 16 (C) 15 (D) 13

9. p: $x + y = 10$
  q: $xy > 25$
If x and y are whole numbers, which of the following *cannot* be true for any (x, y)?
(A) $p \wedge q$ (B) $p \vee q$
(C) $p \rightarrow q$ (D) $q \rightarrow p$

10. p: 5 is the average of x and y.
  q: 10 is the sum of x and y.
Which of the following is true for $x = 3$ and $y = 8$?
(A) $p \vee q$ (B) $p \wedge q$
(C) $\sim p \rightarrow q$ (D) $p \rightarrow \sim q$

11. p: x and y are whole numbers.
  q: The product of x and y is 47.
If the conjunction $p \wedge q$ is true, then the *negation* of which of the following is true?
(A) x avg $y = 24$ (B) x max $y = 47$
(C) x could not be 1. (D) $x + y$ is even.

12. p: x, the square of a counting number, is less than 20.
  q: x, a counting number, is a divisor of 36.
The number of values that make $p \wedge q$ true is what percent of the number of values that make $p \vee q$ true?

(A) 10 (B) 20 (C) 30 (D) $33\frac{1}{3}$

13. Let $\boxed{x} = x + 1$ for all x.

The statement "If $\boxed{x} + 2 = 5$,

then $\boxed{x} + \boxed{x} = 6$" is true when x is
(A) 1 only (B) 2 only
(C) 3 only (D) any real number

SUGGESTED TEST ITEMS (Chapter 5)

1. Tell whether each of the following is or is not a mathematical sentence.
   a. Chicago is a city in France.   b. How old are you?   c. Stop.
   d. Water freezes at 0° Celsius.   e. If I go.   f. x

2. Identify each of the following as *true, false,* or *open.*
   a. There are 7 days in a week.   b. $3^2 = 3 \cdot 2$ c. $2^4 = 4^2$
   d. He is sixteen years old.   e. A triangle has three angles.   f. $x + 7 = 10$

In 3–7:   Let p represent "Peter is a rabbit." (True)
    Let q represent "Peter is an animal." (True)
    Let r represent "Peter lives in a pond." (False)
   a. Write each of the following sentences in symbolic form.
   b. Give the truth value of each sentence.

3. Peter does not live in a pond.
4. Peter is not a rabbit and Peter is an animal.
5. Peter is not an animal or Peter lives in a pond.
6. If Peter is not a rabbit, then Peter is not an animal.
7. Peter is not a rabbit if Peter is an animal.

In 8–11:   Let f represent "I study French." (False)
    Let b represent "I study biology." (True)
    Let s represent "Biology is a science." (True)
   a. Write a complete sentence in words to show what the symbols represent.
   b. Give the truth value of each sentence.

8. $\sim f$ 9. $f \wedge \sim b$ 10. $s \rightarrow \sim b$ 11. $b \vee \sim s$

12. Use the domain $\{1, 2, 3, 4, \ldots, 10\}$ to find the truth set of each of the following.
   a. $x < 5$ b. $x \not< 5$ c. $x \geq 7$
   d. $(x < 5) \wedge (x \not< 5)$ e. $(x \geq 7) \vee (x + 5 = 12)$

In 13 and 14: a. Identify the hypothesis. b. Identify the conclusion.

13. If today is Monday, then tomorrow is not Wednesday.
14. I will walk home if it does not rain.

In 15–20, complete the statement by writing "is true," "is false," or "may be true or false."

15. If p is false, then $\sim(\sim p)$ _____.
16. If p is false, then $p \rightarrow q$ _____.
17. If p is true, then $p \vee q$ _____.
18. If $p \wedge q$ is true, then p _____.
19. If $p \vee q$ is false, then p _____.
20. If p is false, then $p \vee q$ _____.

BONUS: Andy, Ben, Carlos, Donna, and Elsie went to the movies and sat together in one row. Ben sat at the far left. There were two people between Elsie and Andy. Carlos did not sit next to Andy. Donna sat in the middle. In what order were these five friends sitting?

CHAPTER 6

Using Logic

Aims

- To introduce related conditionals.

- To show the relationship of the converse, inverse, and contrapositive to a given conditional.

- To define the biconditional as the conjunction of a conditional and its converse.

- To define a tautology as a compound sentence that is always true.

- To define logical equivalence.

- To use logic to draw conclusions.

By considering logical equivalence, students further strengthen their reasoning powers. Problems chosen in these sections are from real-life situations as well as from the realm of mathematics. Applications of the biconditional statement are seen in the areas of geometry and algebra.

This first exposure to formal logic ends with a preview of how logic is used to draw conclusions. In Course II, we build upon this foundation to develop the laws of inference, and the nature of proof begins to play a major role in the study of mathematics.

6-1 COMPOUND STATEMENTS AND TRUTH VALUES

In order to find the truth value of any compound sentence, we must follow a specific order of operations. Once the truth values within the parentheses are simplified (working with the innermost group first), then the negations must be simplified. The other connectives may then be simplified by working from left to right. For example:

Find the truth value of the compound sentence $(p \wedge q) \vee \sim r$ when p, q, and r are all true.

$$(p \wedge q) \vee \sim r$$
$$(T \wedge T) \vee \sim T$$
$$T \vee \sim T$$
$$T \vee F$$
$$T$$

Make sure that the truth values of conjunction, disjunction, and the conditional are understood by the students before going on to further study of truth tables and tautologies. Encourage students to remember the special cases by asking:

"When is a conjunction true?"

"When is a disjunction false?"

"When is a conditional false?"

Once the unique case is identified, the remainder of the table is easy to reconstruct.

Computer Activity (6-1) Programs can be written to determine the truth values of compound statements in logic involving the three variables P, Q, and R, where each variable represents an arithmetic statement. Note that each compound statement requires a different program. For example, to test the statement $(P \wedge Q) \rightarrow R$, we write:

```
10   REM   THIS PROGRAM WILL TEST THE
20   REM   TRUTH VALUE OF A STATEMENT OF
30   REM   THE FORM (P AND Q) IMPLIES R.
40   IF P AND Q THEN 70
50   PRINT "THE STATEMENT IS TRUE."
60   GOTO 90
70   IF R THEN 50
80   PRINT "THE STATEMENT IS FALSE."
90   END
```

The only time that this compound statement is false is when both P and Q are true and R is false. For example:

```
40   IF 2 + 3 = 5 AND 5 + 1 = 6 THEN 70
70   IF 6 + 6 = 7 THEN 50
```

In all other cases, the compound statement is true.

6-2 COMPOUND SENTENCES AND TRUTH VALUES

Initially, it is best that you supply students with the headings necessary for the completion of truth tables of given compound sentences. Once students become familiar with this structure, have them fill in their own headings before constructing the tables. Those compound sentences that are always true are considered formally in Section 6-4 (Tautologies).

6-3 BICONDITIONALS

The truth table for $p \leftrightarrow q$ is best understood by considering the conjunction of $p \rightarrow q$ and $q \rightarrow p$. It is important that students realize the applications of the biconditional. Precise definitions include the words "if and only if," as seen in Chapter 11 (Geometry) and, to a larger degree, in Course II when the geometry is formalized. Biconditional statements are an integral part of equations: "$2x = 10$ if and only if $x = 5$." If two statements always have the same truth values, these statements are logically equivalent, and one may be substituted for the other in any expression.

In Section 6-5, we will see that $p \rightarrow q$ and its contrapositive $\sim q \rightarrow \sim p$ are logically equivalent statements. The biconditional statement $(p \rightarrow q) \leftrightarrow (\sim q \rightarrow \sim p)$ represents the equivalence. Students will learn other equivalences in Course II when they develop concepts in proof.

Computer Activity (6-3)   When the variables *P* and *Q* in the following program are replaced by simple arithmetic statements, the truth value of the biconditional $P \leftrightarrow Q$ can be determined by the computer.

```
10   REM   THIS PROGRAM WILL TEST THE
20   REM   TRUTH VALUE OF A BICONDITIONAL.
30   IF P THEN 70
40   IF Q THEN 80
50   PRINT "THE BICONDITIONAL IS TRUE."
60   GOTO 90
70   IF Q THEN 50
80   PRINT "THE BICONDITIONAL IS FALSE."
90   END
```

For example, enter:

```
30   IF 3 + 1 = 4 THEN 70
40   IF 3 - 2 = 6 THEN 80
70   IF 3 - 2 = 6 THEN 50
```

The output will be:

```
THE BICONDITIONAL IS FALSE.
```

6-4   TAUTOLOGIES

Tautologies are used to strengthen powers of reasoning. At first, students may approach this topic mechanically: place *T-F* values in the columns of the truth table, and claim a tautology exists only when every value in the last column is true. You should require that more be done. Specifically, in cases where two statements are related in a biconditional form and a tautology exists, the statements are logically equivalent; that is, each can be used as a replacement for the other. Use verbal sentences to illustrate.

For example, $\sim(p \rightarrow q) \leftrightarrow (p \wedge \sim q)$ is a tautology. Using simple verbal statements for *p* and *q,* present one compound statement in words and have students find a logically equivalent verbal statement.

Given: $\sim(p \rightarrow q)$: It is not the case that if it snows, I will swim.
Response: $p \wedge \sim q$: It snows and I do not swim.

Student response can be further reinforced by asking them to take alternate sides of a biconditional. For example, for the tautology $(\sim p \rightarrow q) \leftrightarrow (p \vee q)$, first give the conditional and ask for the disjunction.

Given: $(\sim p \rightarrow q)$:   If I don't eat, I get hungry.
Response: $(p \vee q)$:   I eat or I get hungry.
Then, give the disjunction and ask for the conditional.

Given: $(p \vee q)$:   Ed will eat an orange or an apple.
Response: $(\sim p \rightarrow q)$: If Ed doesn't eat an orange, he'll eat an apple.

6-5   INVERSES, CONVERSES, AND CONTRAPOSITIVES

After you introduce the three related conditionals, ask the students which of these "sounds" logically equivalent to the original. If the students are not sure, construct a truth table consisting of the original conditional, its inverse, its converse, and its contrapositive. Students will see that the contrapositive is logically equivalent to the original, since in each row they have the same truth value. Note also that the converse and inverse, although not logically equivalent to the original, are logically equivalent to each other.

Use the model examples to summarize that although the converse and inverse are not logically equivalent to the given conditional, each may have the same truth value as the given conditional or each may have the opposite truth value of the given conditional. The given conditional itself can be either true or false.

Ask students to supply further examples, with or without mathematical settings, of:
(1) a true conditional that has a true converse and inverse (if a polygon has three sides, then it is a triangle);
(2) a true conditional that has a false converse and inverse (if the figure is a triangle, then it is a polygon);
(3) a false conditional that has a true converse and inverse (if the figure is a polygon, then it is a triangle);
(4) a false conditional that has a false converse and inverse (if a polygon is a triangle, then it is a quadrilateral).

Return to the different examples to stress that no matter what the particular case is, a conditional and its contrapositive always have the same truth value.

From the various settings, students can take away the sense that the forms of a conditional are not limited to mathematical circumstances. Some of the model examples show how certain advertising tries to set logical traps. Later, students in this program can draw on their experiences with conditionals to avoid some logical traps that traditionally arise in the study of geometry.

6-6 DRAWING CONCLUSIONS

In Course II, the rules of inference are developed formally to enable students to recognize patterns in drawing conclusions. This section is intended to prepare students for these formal rules. By referring to the truth table each time in order to decide whether it is possible to determine that a related sentence is true or false, the student will develop a familiarity with the combinations of sentences from which a conclusion can be drawn. At this time, the rules of inference should be used in drawing conclusions only if these rules are the result of the students' observations.

To encourage student observations, it may be useful to "diagram sentences" in a manner similar to that used when translating verbal phrases to algebraic symbols. For example, in Model Problem 1 on page 186:

Today is Monday or I have gym.

$$F \qquad \vee \qquad ? \qquad = \qquad T$$
given $\qquad\qquad\qquad\qquad$ given

Students will see that, since at least one disjunct must be true to produce a true disjunction, the ? must be replaced by a T.

Persons often disagree about the truth of a logical conclusion, not because the logic is incorrect but because they disagree about the truth value of one or more of the premises to which the logic is applied. Present logical arguments such as the following to your students:

1. *Premises:*
If studying is more important than watching TV, then I should study even though my favorite program is on.
Studying is more important than watching TV.
Conclusion:
I should study even though my favorite program is on.

2. *Premises:*
If my favorite group is to perform, it is worth standing in line all day to buy a ticket.
My favorite group is to perform next week.
Conclusion:
It is worth standing in line all day to buy a ticket.

Each conclusion is true when the premises are true. Some students will not accept the conclusions as true because they do not accept the premises as true.

SAT PREPARATION EXERCISES (Chapter 6)

In 1–13, select the letter of the correct answer.

1.   *p:* x is 10.
        q: x is 3 units from 7 on the number line.
    Which of the following is true for all possible values of x?
    (A) $p \rightarrow q$ (B) $q \rightarrow p$
    (C) $p \rightarrow \sim q$ (D) $p \leftrightarrow \sim q$

2.   *p:* $x \div x = 1$
        q: $1(x) = x$
    Which of the following is true for all x?
    (A) p (B) q (C) $p \wedge q$ (D) $p \leftrightarrow q$

3.   *p:* The area is a multiple of 9.
        q: One side is a multiple of 3.
    Which of the following is true for all possible squares?
    (A) $p \wedge \sim q$ (B) $p \rightarrow \sim q$
    (C) $q \rightarrow p$ (D) $\sim p \wedge q$

4.   *p:* $\triangle JKL$ has exactly 2 equal sides.
        q: $\triangle JKL$ has exactly 3 equal sides.
    Which of the following is true for all triangles?
    (A) $p \wedge q$ (B) $p \vee q$
    (C) $p \rightarrow q$ (D) $\sim p \vee \sim q$

5. Given the statement:
        If $x = 0$, then $x + y = y$.
    Which of the following is true?
        I. The converse
        II. The inverse
    (A) I only   (B) II only
    (C) I and II   (D) neither

6. Given the statement:
        If $x = 1$, then $xy = y$.
    Which of the following is true?
        I. The inverse
        II. The contrapositive
    (A) I only   (B) II only
    (C) I and II   (D) neither

7. Given the statement:
        If $x = 0$, then $xy = 0$.
    Which of the following is true?
        I. The converse
        II. The contrapositive
    (A) I only
    (B) II only
    (C) I and II
    (D) neither

8. Given the statement:
        If $x = 2$ and $y = 3$, then $\frac{x}{y} = \frac{2}{3}$.
    Which of the following is true?
        I. The converse
        II. The inverse
    (A) I only
    (B) II only
    (C) I and II
    (D) neither

9. Given the statement:
        If $PQ = QR$, then Q is the midpoint of $\overline{PR}$.
    Which of the following is true?
        I. The converse
        II. The contrapositive
    (A) I only
    (B) II only
    (C) I and II
    (D) neither

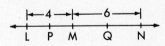

10.   *p:* P is the midpoint of $\overline{LM}$.
        q: Q is the midpoint of $\overline{MN}$.
    Which of the following statements is true for the points shown above when $PQ = 5$?
    (A) $p \wedge q$
    (B) $p \vee q$
    (C) $p \leftrightarrow q$
    (D) $\sim p \vee \sim q$

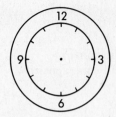

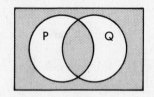

11. *p:* The hour hand is less than 4 units from 3:00 o'clock.

q: The hour hand is less than 4 units from 9:00 o'clock.

If each unit represents an hour on the clock above, what percent of the time is $p \wedge q$ true?

(A) 25 (B) $33\frac{1}{3}$ (C) 50 (D) 100

12. *p:* X is in set P.
q: X is in set Q.

For all points X in the shaded areas above, which of the following statements is true?

(A) $p \wedge q$ (B) $p \vee q$
(C) $p \wedge \sim q$ (D) $p \leftrightarrow q$

13. Let $U = \{1, 2, 3, \ldots, 10\}$.
p: x is in set $P\{1, 2\}$.
q: x is in set $Q\{2, 3\}$.

The truth set for $p \rightarrow q$ is equivalent to

(A) $\overline{P} \cap Q$ (B) $\overline{P} \cup Q$
(C) $P \cap \overline{Q}$ (D) $P \cup \overline{Q}$

SUGGESTED TEST ITEMS (Chapter 6)

In 1–4, *p:* A square is a rectangle. (True)
 q: A square is a polygon. (True)
 r: A circle is a polygon. (False)
 a. Write each of the following in symbolic form using *p, q,* and *r*.
 b. Give the truth value of each.

1. If a square is not a rectangle, then a square is not a polygon.
2. If it is not true that a square is a rectangle and a polygon, then a circle is a polygon.
3. If a circle is a polygon or a circle is not a polygon, then a square is a rectangle.
4. A square is a polygon if and only if a circle is a polygon.

In 5–6, write **a.** the inverse **b.** the converse **c.** the contrapositive.

5. If today is Wednesday, then tomorrow is Thursday.
6. If a carrot is a vegetable, then vegetables do not grow on trees.
7. **a.** Make a truth table for each of the following.
 b. What two sentences are equivalent?
  (1) $p \rightarrow \sim q$ (2) $\sim p \vee \sim q$ (3) $p \wedge \sim q$
8. **a.** Complete the following truth table for the sentence $\sim(p \wedge q) \leftrightarrow (\sim p \vee \sim q)$

p	q	$\sim p$	$\sim q$	$p \wedge q$	$\sim(p \wedge q)$	$\sim p \vee \sim q$	$\sim(p \wedge q) \leftrightarrow (\sim p \vee \sim q)$

 b. Is the statement a tautology? Why?

In 9–12, assume that the first two sentences are true. State whether the truth value of the third sentence is true, false, or cannot be determined.

9. Today is Thursday or Friday.
 Today is not Friday.
 Today is Thursday.
10. If I studied, I passed the test.
 I did not pass the test.
 I studied.
11. I speak Spanish or I speak English.
 I speak English.
 I speak Spanish.
12. If Peter asks Meg to the dance, then Inez will go to the dance with Greg.
 Peter asks Meg to the dance.
 Inez will go the dance with Greg.

BONUS: In the country of Tollifer, the unit of money is a toll. Coins have a value of 3, 7, and 11 tolls. What is the smallest number of coins needed to have exactly 23 tolls? Is there more than one possible set of coins with a value equal to 23 tolls?

CHAPTER 7

Signed Numbers

Aims

- To extend the number line to include signed numbers.

- To order signed numbers.

- To graph solution sets on a number line.

- To formulate the rules for addition, subtraction, multiplication, and division of signed numbers.

- To solve simple algebraic equations using inverses.

The emphasis in this chapter is on the signed aspect of real numbers. Once the number line is extended, all signed numbers are ordered and graphed accordingly.

Similarities exist between signed numbers and logic, since every signed number has an opposite and every sentence in logic has a negation.

The rules for operations are reinforced when signed numbers are used to evaluate algebraic expressions.

7-1 EXTENDING THE NUMBER LINE

The number line is extended to include positive and negative real numbers, which students know as signed numbers. Students are already familiar with rational-number subsets of the real numbers, represented by fractions and decimals. Discussion of irrational numbers is reserved for Chapter 19.

Some students erroneously think of the signed numbers as only the integers. Emphasize that the integers are not all the signed numbers, but only a subset.

A distinction should be made, at the beginning, between the use of positive and negative signs to indicate direction, as in $^+3$ and $^-2$, and plus and minus signs to indicate addition and subtraction: $^+3 + {}^-2$, $^+3 - {}^-2$, etc.

Working with various Celsius temperature readings helps to illustrate the fact that all signed numbers are ordered on the real number line. The symbols $>$ and $<$ are used to order the numbers. Initially, students may have trouble locating numbers such as $-1\frac{3}{4}$ and -2.6 on the number line. Once they understand how to locate points, they will see that the larger of two numbers will always be farther to the right on the number line.

Three distinct numbers are ordered so that one of the three is between the other two. The logical connective *and* is useful to express this concept of betweenness.

The text shows that a conjunction and the interval it represents can be expressed using either symbol of inequality.

Note that although a conjunction such as $(^+7 > {}^+2) \wedge (^+2 < {}^+5)$ can be written using both inequality symbols, the combined inequality must be written with only one symbol or the other. Thus, we can write either $^+7 > {}^+5 > {}^+2$ or $^+2 < {}^+5 < {}^+7$. We cannot write $^+7 > {}^+2 < {}^+5$ because this symbolism does not describe an interval.

Computer Activities (7-1)   A computer program may be used to order signed numbers. For example, in Exercise 6 on page 194, the computer can determine if ‾7 > ‾1 is a true or a false sentence.

```
10   REM  THIS PROGRAM WILL TEST THE
20   REM  TRUTH VALUE OF AN INEQUALITY.
30   IF -7 > -1 THEN 60
40   PRINT "THIS STATEMENT IS FALSE."
50   GOTO 70
60   PRINT "THIS STATEMENT IS TRUE."
70   END
```

The computer will display:

```
THIS STATEMENT IS FALSE.
```

The two programs that follow will allow the students to enter two or three numbers and will write the correct inequality using the numbers that were entered.

```
100   REM  THIS PROGRAM WILL PUT THE
110   REM  CORRECT EQUALITY OR INEQUALITY
120   REM  SIGN BETWEEN ANY TWO NUMBERS.
130   PRINT "ENTER ANY TWO SIGNED NUMBERS"
140   PRINT "SEPARATED BY A COMMA."
150   INPUT A,B
160   IF A < B THEN R$ = "<"
170   IF A = B THEN R$ = "="
180   IF A > B THEN R$ = ">"
190   PRINT A;R$;B
200   END

100   REM  THIS PROGRAM WILL PUT ANY
110   REM  THREE SIGNED NUMBERS IN ORDER.
120   PRINT "ENTER ANY THREE SIGNED NUMBERS"
130   PRINT "SEPARATED BY COMMAS."
140   INPUT A(1),A(2),A(3)
150   FOR J = 1 TO 2
160   FOR K = 1 TO 2
170   IF A(K) <= A(K + 1) THEN 210
180   LET T = A(K)
190   LET A(K) = A(K + 1)
200   LET A(K + 1) = T
210   NEXT K
220   NEXT J
230   PRINT A(1);"<";A(2);"<";A(3)
240   END
```

7-2 GRAPHING THE SOLUTION SET OF AN OPEN SENTENCE INVOLVING ONE VARIABLE ON A NUMBER LINE

The graphs of the solution sets for simple and compound open sentences are considered. These solution sets can be finite or infinite.

The graph of the interval $3 < x < 6$ is viewed as the equivalent conjunction $(3 < x) \wedge (x < 6)$. The graph of the solution set of this open sentence is the intersection of the sets of points represented by each conjunct.

The graph of the disjunction $(3 < x) \vee (x > 6)$ is the union of the sets of points represented by each disjunct.

Students should be able to select specific values on the number line to verify the inequality graphs.

Computer Activity (7-2) To determine the solution set of the open sentence in Exercise 8 on page 197, you can use the following program:

```
10   REM   THIS PROGRAM WILL PRINT THE
20   REM   INTEGERS FROM -4 TO 4 THAT
30   REM   MAKE THE INEQUALITY -1 < Y <= +2
40   REM   TRUE.
50   DATA  -4,-3,-2,-1,0,1,2,3,4
60   READ Y
70   IF Y > -1 THEN 90
80   GOTO 60
90   IF Y <= 2 THEN 110
100   GOTO 60
110   PRINT Y
120   GOTO 60
130   END
```

7-3 THE OPPOSITE OF A DIRECTED NUMBER

To avoid confusion later, take the time to discuss the two uses of the symbols $+$ and $-$.

Note the opportunity for transfer of learning as we relate the logical statement $\sim(\sim p) \leftrightarrow p$ to the sentence $-(-y) = y$. Emphasize the fact that $-y$ does not always represent a negative number: if $y = -3$, then $-y = -(-3) = 3$.

Computer Activity (7-3) The following program will generate random integers between -25 and $+24$ and ask the student to give the opposite. At the end, it will tell the student the number of correct responses given.

Note: On some computers, RND (1) may have to be changed to RND (0).

```
100   REM   THIS PROGRAM WILL PROVIDE
110   REM   PRACTICE WITH THE OPPOSITES
120   REM   OF DIRECTED NUMBERS.
130   LET C = 0
140   LET D = 0
150   LET X =  INT ( RND (1) * 50) - 25
160   PRINT "WHAT IS THE OPPOSITE OF ";X;"?"
170   INPUT A
180   LET D = D + 1
```

```
190    IF A = - 1 * X THEN 260
200    PRINT "THE OPPOSITE OF A POSITIVE OR UNSIGNED"
210    PRINT "NUMBER IS NEGATIVE."
220    PRINT "THE OPPOSITE OF A NEGATIVE NUMBER IS"
230    PRINT "POSITIVE OR UNSIGNED."
240    PRINT "THE OPPOSITE OF 0 IS 0."
250    GOTO 160
260    LET C = C + 1
270    PRINT "THAT'S RIGHT."
280    PRINT "DO YOU WANT TO TRY ANOTHER?"
290    INPUT R$
300    IF R$ = "Y" OR R$ = "YES" THEN 150
310    PRINT "YOU HAD ";C;" OUT OF ";D;" CORRECT ANSWERS."
320    END
```

7-4 THE ABSOLUTE VALUE OF A NUMBER

Since the definition of absolute value is given as the greater of a nonzero number and its opposite, we symbolize this definition as $|x| = x \max (-x)$. Offer some numerical applications of this definition, focusing awareness on the fact that $-x$ does not necessarily represent a negative number. If $x = -2$:

$$|-2| = (-2) \max (-[-2])$$
$$= (-2) \max 2$$
$$= 2$$

Note that, in this example, $-x = 2$, a positive number.

Let students see the effect of the absolute value operation as it is combined with other operations by experimenting, for example, with the following cases.

a. $|-8| + |-4|$ **b.** $|(-8) + (-4)|$
c. $|-8| - |-4|$ **d.** $|(-8) - (-4)|$
e. $|-8| \cdot |-4|$ **f.** $|(-8)(-4)|$
g. $\dfrac{|-8|}{|-4|}$ **h.** $\left|\dfrac{-8}{-4}\right|$

Conclude that the absolute value of a sum (or difference) is not necessarily equivalent to the sum (or difference) of the absolute values. But, the absolute value of a product (or quotient) is equivalent to the product (or quotient) of the absolute values.

To find the value of an expression such as $|9| - |-2| \cdot |2|$, we must first evaluate the absolute values and then follow the correct order of operations, thus obtaining 5.

Computer Activities (7-4) To have the computer find the value of $|-10| - |-5|$ in Exercise 22 on page 202, we can enter a simple PRINT statement, using the absolute-value function:

PRINT ABS (-10) − ABS (-5)

When the RETURN key is hit, the computer will display the answer, 5.

The following program will provide practice in finding the absolute value of a number, using integers from -20 to $+19$.

Note: On some computers, RND (1) may have to be changed to RND (0).

```
100    REM   THIS PROGRAM WILL TEST
110    REM   ABSOLUTE VALUE.
120    LET C = 0
130    LET D = 0
140    LET X =   INT ( RND (1) * 40) - 20
```

```
150   PRINT "WHAT IS THE ABSOLUTE VALUE OF ";X;"?"
160   INPUT A
170   LET C = C + 1
180   IF A =  ABS (X) THEN 230
190   PRINT "THE ABSOLUTE VALUE OF A NUMBER IS"
200   PRINT "ALWAYS POSITIVE OR ZERO."
210   PRINT "TRY AGAIN."
220   GOTO 150
230   PRINT "THAT'S RIGHT."
240   LET D = D + 1
250   PRINT "DO YOU WANT TO TRY ANOTHER?"
260   INPUT R$
270   IF R$ = "YES" OR R$ = "Y" THEN 140
280   PRINT "YOU HAVE ";D;" CORRECT ANSWERS OUT OF ";C;"."
290   END
```

7-5 ADDING SIGNED NUMBERS ON A NUMBER LINE

Adding signed numbers on a number line helps students see how the sum of two positive numbers, the sum of two negative numbers, and the sum of a negative and a positive number are arrived at. The need for rules for addition of signed numbers becomes obvious when you ask students to find sums such as $(+52) + (-131)$. These rules are formalized in the next section.

7-6 ADDITION OF SIGNED NUMBERS

In this section, each of the rules for adding signed numbers without the use of a number line is defined in terms of absolute values. The addition properties studied in Chapter 1 apply to signed numbers. Other addition properties are also mentioned here: the addition property of opposites and the property of the opposite of a sum.

In Chapter 1, there was no mention of the additive inverse, since the numbers of arithmetic do not include negative numbers. Now, since every signed number, n, has an opposite, $-n$, the additive inverse is introduced.

Computer Activity (7-6) The following program will generate a pair of random integers between -20 and $+19$ and ask the student to enter the sum. If an incorrect sum is entered, the program will suggest a rule for adding signed numbers that corresponds to the student error. After three tries, the correct answer is given.

Note: On some computers, RND (1) may have to be changed to RND (0).

```
100   REM    THIS PROGRAM WILL TEST THE
110   REM    ADDITION OF SIGNED NUMBERS.
120   LET C = 0
130   LET D = 0
140   LET X =  INT ( RND (1) * 40) - 20
150   LET Y =  INT ( RND (1) * 40) - 20
160   LET T = 0
170   PRINT "WHAT IS THE SUM OF ";X;" AND ";Y;"?"
180   LET D = D + 1
190   LET T = T + 1
200   INPUT A
```

```
210   IF A = X + Y THEN 450
220   IF T > 2 THEN 430
230   IF  ABS (A) =  ABS (X - Y) AND X * Y < 0 THEN 270
240   IF A =  - 1 * (X + Y) THEN 310
250   PRINT "CHECK YOUR ADDITION. TRY AGAIN."
260   GOTO 170
270   PRINT "IF TWO NUMBERS HAVE OPPOSITE SIGNS,"
280   PRINT "FIND THE DIFFERENCE OF THE ABSOLUTE"
290   PRINT "VALUES. TRY AGAIN."
300   GOTO 170
310   IF X < 0 AND Y < 0 THEN 400
320   IF X > 0 AND Y > 0 THEN 370
330   PRINT "IF TWO NUMBERS HAVE OPPOSITE SIGNS,"
340   PRINT "THE SUM HAS THE SIGN OF THE NUMBER WITH"
350   PRINT "THE LARGER ABSOLUTE VALUE. TRY AGAIN."
360   GOTO 170
370   PRINT "REMEMBER THAT THE SUM OF TWO POSITIVE"
380   PRINT "NUMBERS IS POSITIVE. TRY AGAIN."
390   GOTO 170
400   PRINT "REMEMBER THAT THE SUM OF TWO NEGATIVE"
410   PRINT "NUMBERS IS NEGATIVE. TRY AGAIN."
420   GOTO 170
430   PRINT X;" + ";Y;" = ";X + Y
440   GOTO 470
450   PRINT "THAT'S CORRECT."
460   LET C = C + 1
470   PRINT "DO YOU WANT TO TRY ANOTHER?"
480   INPUT R$
490   IF R$ = "YES" OR R$ = "Y" THEN 140
500   PRINT "YOU ANSWERED ";C;" CORRECTLY OUT OF ";D;"."
510   END
```

7-7 SUBTRACTION OF SIGNED NUMBERS

We defined subtraction in the set of numbers of arithmetic as the inverse operation of addition. That set is not closed with respect to subtraction. However, the difference of any two signed numbers is a unique signed number. Thus, the set of signed numbers is closed with respect to subtraction.

Since there are various approaches to teaching subtraction of signed numbers, it is recommended that you use your favorite method.

One visual approach emphasizes the definition of subtraction as adding the opposite by circling the sign of the subtrahend and replacing the sign by its opposite. For example, to subtract -3 from -9:

$$
\begin{array}{r}
-9 \\
\underline{\ominus 3} \\
-6
\end{array}
$$

This device is helpful later when there are several signs in the subtrahend, as in subtraction of polynomials.

Computer Activity (7-7) The following program will generate a pair of random integers between -20 and $+19$ and ask the student to enter the difference. If an incorrect difference is entered, the program will suggest a rule for subtracting signed numbers that corresponds to the student error. After three tries, the correct answer is given.

Note: On some computers, RND (1) may have to be changed to RND (0).

```
100   REM   THIS PROGRAM WILL TEST THE
110   REM   SUBTRACTION OF SIGNED NUMBERS.
120   LET C = 0
130   LET D = 0
140   LET X =   INT ( RND (1) * 40) - 20
150   LET Y =   INT ( RND (1) * 40) - 20
160   LET T = 0
170   PRINT "WHAT IS THE DIFFERENCE:(";X;") - (";Y;")"
180   LET D = D + 1
190   LET T = T + 1
200   INPUT A
210   IF A = X - Y THEN 360
220   IF T > 2 THEN 340
230   IF A = X + Y THEN 270
240   IF A = -1 * (X - Y) THEN 310
250   PRINT "CHECK YOUR ARITHMETIC. TRY AGAIN."
260   GOTO 170
270   PRINT "REMEMBER TO ADD THE OPPOSITE OF THE"
280   PRINT "NUMBER YOU ARE SUBTRACTING."
290   PRINT "TRY AGAIN."
300   GOTO 170
310   PRINT "CHECK THE SIGN OF YOUR ANSWER."
320   PRINT "TRY AGAIN."
330   GOTO 170
340   PRINT "(";X;") - (";Y;") = ";X - Y
350   GOTO 380
360   PRINT "THAT'S RIGHT."
370   LET C = C + 1
380   PRINT "DO YOU WANT TO TRY ANOTHER?"
390   INPUT R$
400   IF R$ = "YES" OR R$ = "Y" THEN 140
410   PRINT "YOU ANSWERED ";C;" CORRECTLY OUT OF ";D;"."
420   END
```

7-8 MULTIPLICATION OF SIGNED NUMBERS

In this section, examples are used to illustrate multiplication of signed numbers. Rules are also defined in terms of absolute values.

The multiplication properties studied in Chapter 1 are extended to the set of signed numbers, and the property involving multiplication by -1 is now mentioned. Guide students to conclude that raising a negative number to an odd exponent will yield a negative answer, while raising a negative number to an even exponent will yield a positive answer.

In the exercises, students are asked to find the similarities that exist between the product of two signed numbers and the truth table for the biconditional statement $(p \leftrightarrow q)$ in logic, another example of integration of topics.

Computer Activity (7-8) The following program tests the multiplication of signed numbers, using integers from −10 to +9 as the multiplier and integers from −20 to +19 as the multiplicand.

Note: On some computers, RND (1) may have to be changed to RND (0).

```
100   REM    THIS PROGRAM WILL TEST THE
110   REM    MULTIPLICATION OF SIGNED
120   REM    NUMBERS.
130   LET C = 0
140   LET D = 0
150   LET X =  INT ( RND (1) * 20) - 10
160   LET Y =  INT ( RND (1) * 40) - 20
170   LET T = 0
180   PRINT "WHAT IS THE PRODUCT OF ";X;" AND ";Y;"?"
190   LET D = D + 1
200   LET T = T + 1
210   INPUT A
220   IF A = X * Y THEN 420
230   IF T > 2 THEN 400
240   IF A =  - 1 * X * Y OR X * Y = 0 THEN 270
250   PRINT "CHECK YOUR ARITHMETIC. TRY AGAIN."
260   GOTO 180
270   IF X * Y > 0 THEN 320
280   IF X * Y < 0 THEN 360
290   PRINT "REMEMBER THAT 0 TIMES ANY NUMBER IS 0."
300   PRINT "TRY AGAIN."
310   GOTO 180
320   PRINT "REMEMBER THAT THE PRODUCT OF TWO"
330   PRINT "NUMBERS WITH THE SAME SIGN IS POSITIVE."
340   PRINT "TRY AGAIN."
350   GOTO 180
360   PRINT "REMEMBER THAT THE PRODUCT OF TWO"
370   PRINT "NUMBERS WITH OPPOSITE SIGNS IS NEGATIVE."
380   PRINT "TRY AGAIN."
390   GOTO 180
400   PRINT X;" TIMES ";Y;" EQUALS ";X * Y
410   GOTO 440
420   PRINT "THAT'S RIGHT."
430   LET C = C + 1
440   PRINT " DO YOU WANT TO TRY ANOTHER?"
450   INPUT R$
460   IF R$ = "YES" OR R$ = "Y" THEN 150
470   PRINT "YOU ANSWERED ";C;" CORRECTLY OUT OF ";D;"."
480   END
```

7-9 DIVISION OF SIGNED NUMBERS

Since division is defined as the inverse operation of multiplication, the rules for dividing signed numbers parallel those for multiplying signed numbers.

Ask if the set of signed numbers is closed for division. (This set is not closed for division because division by zero is undefined.)

Computer Activity (7-9) The following program tests the division of signed numbers, using integers from -180 to $+200$ as the dividend and integers from -10 to $+9$ as the divisor.

Note: On some computers, RND (1) may have to be changed to RND (0).

```
100     REM   THIS PROGRAM WILL TEST THE
110     REM   DIVISION OF SIGNED NUMBERS.
120     LET C = 0
130     LET D = 0
140     LET X =   INT ( RND (1) * 40) - 20
150     LET Y =   INT ( RND (1) * 20) - 10
160     LET T = 0
170     IF Y = 0 THEN 150
180     PRINT "WHAT IS THE QUOTIENT: ";X * Y;" DIVIDED BY ";Y
190     LET D = D + 1
200     LET T = T + 1
210     INPUT A
220     IF A = X THEN 430
230     IF T > 2 THEN 410
240     IF A =  - 1 * X OR X = 0 THEN 270
250     PRINT "CHECK YOUR ARITHMETIC. TRY AGAIN."
260     GOTO 180
270     IF X > 0 THEN 330
280     IF X < 0 THEN 370
290     PRINT "REMEMBER THAT 0 DIVIDED BY ANY NUMBER"
300     PRINT "IS 0."
310     PRINT "TRY AGAIN."
320     GOTO 180
330     PRINT "REMEMBER THAT THE QUOTIENT OF TWO"
340     PRINT "NUMBERS WITH THE SAME SIGN IS POSITIVE."
350     PRINT "TRY AGAIN."
360     GOTO 180
370     PRINT "REMEMBER THAT THE QUOTIENT OF TWO"
380     PRINT "NUMBERS WITH OPPOSITE SIGNS IS NEGATIVE."
390     PRINT "TRY AGAIN."
400     GOTO 180
410     PRINT X * Y;" DIVIDED BY ";Y;" EQUALS ";X;"."
420     GOTO 450
430     PRINT "THAT'S RIGHT."
440     LET C = C + 1
450     PRINT "DO YOU WANT TO TRY ANOTHER?"
460     INPUT R$
470     IF R$ = "Y" OR R$ = "YES" THEN 140
480     PRINT "YOU ANSWERED ";C;" CORRECTLY OUT OF ";D;"."
490     END
```

7-10 USING SIGNED NUMBERS IN EVALUATING ALGEBRAIC EXPRESSIONS

Evaluating algebraic expressions by using signed numbers follows the same procedures outlined in Chapter 3 when the variables were replaced by the numbers of arithmetic. Although the order of operations remains the same, the use of signed numbers presents a greater challenge.

Computer Activity (7-10) A computer program may be used to evaluate algebraic expressions involving signed numbers. Using Exercise 37 on page 226, we can write the following program:

```
10  LET D = - 3
20  PRINT 2 * D ^ 2 - D
30  END
```

The output will be:

21

The computer activities suggested in Section 4 of Chapter 3 can be repeated here, using signed numbers as the values of the variables.

7-11 USING THE ADDITIVE INVERSE IN SOLVING EQUATIONS

In Section 4-2, simple equations were introduced using the set of numbers of arithmetic as the domain. Either the addition or subtraction property of equality was used to solve these first-degree equations.

Since these properties hold true for the set of signed numbers and since every signed number has an opposite (additive inverse), equations can now be solved by using only the addition property of equality. For example:

$$x + 3 = 7$$
$$x + 3 + (-3) = 7 + (-3)$$
$$x + 0 = 4$$
$$x = 4$$

$$y - 5 = -8$$
$$y - 5 + (5) = -8 + (5)$$
$$y + 0 = -3$$
$$y = -3$$

7-12 USING THE MULTIPLICATIVE INVERSE IN SOLVING EQUATIONS

In Section 4-3, simple equations were solved by using either the division or multiplication property of equality. Here, equations such as $2x = 8$ and $\frac{2}{3}x = 14$ are now solved by using only the multiplication property of equality.

Although one property is now stated, students should be given the option to solve equations using any mathematically correct procedure. For example, to solve $2x = 8$, students may use either:

the multiplication property	or	the division property
$2x = 8$		$2x = 8$
$\frac{1}{2} \cdot 2x = \frac{1}{2} \cdot 8$		$\frac{2x}{2} = \frac{8}{2}$
$x = 4$		$x = 4$

SAT PREPARATION EXERCISES (Chapter 7)

Questions 1–9 each consist of two quantities, one in Column A and one in Column B. You are to compare the two quantities and choose:

A if the quantity in Column A is greater;
B if the quantity in Column B is greater;
C if the two quantities are equal;
D if the relationship cannot be determined from the information given.

Notes

1. In certain questions, information concerning one or both of the quantities to be compared is centered above the two columns.
2. In a given question, a symbol that appears in both columns represents the same thing in Column A as it does in Column B.
3. Letters such as x, n, and k stand for real numbers.

Column A	**Column B**
1. $-1 - 2 - 3$	$(-1)(-2)(-3)$
2. $-1 - 3 - 5$	$(-1)(-3)(-5)$

$$x > 0, y < 0$$

3. $\lvert x + y \rvert$	$\lvert x \rvert + \lvert y \rvert$

$$y = 0$$

4. $-5axy^3$	$axy^3 - 5$

$$a > 0, b < 0$$

5. ab	$-\lvert a \rvert \cdot \lvert b \rvert$

$$h < 0$$

6. h	h^3

$$x = -3$$

7. $\dfrac{x - 2}{\lvert x - 2 \rvert}$	$\dfrac{x - 2}{\lvert x \rvert - 2}$

8. The solution of $-x + 7 = 14$	The solution of $x - (-7) = 7$

9. The solution of $-\dfrac{1}{2}x = -6$	The solution of $-6x = -2$

In 10–24, select the letter of the correct answer.

10. The product of a negative odd number and a positive even number is
    (A) negative and odd
    (B) positive and even
    (C) negative and even
    (D) positive and odd

11. Which set of numbers is listed in ascending order (from smallest to greatest)?
    (A) $-\dfrac{1}{3}, -\dfrac{1}{2}, \dfrac{2}{3}, \dfrac{3}{4}$ (B) $-\dfrac{1}{2}, -\dfrac{1}{3}, \dfrac{2}{3}, \dfrac{3}{4}$
    (C) $-\dfrac{1}{3}, -\dfrac{1}{2}, \dfrac{3}{4}, \dfrac{2}{3}$ (D) $-\dfrac{1}{2}, -\dfrac{1}{3}, \dfrac{3}{4}, \dfrac{2}{3}$

12. If $x + 7 = 3$, what is the value of $3x + 21$?
    (A) 9   (B) 11   (C) 33   (D) -33

13. If the product of $\dfrac{3}{4}$ of -12 and $\dfrac{2}{3}$ of x is 90, then x is
    (A) -10 (B) 10   (C) -15 (D) 15

14. If $3 = x + (-3)$, and $4 = y + (-2)$, then the product of x and y is
    (A) 6   (B) 12   (C) 24   (D) 36

15. If $x = -2$, which of the following gives the largest value?
    (A) $2x^3$ (B) $(2x)^3$ (C) $(-2x)^3$ (D) $-2x^3$

16. If $x = -3 + 5 + (-1)$ and $y = -8 + (-9) + 4$, then the average of x and y is
    (A) -2 (B) 2   (C) 6   (D) -6

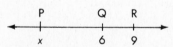

17. QR is 50% of PQ. Then $(3 + x)(3 - x)$ is how far from x?
    (A) 0   (B) 3   (C) 6   (D) 9

18. If $\boxed{x} = \dfrac{x}{\lvert x - 1 \rvert}$, then which of the following values is closest to zero?
    (A) $\boxed{2}$ (B) $\boxed{3}$ (C) $\boxed{-2}$ (D) $\boxed{-3}$

19. Which of the following has the least value if $x = -1$ and $y = -2$?
(A) $|x + y|$ (B) $|x - y|$
(C) $|x| + |y|$ (D) $|x| - |y|$

20. If $\boxed{x} = \dfrac{x}{|x|} + \dfrac{1}{x}$, then which of the following has the largest value?

(A) $\boxed{1}$ (B) $\boxed{2}$ (C) $\boxed{-1}$ (D) $\boxed{-2}$

21. If x is a number between -1 and 2, and y is a number between 4 and 10, then the expression $\dfrac{xy}{2}$ represents a number between

(A) -4 and 20   (B) -4 and 8
(C) -5 and 10   (D) -2 and 10

22. For the statement "If $x^2 > x$, then $x > 1$" which of the following is always true?
  I. the inverse
  II. the contrapositive
(A) I only   (B) II only
(C) I and II   (D) neither

23. For the statement "If $x = 5$, then $x^2 = 25$" which of the following is always true?
  I. the converse
  II. the inverse
(A) I only   (B) II only
(C) I and II   (D) neither

24. $p: x > 0$
            $q: x^2 = 4$
Which of the following must be true to lead to the conclusion that $x = -2$?
(A) $p \wedge q$ (B) $p \vee q$
(C) $\sim p \wedge q$ (D) $\sim p \vee q$

SUGGESTED TEST ITEMS (Chapter 7)

In 1–4, find the value of the expression.

1. $|-4|$ **2.** $|7|$ **3.** $|3 - 9|$ **4.** $|3| - |9|$

In 5–12, find the sum.

5. $\begin{array}{r} +7 \\ -3 \\ \hline \end{array}$ **6.** $\begin{array}{r} +12 \\ +18 \\ \hline \end{array}$ **7.** $\begin{array}{r} -6 \\ -16 \\ \hline \end{array}$ **8.** $\begin{array}{r} -17 \\ +4 \\ \hline \end{array}$ **9.** $\begin{array}{r} -5 \\ +5 \\ \hline \end{array}$ **10.** $\begin{array}{r} -7.4 \\ -6.7 \\ \hline \end{array}$

11. $-6 + 6 - 4$ **12.** $-4 + 0 + 8 - 4$

In 13–20, find the difference.

13. $\begin{array}{r} +7 \\ +10 \\ \hline \end{array}$ **14.** $\begin{array}{r} +7 \\ -10 \\ \hline \end{array}$ **15.** $\begin{array}{r} +3 \\ -1 \\ \hline \end{array}$ **16.** $\begin{array}{r} 0 \\ -3 \\ \hline \end{array}$ **17.** $\begin{array}{r} +6 \\ 0 \\ \hline \end{array}$ **18.** $\begin{array}{r} +6 \\ -6 \\ \hline \end{array}$

19. $-6 - \left(+9\frac{1}{4}\right)$ **20.** $-14.2 - (-8.5)$

In 21–26, find the product.

21. $\begin{array}{r} +3 \\ +5 \\ \hline \end{array}$ **22.** $\begin{array}{r} -7 \\ -8 \\ \hline \end{array}$ **23.** $\begin{array}{r} +7 \\ -7 \\ \hline \end{array}$ **24.** $\begin{array}{r} -14 \\ +3 \\ \hline \end{array}$ **25.** $\begin{array}{r} -3.8 \\ 0 \\ \hline \end{array}$ **26.** $\begin{array}{r} -8 \\ +.2 \\ \hline \end{array}$

In 27–32, find the quotient.

27. $\dfrac{+30}{-6}$ **28.** $\dfrac{+72}{+8}$ **29.** $\dfrac{-28}{-7}$ **30.** $\dfrac{-51}{+3}$ **31.** $\dfrac{-12}{-.2}$ **32.** $\dfrac{0}{-5}$

33. From the sum of -7 and $+14$, subtract -5.

In 34–37, find the value of the expression when $a = -6$, $b = +8$ and $c = -.5$.

34. $-7a$ **35.** a^2c **36.** $b - a$ **37.** $(a + b)^2$

In 38–41, graph the solution set of the open sentence using a replacement set of all real numbers.

38. $-5 < x \leq +2$ **39.** $(x < -2) \lor (x > 2)$ **40.** $(x > -1) \land (x \geq 1)$ **41.** $0 < x < 3$

In 42–47, solve for x and check.

42. $x + 5 = 7$ **43.** $x - 3 = -2$ **44.** $x + 8 = 2$

45. $7x = -14$ **46.** $\frac{2}{3}x = 12$ **47.** $-6x = 24$

BONUS: In the country of Tollifer, the unit of money is a *toll*. Coins have a value of 3, 7, and 11 tolls. A purchase that costs any whole number of tolls can be made but often only by giving in payment a larger sum and receiving change. For each whole number from 1 to 30, show how a purchase that costs that number of tolls can be paid. (*Hint*: One way to pay for a purchase worth 1 toll would be to pay a 7-toll coin and receive 2 coins that are each worth 3 tolls in change. If change is considered to be a negative value, we can write $7 + 2(-3) = 1$. Other combinations of coins are possible.)

CHAPTER 8

Operations With Monomials

Aims

- To present the rules for adding, subtracting, multiplying, and dividing monomials.

- To explain the concepts of negative and zero exponents.

- To introduce students to the use of scientific notation.

Student mastery of both the principles and the skills of this chapter and the following chapter on polynomials is essential for success in algebra. The chapters are arranged so that students may achieve competence in dealing with monomials before going on to work with polynomials. However, some teachers may wish to change the order in which these topics are presented and follow each section in Chapter 8 by the section that considers the same operation on polynomials from Chapter 9. Such an approach may enable students to acquire greater competence in the use of a particular operation before proceeding to the next operation. For example, the following order could be used: 8-1, 9-1, 8-2, 9-2, 8-3, 8-4, 9-3, 9-4, 9-5, 8-5, 8-6, 9-6, 9-7, 8-7, 8-8, 8-9.

In a natural integration of topics, algebraic operations are applied to geometric models. Also, verbal settings are used to reinforce such concepts as Rate × Time = Distance and Unit Price × Number of Units = Total Cost.

8-1 ADDING LIKE MONOMIALS

Students should understand how the distributive property is used as the basic principle that enables us to add like terms. They are accustomed to seeing the form $a(b + c) = ab + ac$, and may need help in recognizing the altered form used here, $ba + ca = (b + c)a$. Show them how the text examples, such as $9x + 2x = (9 + 2)x$, follow this pattern.

Emphasize that other additions also use this principle. For example, in order to add fractions, we need common denominators:

$$\frac{3}{7} + \frac{2}{7} = 3 \cdot \frac{1}{7} + 2 \cdot \frac{1}{7} = (3 + 2)\frac{1}{7} = 5 \cdot \frac{1}{7} = \frac{5}{7}$$
$$3x + 2x = (3 + 2)x = 5x$$

Later in the course, we will add irrational numbers having the same radical factor:

$$3\sqrt{5} + 2\sqrt{5} = (3 + 2)\sqrt{5} = 5\sqrt{5}$$

A clear understanding of this application of the distributive property will help students avoid such common errors as $3x^2 + 2x^2 = 5x^4$.

Computer Activity (8-1) The following program could be used to check the answers for Exercises 1–26 on page 234, or for problems involving the sum of two monomials:

```
100   REM  THIS PROGRAM WILL FIND THE SUM
110   REM  OF TWO MONOMIALS.
120   PRINT "IF TWO MONOMIALS HAVE THE SAME LITERAL"
130   PRINT "FACTOR, THEIR SUM CAN BE WRITTEN AS A"
140   PRINT "MONOMIAL."
150   PRINT "TO USE THIS PROGRAM TO FIND THE SUM OF"
160   PRINT "TWO MONOMIALS, WRITE A LITERAL FACTOR"
170   PRINT "THAT CONTAINS AN EXPONENT BY USING ^."
180   PRINT "FOR EXAMPLE, WRITE X CUBED AS X ^ 3"
190   PRINT
200   PRINT "ENTER THE LITERAL FACTOR OF THE"
210   PRINT "MONOMIALS TO BE ADDED."
220   INPUT V$
230   PRINT "ENTER THE TWO COEFFICIENTS OF ";V$
240   PRINT "SEPARATED BY A COMMA. REMEMBER THAT"
250   PRINT "IF NO NUMERICAL COEFFICIENT IS WRITTEN,"
260   PRINT "IT IS UNDERSTOOD TO BE 1."
270   INPUT A,B
280   PRINT A;V$;" ";
290   IF B > 0 THEN  PRINT " + ";
300   PRINT B;V$;" = ";A + B;V$
310   PRINT
320   PRINT "DO YOU WANT TO DO ANOTHER?"
330   INPUT R$
340   IF R$ = "YES" OR R$ = "Y" THEN 200
350   END
```

8-2 SUBTRACTING LIKE MONOMIALS

Subtraction of like monomials calls for the same method as that used in subtracting signed numbers. Thus, students who did not quite understand subtraction of signed numbers will find this section confusing. Thinking of subtraction as the addition of the additive inverse can help. Also, circling signs to be changed is a good visual device.

The introduction of words in Exercises 43–50 on page 237 requires that some time be spent in discussing order.

You may wish to use subtraction of monomials in perimeter problems. For example, the perimeter of a triangle is $12xy^2$. If the sum of the lengths of two sides of the triangle is $7xy^2$, express the length of the third side.

Computer Activity (8-2) The following program could be used by students to check their answers to Exercises 1–46 on pages 236 and 237, or to do similar exercises of their own choosing:

```
100  REM  THIS PROGRAM WILL FIND THE
110  REM  DIFFERENCE OF TWO MONOMIALS.
120  PRINT "IF TWO MONOMIALS HAVE THE SAME LITERAL"
130  PRINT "FACTOR, THEIR DIFFERENCE CAN BE WRITTEN"
140  PRINT "AS A MONOMIAL. TO USE THIS PROGRAM"
150  PRINT "TO SUBTRACT MONOMIALS, ENTER A LITERAL"
160  PRINT "FACTOR THAT HAS AN EXPONENT BY USING ^."
170  PRINT "FOR EXAMPLE, WRITE X CUBED AS X ^ 3"
180  PRINT
190  PRINT "ENTER THE LITERAL FACTOR."
200  INPUT V$
210  PRINT "ENTER THE NUMERICAL COEFFICIENT OF ";V$
220  PRINT "FROM THE MINUEND. REMEMBER THAT IF NO"
230  PRINT "NUMERICAL COEFFICIENT IS WRITTEN, IT IS"
240  PRINT "UNDERSTOOD TO BE 1."
250  INPUT A
260  PRINT "ENTER THE NUMERICAL COEFFICIENT OF ";V$
270  PRINT "FROM THE SUBTRAHEND."
280  INPUT B
290  PRINT A;V$;" - (";B;V$;") = ";A - B;V$
300  PRINT "DO YOU WANT TO DO ANOTHER?"
310  INPUT R$
320  IF R$ = "YES" OR R$ = "Y" THEN 190
330  END
```

8-3 MULTIPLYING POWERS OF THE SAME BASE

Students often find working with numerical bases confusing. Perhaps they feel they should be able to do more with the known values. Whatever the reasons, they are happy to leave $x^2 \cdot x^3 = x^5$, but they tend to tamper with $2^2 \cdot 2^3 = 2^5$. Throughout all work with the laws of exponents, stress that each procedure is defined, whether the base is literal or numerical. The exercises in the text have a good sprinkling of numerical bases.

To avoid confusion about when to add exponents, as in $x^a \cdot x^b = x^{a+b}$, and when to multiply exponents, as in $(x^a)^b = x^{a \cdot b}$, have students rewrite finding the power of a power as a product of powers. For example:

$$(x^4)^3 = x^4 \cdot x^4 \cdot x^4 = x^{12}$$

Remind students that *every* base has an exponent. Thus, when working with the laws of exponents, they must remember that x means x^1 and that the exponent of 1 must be taken into account when doing a multiplication such as $x \cdot x^2 = x^1 \cdot x^2 = x^{1+2} = x^3$.

The text indicates that the product of powers with different bases cannot be simplified (for example, $c^2 d^3$). On the other hand, you may wish to point out that different bases with the same exponent can be combined so that the exponent is written only once, as in $c^2 d^2 = (cd)^2$.

Computer Activity (8-3) The following program could be used by students to check their answers to the opening exercises on page 239, or to do similar exercises of their own choosing:

```
100  REM    THIS PROGRAM WILL MULTIPLY
110  REM    TWO POWERS OF THE SAME BASE.
120  PRINT "TO MULTIPLY POWERS WITH LIKE BASES, ADD"
130  PRINT "THE EXPONENTS OF THE FACTORS. THE"
140  PRINT "BASE OF THE PRODUCT IS THE SAME AS THE"
150  PRINT "BASE OF EACH OF THE FACTORS."
160  PRINT "REMEMBER THAT IF NO EXPONENT IS"
170  PRINT "WRITTEN, IT IS UNDERSTOOD TO BE 1."
180  PRINT
190  PRINT "ENTER THE BASE."
200  INPUT B$
210  PRINT "ENTER THE TWO EXPONENTS TO BASE ";B$
220  PRINT "SEPARATED BY A COMMA."
230  INPUT X,Y
240  PRINT
250  PRINT B$;"^";X;"*";B$;"^";Y;" = ";B$;"^";X + Y;
260  IF X + Y = 1 THEN  PRINT " OR ";B$
270  IF X + Y = 0 THEN  PRINT " OR 1"
280  PRINT
290  PRINT "DO YOU WANT TO DO ANOTHER? (Y OR N)"
300  INPUT A$
310  IF A$ = "YES" OR A$ = "Y" THEN 180
320  END
```

8-4 MULTIPLYING A MONOMIAL BY A MONOMIAL

Compare again operations with fractions and operations with monomials. The sum or difference of two fractions can be written as a single fraction only if the fractions to be combined have a common denominator, just as the sum or difference of two monomials can be written as a monomial only if the monomials have the same literal factor. The product of two fractions can be written as a single fraction even if the fractions have different denominators and the product of two monomials can be written as a monomial even if the monomials have different literal factors.

For example:

$$(3x)(5y^2) = (3 \cdot 5)(x \cdot y^2) = 15xy^2$$

Note that the commutative and associative properties are applied to the multiplication of monomials. In time, students need not show the middle step.

Using Model Problem 2 on page 241, show how the area of a rectangle $3x$ by $2x$ can be determined both algebraically and geometrically. Visualizing a geometric representation helps to present the solution in a less abstract manner.

Continue to emphasize that solutions to problems should specify units of measure wherever appropriate, as in Exercises 61 and 62. Again, "cancellation" is a helpful visual device. In Exercise 62:

$$\frac{10z \text{ miles}}{\cancel{\text{hour}}} \cdot 4z \; \cancel{\text{hours}} = 40z^2 \text{ miles}$$

8-5 DIVIDING POWERS OF THE SAME BASE

Since division and multiplication are inverse operations, students should check their division by multiplication. For example, if $\frac{x^5}{x^2} = x^3$ then $x^2 \cdot x^3 = x^5$. To help students avoid making common errors such as $5^5 \div 5^2 = 1^3$, emphasize that there is only one procedure for dividing powers of the same base, whether the base is literal or numerical.

Computer Activity (8-5) The following program could be used by students to check their answers to Exercises 1–20 on page 244, or to do similar exercises of their own choosing:

```
100   REM  THIS PROGRAM WILL DIVIDE
110   REM  TWO POWERS OF THE SAME BASE.
120   PRINT "TO FIND THE QUOTIENT OF TWO POWERS OF"
130   PRINT "THE SAME BASE, THE EXPONENT OF THE"
140   PRINT "DIVISOR IS SUBTRACTED FROM THE"
150   PRINT "EXPONENT OF THE DIVIDEND.  THE BASE OF"
160   PRINT "THE QUOTIENT IS THE SAME AS THE BASE"
170   PRINT "OF THE DIVIDEND AND OF THE DIVISOR."
180   PRINT "ENTER THE BASE."
190   INPUT B$
200   PRINT "ENTER THE EXPONENT OF THE DIVIDEND."
210   INPUT X
220   PRINT "ENTER THE EXPONENT OF THE DIVISOR."
230   INPUT Y
240   PRINT B$;"^";X;" DIVIDED BY ";B$;"^";Y;" = ";
250   PRINT B$;"^";X - Y;
260   IF X - Y = 1 THEN  PRINT " OR ";B$
270   IF X - Y = 0 THEN  PRINT " OR 1"
280   PRINT
290   PRINT "DO YOU WANT TO DO ANOTHER? (Y OR N)"
300   INPUT A$
310   IF A$ = "YES" OR A$ = "Y" THEN 180
320   END
```

8-6 DIVIDING A MONOMIAL BY A MONOMIAL

The quotient of two monomials is a monomial if and only if all of the literal factors of the divisor are factors of the dividend, that is, no variable remains in the divisor. All of the divisions of this section are of this kind. In Chapter 14, division in which the quotient of monomials may not be a monomial will be considered.

Students should be encouraged to check division by multiplication, thus forming a good habit as well as continuing to practice multiplication. The check may be written or performed mentally.

8-7 NONPOSITIVE INTEGRAL EXPONENTS

After you establish that $x^0 = 1$, discuss why $x \neq 0$ in the definition. Point out that the definition $x^0 = 1$ is related to the fact that $\frac{x^a}{x^a} = 1$, a quotient that is not valid if $x = 0$. Emphasize the difference between $2y^0$, which is equal to 2, and $(2y)^0$, which is equal to 1.

Once the definition $x^{-n} = \frac{1}{x^n}$ ($x \neq 0$) is formalized, you may show how all the laws of exponents remain valid. For example:

$$5^3 \cdot 5^{-1} = \frac{5^3}{1} \cdot \frac{1}{5^1} = \frac{5^3}{5^1} = 5^2$$

or

$$5^3 \cdot 5^{-1} = 5^{3+(-1)} = 5^2$$

Stress the point that raising a number to a negative exponent does not imply that the answer is negative. Ask for two examples involving negative exponents, one where the answer is positive and one where the answer is negative. For example:

a. $(-2)^{-2} = \dfrac{1}{(-2)^2} = \dfrac{1}{4}$

b. $(-2)^{-3} = \dfrac{1}{(-2)^3} = \dfrac{1}{-8} = -\dfrac{1}{8}$

Conclude that if the base is negative, the value of the power can be positive or negative depending on whether the exponent is even or odd. If the base is positive, the value of the power is always positive.

In the problem $4^{-3} \div 4^{-6}$, a common response is 4^{-9} rather than the correct solution $4^{-3-(-6)} = 4^3$. If this error occurs, demonstrate another method of solution. For example:

$$4^{-3} \div 4^{-6}$$
$$= \frac{1}{4^3} \div \frac{1}{4^6} = \frac{1}{4^3} \cdot \frac{4^6}{1} = \frac{4^6}{4^3} = 4^{6-3} = 4^3$$

From the viewpoint of manipulation, the definition $x^{-n} = \dfrac{1}{x^n}$ $(x \neq 0)$ has the effect that a negative exponent originally found in a numerator is changed to a positive exponent that then appears in a denominator.

$$x^{-3} \searrow \frac{1}{x^3}$$

A corollary of the definition can be established from Model Problem 1d on page 247.

$$\frac{1}{x^{-n}} = x^n \; (x \neq 0)$$

This corollary has the effect that a negative exponent originally found in a denominator is changed to a positive exponent that then appears in a numerator.

$$\frac{1}{x^{-3}} \nearrow x^3$$

When switching positions of the power with respect to numerator or denominator, students must be especially careful to move only the base that belongs with the negative exponent.

$$\frac{2}{x^{-3}} = 2x^3 \qquad \frac{1}{2x^{-3}} = \frac{x^3}{2}$$

Note that the coefficient 2, independent of the exponent, remains in its original position in the two cases shown above. The coefficient 3, which is affected by the exponent, moves as part of the base in the two cases shown below.

$$(3x)^{-2} = \frac{1}{(3x)^2} \qquad \frac{1}{(3x)^{-2}} = (3x)^2$$

8-8 EXPRESSING LARGE NUMBERS IN SCIENTIFIC NOTATION

Before you explain scientific notation, it is important for students to see the need for a notation that will neatly handle very large numbers. A discussion about very large and very small measurements will establish that need. Concepts normally taught in science class, such as distances of planets from the sun, can be reviewed as you prepare to put these numbers into scientific notation.

Students usually have more trouble converting *to* scientific notation than they do converting *from* scientific notation. After they have determined the first factor of the scientific notation, the number between 1 and 10, suggest a visual counting procedure to determine the required exponent.

$$270,000 = 2.7 \times 10^?$$

Count off from where the decimal point *will be* to where the decimal point *is*.

$$2 \underbrace{7\,0\,0\,0\,0}_{1\;2\;3\;4\;5} = 2.7 \times 10^5$$

Note that when we count to the right, we use a positive exponent.

Calculator Activity (8-8) You can use a handheld calculator as a motivational device. Most calculators have a display limited to 8 digits. Ask for the calculator displays for the following problems (displays will vary according to manufacturer and model):

	Answers
a. 600×600	360000
b. $600 \times 600 \times 600$	2.16 *E*8
	2.16 *E*+8
	2.16 8

The answer to **b** is given in *E*-notation, which is a form of scientific notation used in calculators and computers.

Computer Activities (8-8)   Exercises 4–15 on page 250 can be done on a computer. For example, to change 1.27×10^3 into decimal notation, a simple computer program is:

```
10   PRINT 1.27 * 10 ^ 3
20   END
```

Once the RETURN key is hit, the computer will display 1270.

Exercises 16–23 on page 250 can also be done on a computer. For example, to change 20,000,000,000 into scientific notation, a program is:

```
10   LET A = 20000000000
20   PRINT A
30   END
```

Depending on the computer used, a display of 2 *E* + 10 or some alternate form will result when the number is large enough. In most computers, a number has to be very large—say 8 or more digits—before it is changed into scientific notation.

8-9 EXPRESSING SMALL NUMBERS IN SCIENTIFIC NOTATION

In this section, a discussion of negative integral powers of ten is first introduced before very small numbers are expressed in scientific notation.

To help students avoid errors when converting to scientific notation, you can repeat the previously suggested counting procedure.

$$.00382 = 3.82 \times 10^?$$

Count off from where the decimal point *will be* to where the decimal point *is*.

$$\underset{3 \quad 2 \quad 1}{.0\,0\,3}\,8\,2 \ = 3.82 \times 10^{-3}$$

Note that when we count to the left, we use a negative exponent.

Computer Activity (8-9)   As a rule, numbers must be very small before the computer will change them into scientific notation. Proceed according to the computer activity in Section 8-8 to determine when the specific computer being used will display the *E*-notation.

The following program will generate random numbers and provide practice in expressing those numbers in scientific notation:

Note: On some computers, RND (1) may have to be changed to RND (0).

```
100    REM   THIS PROGRAM WILL TEST THE USER
110    REM   OF SCIENTIFIC NOTATION.
120    LET T = 0
130    PRINT
140    LET N =   INT ( RND (1) * 900) + 100
150    LET E =   INT ( RND (1) * 9) - 4
160    LET D = N * 10 ^ E
170    PRINT "A NUMBER IN SCIENTIFIC NOTATION IS THE"
180    PRINT "PRODUCT OF TWO NUMBERS: THE FIRST"
190    PRINT "NUMBER IS 1 OR MORE BUT LESS THAN 10;"
200    PRINT "THE SECOND NUMBER IS A POWER OF 10."
210    PRINT
220    PRINT "EXPRESS ";D;" IN SCIENTIFIC NOTATION."
230    PRINT
240    PRINT "WHAT IS THE NUMBER BETWEEN 1 AND 10?"
250    INPUT A
260    PRINT
270    PRINT "WHAT IS THE POWER OF 10?"
280    INPUT B
290    PRINT
300    LET T = T + 1
310    IF T > 2 THEN 480
320    IF A < 1 OR A >= 10 THEN 430
330    IF   ABS (A * 100 - N) > .01 THEN 390
340    IF B = E + 2 THEN 470
350    PRINT "CHECK YOUR EXPONENT."
360    PRINT "TRY AGAIN."
370    PRINT
380    GOTO 270
390    PRINT "CHECK YOUR VALUE BETWEEN 1 AND 10."
400    PRINT "TRY AGAIN."
410    PRINT
420    GOTO 240
430    PRINT "TO WRITE A NUMBER BETWEEN 1 AND 10,"
440    PRINT "PLACE THE DECIMAL POINT AFTER THE FIRST"
450    PRINT "NONZERO DIGIT."
460    GOTO 240
470    PRINT "THAT'S RIGHT."
480    PRINT D;" = ";N / 100;" * 10 ^ ";E + 2
490    PRINT
500    PRINT " DO YOU WANT TO TRY ANOTHER? (Y OR N)"
510    INPUT R$
520    IF R$ = "Y" OR R$ = "YES" THEN 120
530    END
```

Note: This program should run on most computers. The number D, on line 220, must appear in decimal notation for this program to make sense. On some computers, but not all, the field of acceptable decimal numbers can be expanded by changing line 150 to read:

```
150    LET E =   INT ( RND (1) * 12) - 7
```

SAT PREPARATION EXERCISES (Chapter 8)

In 1–11, select the letter of the correct answer.

1. If the base of a triangle is $4x^2$, and the height is $2x^3$, then the area is
   (A) $4x^5$ (B) $4x^6$ (C) $8x^5$ (D) $8x^6$

2. If the bases of a trapezoid are x and $2x$, and the height is $2x$, then the area is
   (A) $6x^3$ (B) $6x^2$ (C) $3x^3$ (D) $3x^2$

3. If x and x^2 represent consecutive even integers, then the average of these two integers is
   (A) 1 (B) 2 (C) 3 (D) 4

4. If x is 10, then $2(x^3 + x)$ has the same value as
   (A) 2.2×10^2 (B) 2.02×10^2
   (C) 2.2×10^3 (D) 2.02×10^3

5. How many integers from 95 through 99 can be expressed as xy^2, where x and y are integers greater than 1?
   (A) 1 (B) 2 (C) 3 (D) 4

6. If a person drives x^2y^2 miles at a rate of xy^2 miles per hour, then the number of hours required is represented by
   (A) 1 (B) x (C) x^2y^4 (D) x^3y^4

7. If x^2 is the same as $8x$ increased by 50% of $8x$, then x could be
   (A) 4 (B) 8 (C) 12 (D) 16

8. The product of $4x$ and $5x$ gives the same result as the sum of $10x^2$ and
   (A) $2x^2$ (B) $2x$ (C) $10x^2$ (D) $10x$

9. If x is between -1 and 2, and y is between 3 and 4, then x^2y is between
   (A) 0 and 16   (B) 3 and 16
   (C) 3 and 8   (D) 0 and 8

10. If x and y are integers, and $\frac{x}{y} = 3$, then the average of x^3 and y^3 is a multiple of
    (A) 3 (B) 5 (C) 9 (D) 14

11. If $x + y^2 = 6$ and $y = -2$, then $x^2 - y$ is
    (A) 2 (B) -2 (C) 6 (D) -6

Questions 12–19 each consist of two quantities, one in Column A and one in Column B. You are to compare the two quantities and choose:

A if the quantity in column A is greater;
B if the quantity in Column B is greater;
C if the two quantities are equal;
D if the relationship cannot be determined from the information given.

Notes

1. In certain questions, information concerning one or both of the quantities to be compared is centered above the two columns.
2. In a given question, a symbol that appears in both columns represents the same thing in Column A as it does in Column B.
3. Letters such as x, n, and k stand for real numbers.

Column A	*Column B*
12. The sum of x^2 and $4x^2$	The product of $0.1x$ and $50x$

x is negative.

13. $(-3x^3)(-2x^2)$	$6x^6 \div 2x^2$

$x = y$

14. $5xy - xy$	y^2 avg $7y^2$

$x > 2$

15. The sum of 2 and $6x$	12 max $(6x + x)$

$$Px^Q = (4x^4)^2$$
for $x \neq 1$ and $x \neq 0$

16. P	Q

The length of a rectangle is $3x$ and the area is $27x^2$.

17. The width of the rectangle	$9x^2$

$P \neq Q$ and $Px^P \cdot Px^P = Qx^Q$
for $x \neq 1$ and $x \neq 0$

18. Q	5

$$x^2 + y^2 = 1$$

19. $|x| + |y|$	1

SUGGESTED TEST ITEMS (Chapter 8)

In 1–12, simplify the expression.

1. $5a^3 - 8a^3$ **2.** $-6ab + 5ab$ **3.** $-6ab(5ab)$ **4.** $(-3x)^3$

5. $-2x^4 - 4x^4$ **6.** $-ab^2(4a^2b)$ **7.** $7y - (-3y)$ **8.** $9cd - cd$

9. $3r(-4rs^2)^2$ **10.** $\dfrac{28ab}{4b}$ **11.** $\dfrac{36x^4y^2}{-9xy^2}$ **12.** $\dfrac{5^3 \cdot 5^2}{5^4}$

13. Express in terms of x the distance traveled in $\frac{1}{5}x$ hours by a car traveling at a rate of $15x^2$ miles per hour.

14. If the area of a rectangle is represented by $24x^2y^2$ and the length is represented by $8xy$, represent in terms of x and y: **a.** the width   **b.** the perimeter

In 15–19, select the numeral that precedes the correct answer.

15. When $-96x^{15}$ is divided by $-8x^3$, the quotient is
   (1) $-12x^5$ (2) $12x^5$ (3) $-12x^{12}$ (4) $12x^{12}$

16. The product $(3cd^2)(2c^3d)$ is
   (1) $5c^3d^2$ (2) $6c^3d^2$ (3) $6c^4d^3$ (4) $5c^4d^3$

17. The expression $y^5 + y^5$ is equivalent to
   (1) $2y^5$ (2) $2y^{10}$ (3) y^{10} (4) y^{25}

18. The expression $(-3x^4)^3$ is equivalent to
   (1) $-27x^7$ (2) $-9x^7$ (3) $-9x^{12}$ (4) $-27x^{12}$

19. The value of $8^{-2} \cdot 8^3$ is

   (1) 8 (2) -8 (3) $-\dfrac{1}{8}$ (4) $\dfrac{1}{8}$

In 20–23, express each number in scientific notation.

20. 3,200   **21.** 93,000,000   **22.** 0.054   **23.** 0.000002

In 24–27, express each number in decimal notation.

24. 8×10^4 **25.** 1.7×10^9 **26.** 7.3×10^{-2} **27.** 5×10^{-7}

BONUS: A grocer sells sugar by weighing it into sacks from a large container. Today, his scale is out of order but he has two containers, one that holds exactly 2 kilograms of sugar and the other that holds exactly 5 kilograms of sugar. Explain how he could prepare sacks of 1 k, 2 k, 3 k, 4 k, and 5 k of sugar without wasting any sugar or without putting any back into the large container.

CHAPTER 9

Operations With Polynomials

Aims

- To explain the addition, subtraction, multiplication, and division of polynomials.

Once students have learned to add, subtract, multiply, and divide monomials, the same skills can be applied to polynomials. In performing these operations, students should recognize that they are using the commutative, associative, and distributive properties. Division of a polynomial by a polynomial may be considered an optional topic.

Geometric applications and examples from common experience are included to prepare for the use of algebraic strategies in solving more complex problems.

9-1 ADDING POLYNOMIALS

A polynomial is defined as the sum of monomials. Note that monomials, binomials, and trinomials, are all examples of polynomial expressions.

Once a polynomial is expressed in simplest form, the degree of the polynomial can then be determined. Although the terms of a polynomial can be arranged in any order, it is suggested that standard form (a polynomial in one variable in descending order) be used wherever possible. You may wish to discuss a polynomial in two variables in which one variable is arranged in descending powers, while the other is arranged in ascending powers. For example:

$$3x^2 + 2xy + 3y^2$$

When rearranging the terms of a polynomial, as in Model Problem 2, students may be careless about signs. An expression like $3xy - x^2$, for example, may be incorrectly written as $x^2 - 3xy$. Before transposing the terms, take time, at the start, to write $3xy - x^2$ as $3xy + (-x^2)$, and remind students that the operation of addition is commutative, while the operation of subtraction is not. In effect, a sign "belongs to" the term that follows it.

Students should become accustomed to a horizontal format as well as to a vertical format. To begin, a vertical format is convenient to reinforce the combination of like terms, and to highlight any missing terms. Later, an important application of a horizontal format arises when combining like terms in the solution of an equation.

Perimeters of geometric figures can be expressed as polynomials. For example, find the perimeter of a square each of whose sides is represented by $x - 4$:

$$(x - 4) + (x - 4) + (x - 4) + (x - 4)$$
$$= 4x - 16$$

Ask students why the value of the variable x must be greater than 4 in the stated problem. Stress that length cannot be represented by a negative number or zero.

9-2 SUBTRACTING POLYNOMIALS

Subtraction of polynomial expressions calls for procedures similar to the subtraction of like terms. The subtraction of a polynomial is best handled as the addition of its opposite (additive inverse). For example:

$$\begin{aligned} &(2x^2 - 3x + 4) - (x^2 + 2x - 6) \\ &= (2x^2 - 3x + 4) + (-x^2 - 2x + 6) \\ &= 2x^2 - 3x + 4 - x^2 - 2x + 6 \\ &= x^2 - 5x + 10 \end{aligned}$$

This problem can also be done in a vertical format. The visual technique previously suggested for subtraction of signed numbers (Chapter 7) can again be employed here. Circle the original signs of the subtrahend and write the new sign above each circled sign.

$$\begin{aligned} 2x^2 &- 3x +\ \ 4 \\ \ominus\ \ x^2 &\oplus 2x \ominus\ \ 6 \\ \hline x^2 &- 5x + 10 \end{aligned}$$

Subtraction can be checked by adding the subtrahend and the difference. The result should equal the minuend. In the preceding problem:

$$\begin{aligned} x^2 + 2x -\ \ 6 &\quad \text{subtrahend} \\ x^2 - 5x + 10 &\quad \text{difference} \\ \hline 2x^2 - 3x +\ \ 4 &\quad \text{minuend} \end{aligned}$$

You may wish to reinforce understanding by having students find first the sum, then the difference, of the same pair of polynomials. For example:

	Add	*Subtract*
1.	$2x + y$	$2x + y$
	$-2x - y$	$-2x - y$
	0	$4x + 2y$
2.	$-2x - y$	$-2x - y$
	$-2x - y$	$-2x - y$
	$-4x - 2y$	0

9-3 MULTIPLYING A POLYNOMIAL BY A MONOMIAL

The text provides a geometric illustration of how the distributive property is applied to multiplying a polynomial by a monomial. Spend some time with this so that the analogy is clear.

Although the distributive property is stated as $a(b + c) = ab + ac$, the property can be extended to polynomials containing more than two terms:

$$\begin{aligned} a(b + c + d + &\ldots + x) \\ = ab + ac + ad + &\ldots + ax \end{aligned}$$

If powers with like bases are multiplied, the rule $x^a \cdot x^b = x^{a+b}$, studied in Section 8-3, is applied. For example:

$$-2x^2(3x^2 - 2x - 3) = -6x^4 + 4x^3 + 6x^2$$

Note, however, that like terms are not necessary for multiplication.

9-4 USING MULTIPLICATION TO SIMPLIFY ALGEBRAIC EXPRESSIONS CONTAINING SYMBOLS OF GROUPING

Before all like terms of the expression $2x - 3(x + 2)$ can be combined (or *collected*), the distributive property is first applied to simplify the expression. Encourage students to think of this as the sum of $2x$ and -3 times the expression in parentheses rather than as the difference between $2x$ and 3 times the expression in parentheses.

Call attention to the fact that the opposite, or additive inverse, of a polynomial is always the same as the polynomial multiplied by -1. In both cases, the sign of each term of the polynomial is changed.

$$-(3x - 7) = -3x + 7$$
$$-1(3x - 7) = -3x + 7$$

9-5 MULTIPLYING A POLYNOMIAL BY A POLYNOMIAL

To multiply a polynomial by a polynomial, you should first arrange the multiplicand and multiplier in descending or ascending powers of a common variable. Then, apply the distributive property and combine like terms.

You may wish to use FOIL as a memory aid in the multiplication of two binomials. For example, to multiply $(x + 5)(2x - 3)$, follow these steps:

1. Multiply the *first* terms of the binomials.

$$F: \quad x \cdot 2x = 2x^2$$

2. Multiply the *outer* terms of the binomials.

$$O: \quad x \cdot -3 = -3x$$

3. Multiply the *inner* terms of the binomials.

$$I: \quad 5 \cdot 2x = 10x$$

4. Multiply the *last* terms of the binomials.

$$L: \quad 5 \cdot -3 = -15$$

5. Add the results of these steps, combining like terms.

$$2x^2 + (-3x) + 10x + (-15) = 2x^2 + 7x - 15$$

Diagrammatically: $(x + 5)(2x - 3)$

Encourage students to rewrite the square of a binomial as the product of two equal binomials. For example, when $(x + 3)^2$ is written as $(x + 3)(x + 3)$, students usually get the correct result $x^2 + 6x + 9$, and are not likely to make the common error of writing $x^2 + 9$.

In general, students must remember that every term of one factor must multiply every term of the other factor.

Included in the exercises are a few that require multiplication of three factors. Suggest that students simplify the product of the first two factors before multiplying by the third factor. For example:

$$\begin{aligned}(x + 3)^3 &= (x + 3)(x + 3)(x + 3) \\ &= (x^2 + 6x + 9)(x + 3) \\ &= x^3 + 6x^2 + 9x + 3x^2 + 18x + 27 \\ &= x^3 + 9x^2 + 27x + 27\end{aligned}$$

Problems concerning areas of rectangles whose sides are binomials are provided in the exercises.

Computer Activity (9-5) The following program could be used by students to check their answers to Exercises 1–24 on page 269, or to do similar problems of their own choosing.

```
100   REM    THIS PROGRAM WILL FIND THE
110   REM    PRODUCT OF TWO BINOMIALS.
120   PRINT "THIS PROGRAM WILL FIND THE PRODUCT OF"
130   PRINT "TWO BINOMIALS IF THE FIRST TERMS OF THE"
140   PRINT "BINOMIALS ARE LIKE TERMS WHOSE VARIABLES"
150   PRINT "HAVE EXPONENTS OF 1, AND THE LAST TERMS"
160   PRINT "OF THE BINOMIALS ARE CONSTANTS."
170   PRINT
180   PRINT "ENTER THE VARIABLE FACTOR."
190   INPUT V$
200   PRINT
210   PRINT "ENTER THE COEFFICIENT OF ";V$;" FROM THE"
220   PRINT "FIRST BINOMIAL.  REMEMBER THAT IF NO"
230   PRINT "COEFFICIENT IS WRITTEN, IT IS 1."
```

```
240    INPUT A
250    PRINT
260    PRINT "ENTER THE CONSTANT FROM THE FIRST"
270    PRINT "BINOMIAL."
280    INPUT B
290    PRINT
300    PRINT "ENTER THE COEFFICIENT OF ";V$;" FROM THE"
310    PRINT "SECOND BINOMIAL."
320    INPUT C
330    PRINT
340    PRINT "ENTER THE CONSTANT FROM THE SECOND"
350    PRINT "BINOMIAL."
360    INPUT D
370    PRINT
380    PRINT "THE PRODUCT IS ";A * C;V$;"^ 2 ";
390    IF A * D + B * C = 0 THEN 440
400    IF A * D + B * C > 0 THEN  PRINT " + ";
410    PRINT A * D + B * C;V$;" ";
420    IF B * D = 0 THEN 450
430    IF B * D > 0 THEN  PRINT " + ";
440    PRINT B * D
450    PRINT
460    PRINT "DO YOU WANT TO DO ANOTHER? (Y OR N)"
470    INPUT R$
480    IF R$ = "Y" OR R$ = "YES" THEN 180
490    END
```

9-6 DIVIDING A POLYNOMIAL BY A MONOMIAL

There are several methods for dividing a polynomial by a monomial. In this section, we divide *each* term of the polynomial by the monomial:

$$\frac{2x^4 - 10x}{2x} = \frac{2x^4}{2x} - \frac{10x}{2x} = x^3 - 5$$

At this point, it is advisable to stay with this method of division. Later, in Chapter 13, factoring procedures will be discussed. It can then be shown that:

$$\frac{2x^4 - 10x}{2x} = \frac{\overset{1}{\cancel{2x}}(x^3 - 5)}{\underset{1}{\cancel{2x}}} = x^3 - 5$$

When the last term of a quotient is 1, students often make the error of omitting that term. Stress that $\frac{x^2 + x}{x}$, for example, is equal to $x + 1$, and is not equal to x. This error can be avoided if students check the reasonableness of the answer with respect to multiplication. It is not reasonable for a quotient with one term to be multiplied by one term and yield a dividend of two terms.

In the exercises in this section, the exponents of the divisor are always less than or equal to the exponents of the dividend. As a challenge, you may wish to give a problem such as:

$$\frac{5x^4y - 15x^3y^5}{5xy^2} = \frac{5x^4y}{5xy^2} - \frac{15x^3y^5}{5xy^2}$$
$$= x^3y^{-1} - 3x^2y^3 \text{ or } \frac{x^3}{y} - 3x^2y^3$$

Note that $\frac{x^3}{y} - 3x^2y^3$ is not a polynomial since $\frac{x^3}{y}$ is not a monomial.

72

9-7 DIVIDING A POLYNOMIAL BY A POLYNOMIAL

As illustrated in this section, the division of a polynomial by another polynomial follows a procedure similar to the division of two arithmetic numbers. The division process naturally comes to an end when the remainder is 0 or when the degree of the remainder is less than the degree of the divisor. It is advisable to arrange the terms of both the divisor and the dividend in descending powers of the variable. Start out with several division problems whose remainders are 0 until students feel at ease with this method. When there is no remainder, the problem can be checked by multiplying the quotient and the divisor. That is, this product is the original dividend. If there is a remainder other than 0, this remainder is now added to the product of the quotient and divisor, resulting in the original dividend.

You may wish to challenge your students with a division problem such as:

$$x + 1 \overline{)\, x^4 - x^3 - 3x - 3}$$

The term $0x^2$ should be inserted as a placeholder in the dividend.

$$x + 1 \overline{)\, x^4 - x^3 + 0x^2 - 3x - 3}$$

Questions 1–9 each consist of two quantities, one in column A and one in Column B. You are to compare the two quantities and choose:

A if the quantity in Column A is greater;
B if the quantity in Column B is greater;
C if the two quantities are equal;
D if the relationship cannot be determined from the information given.

Notes

1. In certain questions, information concerning one or both of the quantities to be compared is centered above the two columns.
2. In a given question, a symbol that appears in both columns represents the same thing in Column A as it does in Column B.
3. Letters such as x, n, and k stand for real numbers.

Column A	Column B
1. $8(x^2 + x) + 9(x^2 + x)$	$18(x^2 + x) - (x^2 + x)$
2. $3(x + 3) + 4(x - 1)$	$5x + 2(x + 1)$

$$x > 0$$

Column A	Column B
3. $(x + 3)(x - 4)$	$(x - 3)(x + 4)$

$$y = x + 1$$

Column A	Column B
4. $(y + 3)^3$	$(x + 4)^3$

$$k \neq 0$$

Column A	Column B
5. $\dfrac{9k^3 + 6k^2}{3k^2}$	$\dfrac{12k^2 + 12k}{4k}$

$$k \neq 0$$

Column A	Column B
6. $\dfrac{12k + 6k^2}{6k}$	$\dfrac{16k - 8k^2}{8k}$

 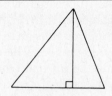

7. The area of a rectangle, with dimensions of $2x$ and $4x + 3$	The area of a triangle, with base of $6x$ and height of $3x + 2$
8. The area of a rectangle, with dimensions of $2y$ and $5y + 2$	The area of a triangle, with base of $3y$ and height of $5y + 2$

$$y < 6$$

9. $6y - (y - 6)$	$6y - (6 - y)$

In 10–17, select the letter of the correct answer.

10. The side of a rhombus is $x + 5$ and the side of a square is $x + 2$. Then the perimeter of the rhombus exceeds the perimeter of the square by
(A) 3   (B) 9   (C) 12   (D) $6x + 21$

11. If $x + 3$ is an even integer, then which of the following is an odd integer?
(A) $(x + 3)(x + 4)$ (B) $(x + 3)^2$
(C) $(x + 4)(x + 5)$ (D) $(x + 4)^2$

12. The area of a rectangle is $x^2 + 6x + 5$ and its length is $x + 1$. Then the width of the rectangle is
(A) $x + 6$ (B) $x + 5$
(C) $x + 3$ (D) $x + 2$

13. What is the average of $3(5x^2 + 2)$ and $7(5x^2 + 2)$?
(A) $20x^2 + 8$ (B) $25x^2 + 10$
(C) $40x^2 + 16$ (D) $50x^2 + 20$

14. The expression $(x - (x - (x - (x - 1))))$ equals
(A) $+1$ (B) -1
(C) $2x + 1$ (D) $2x - 1$

15. If the side of a square is $x + 4$, then a measure 2 less than its area is
(A) $x^2 + 4$ (B) $x^2 + 14$
(C) $x^2 + 4x + 4$ (D) $x^2 + 8x + 14$

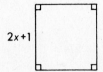
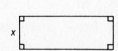

16. The square on the left and the rectangle on the right have the same perimeters. What is the area of the rectangle on the right?
(A) $4x^2 + 4x + 1$ (B) $8x^2 + 4x$
(C) $6x^2 + 4x$ (D) $3x^2 + 2x$

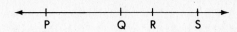

17. If PR is $4x + 5$, RS is $2x + 3$, and Q is the midpoint of $\overline{PS}$, then QR is
(A) $6x + 8$ (B) $3x + 4$
(C) $2x + 2$ (D) $x + 1$

SUGGESTED TEST ITEMS (Chapter 9)

1. Arrange each of the following in descending order and state the degree of the polynomial.
   a. $12x - 3x^2 + x^3 - 2$ **b.** $5y + y^4 - 7$

2. Write the polynomial that is the additive inverse or opposite of $7a - 6b$.

In 3–12, write the expression as a polynomial in simplest form.

3. $8x + 7 - 5x + 1$ 4. $c(3c^2 - cd + d^2)$

5. $-ab + 3a(b + 7)$ 6. $-3m + 2m^2 + m - 2m^2 - 2m$

7. $7 - 3(x - 5)$ 8. $(2x - 1)(x + 4)$

9. $(2a - 5)^2$ 10. $(7y + 3x) - (4x - 7y)$

11. $(3r + 5)(3r - 5)$ 12. $12x^2 - [x^2 - (x + 3)]$

13. The length of a rectangle is represented by $(3x - 7)$ and the width by $(x + 4)$.
    a. Represent the perimeter as a polynomial in simplest form.
    b. Represent the area as a polynomial in simplest form.
    c. Give a value for x that is not possible.

14. The perimeter of a square is represented by $8a - 12$. Express the area as a polynomial.

15. A mail order catalog offers shirts for 5 dollars less than the regular price. Shipping charges of 3 dollars are added to every order. Represent in simplest form the cost of ordering 4 shirts if the regular price of a shirt is x dollars.

BONUS: Find two consecutive counting numbers whose squares differ by 35.
  Is it possible to find two consecutive counting numbers whose squares differ by 24? Explain.

CHAPTER **10**

First-Degree Equations and Inequalities in One Variable

Aims

- To use inverses in solving equations whose solutions require more than one operation.

- To solve equations of increasing variety and complexity.

- To apply an algebraic approach to verbal problems.

- To introduce the properties of inequality.

- To determine and to graph the solution sets of inequalities.

Now that students have learned skills in algebraic manipulation, they are prepared to solve more difficult equations, such as those containing parentheses and those with variables in both members. Further attention is given to equations containing more than one variable, that is, formulas and literal equations.

A major emphasis in this chapter is on establishing a sound understanding of algebraic solution of verbal problems. At the same time, it is desirable, in class discussion, to consider parallel solutions that reinforce students' ability to apply the problem-solving strategies that were learned earlier in the course. Apart from the broad usefulness of such strategies beyond the area of mathematics, they can help

students succeed in some types of formal testing situations, such as college entrance examinations. Comments are included in this manual to suggest where such references to strategies may be appropriate. It must be remembered, however, that the algebraic foundation is essential for further work in mathematics, and that algebraic solution is a principal focus in this course.

10-1 USING BOTH THE ADDITIVE AND MULTIPLICATIVE INVERSES IN SOLVING EQUATIONS

In Section 4–7, equations were solved using several operations. Although the order in which the inverse operations were performed was shown not to matter, it is usually easier to perform any additions or subtractions first, followed by any multiplications or divisions. In this section, it is preferable to use the additive inverse before the multiplicative inverse.

Model Problem 3 presents an algebraic solution and its geometric interpretation. Some students may recognize that the problem could be solved by the strategy of working backward: If 41 results from increasing by 5, subtract 5 to get 36. If 4 times a number is 36, divide by 4 to get 9. Emphasize again that writing and solving an equation is an organized way of working backward.

Remind students of the steps to use when solving a verbal problem by algebraic processes:

1. Read the problem carefully to determine what is known and what has to be found.
2. Represent the unknown quantities in terms of a single variable.
3. Translate the word statement into an equation or an inequality.
4. Solve the equation or the inequality.
5. Check the solution in the words of the problem.

10-2 SOLVING EQUATIONS THAT HAVE THE VARIABLE IN BOTH MEMBERS

An equation may have a variable in both of its members. Since a variable represents a number, the variable may also be added to or subtracted from both members of an equation without changing the solution set. In essence, we are simply collecting like terms by this process.

Students have a tendency to collect variables at the left. In certain situations, some students may realize that negative values can be avoided by collecting variables at the right. Both approaches should be presented in class. For example:

Solution 1

$$x + 10 = 3x + 2$$
$$x + (-3x) + 10 = 3x + (-3x) + 2$$
$$-2x + 10 = 2$$
$$-2x + 10 + (-10) = 2 + (-10)$$
$$-2x = -8$$
$$x = 4$$

Solution 2

$$x + 10 = 3x + 2$$
$$x + (-x) + 10 = 3x + (-x) + 2$$
$$10 = 2x + 2$$
$$10 + (-2) = 2x + 2 + (-2)$$
$$8 = 2x$$
$$4 = x$$

Again, various strategies may be used in some of the problems. To apply guessing and checking to Model Problem 2, for example, guess at two numbers that satisfy the first condition, and check whether they also satisfy the second condition. Thus, 8 and 2, 12 and 3, 16 and 4, and 20 and 5 all are number pairs such that the larger is 4 times the smaller, but only 20 and 5 meet the requirement that the larger exceeds the smaller by 15. It is likely that students will recognize the greater efficiency of the algebraic approach.

10-3 SOLVING EQUATIONS CONTAINING PARENTHESES

To solve an equation containing parentheses, we must first eliminate all parentheses by performing the indicated operations on the members contained within the parentheses. A review of subtracting polynomials and multiplying a polynomial by a monomial is advisable.

We have been using the distributive property to remove parentheses. You may wish to mention an alternative that is sometimes useful. For example, to solve the equation $2(4x - 2) = 20$, we use the distributive property to form the equivalent equation $8x - 4 = 20$. Or, we can divide both members of the original equation by 2 to form the equivalent equation $4x - 2 = 10$. In both cases, the value for x is 3.

Computer Activity (10-3) The following program will allow students to check their solutions of equations, such as those in Exercises 1–32 on page 284, or to solve similar equations of their own choosing.

```
100    REM    THIS PROGRAM WILL SOLVE A
110    REM    FIRST-DEGREE EQUATION AFTER
120    REM    PARENTHESES HAVE BEEN REMOVED.
130    PRINT "THE COMPUTER WILL SOLVE A FIRST-DEGREE"
140    PRINT "EQUATION FOR YOU. BEFORE YOU BEGIN,"
150    PRINT "USE THE DISTRIBUTIVE PROPERTY TO REMOVE"
160    PRINT "PARENTHESES."
170    PRINT
180    PRINT "WHAT IS THE VARIABLE IN THE EQUATION?"
190    INPUT V$
200    PRINT "HOW MANY TERMS IN ";V$;" ARE IN THE LEFT"
210    PRINT "MEMBER OF THE EQUATION?"
220    INPUT N
230    LET S = 0
240    IF N = 0 THEN 320
250    PRINT "ENTER THE COEFFICIENTS OF ";V$;" FROM THE"
260    PRINT "LEFT MEMBER, PRESSING THE RETURN KEY"
270    PRINT "AFTER EACH ENTRY."
280    FOR I = 1 TO N
290    INPUT A
300    LET S = S + A
310    NEXT I
320    PRINT "HOW MANY CONSTANTS ARE IN THE LEFT"
330    PRINT "MEMBER OF THE EQUATION?"
340    INPUT N
350    LET C = 0
360    IF N = 0 THEN 440
370    PRINT "ENTER THE CONSTANTS FROM THE LEFT"
380    PRINT "MEMBER, PRESSING THE RETURN KEY AFTER"
390    PRINT "EACH ENTRY."
400    FOR I = 1 TO N
410    INPUT B
420    LET C = C - B
430    NEXT I
440    PRINT "HOW MANY TERMS IN ";V$;" ARE IN THE RIGHT"
450    PRINT "MEMBER OF THE EQUATION?"
460    INPUT N
470    IF N = 0 THEN 550
480    PRINT "ENTER THE COEFFICIENTS OF ";V$;" FROM THE"
490    PRINT "RIGHT MEMBER OF THE EQUATION, PRESSING"
500    PRINT "THE RETURN KEY AFTER EACH ENTRY."
510    FOR I = 1 TO N
520    INPUT A
530    LET S = S - A
540    NEXT I
550    PRINT "HOW MANY CONSTANTS ARE IN THE RIGHT"
560    PRINT "MEMBER OF THE EQUATION?"
```

```
570    INPUT N
580    IF N = 0 THEN 660
590    PRINT "ENTER THE CONSTANTS FROM THE RIGHT"
600    PRINT "MEMBER, PRESSING THE RETURN KEY AFTER"
610    PRINT "EACH ENTRY."
620    FOR I = 1 TO N
630    INPUT B
640    LET C = C + B
650    NEXT I
660    PRINT
670    PRINT V$;" = ";C / S
680    PRINT
690    PRINT "DO YOU WANT TO SOLVE ANOTHER?(Y OR N)"
700    INPUT R$
710    IF R$ = "Y" OR R$ = "YES" THEN 180
720    END
```

10-4 CONSECUTIVE INTEGER PROBLEMS

Exercises are provided in this section prior to the solving of consecutive integer problems so that students are prepared to identify consecutive integers, consecutive even integers, and consecutive odd integers. Although students may seem to understand the fact that consecutive integers differ by 1, while consecutive even integers and consecutive odd integers differ by 2, difficulties still occur with these concepts. In the solution of consecutive odd integer problems, a common error is to represent the first odd integer as x, the second consecutive odd integer as $x + 1$, the third by $x + 3$, and so on. Take the time needed to show why x, $x + 2$, $x + 4$ are the correct representations.

Emphasize that an answer containing a fraction cannot be a correct answer to a problem that asks for an integer, and an answer that is even cannot be correct in a problem requiring an odd solution.

Estimation can be used in some consecutive integer problems to assess the reasonableness of an answer. In Model Problem 1, for example, two consecutive integers must be almost equal in value. If their sum is 95, each would be about half of 95, thus confirming that 47 and 48 are reasonable answers.

10-5 FINDING THE VALUE OF A VARIABLE IN A FORMULA

In Section 3-6, students were required to evaluate the subject of a formula by first replacing the other variables with their numerical values and then computing. Now, students are asked to find the value of *any* variable in the formula, when values are provided for all but the specified variable.

As a counterpart to the solution in the model problem, you may wish to mention an approach that combines the strategies of drawing a diagram that shows the given information and then working backward:

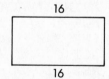

Since the length is 16, the sum of the lengths is 32. Subtract 32 from the perimeter, 48, to obtain 16 as the sum of the widths, and, therefore, 8 as the missing width.

10-6 PERIMETER PROBLEMS

Students are expected to find the perimeter of any regular polygon, given the length of a side of the polygon. They should also be able to find the length of any side of a regular polygon, given the perimeter of the polygon.

Wherever possible, students should be required to draw and label a diagram for a geometric problem. For example, if the length of a rectangle is three less than twice the width, the width is represented by w and the length by $2w - 3$.

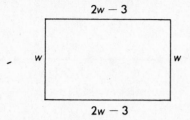

Given that the perimeter of the rectangle is 42, students may write an equation using either the definition of perimeter:

$$w + (2w - 3) + w + (2w - 3) = 42$$

or the formula for the perimeter of a rectangle:

$$2(2w - 3) + 2w = 42$$

10-7 SOLVING EQUATIONS THAT HAVE VARIABLES IN THE ANSWERS

To solve equations containing more than one variable, we will use a simpler related problem. Write an equation similar to the one to be solved by replacing with constants all variables except the one for which the equation is to be solved. Use the same steps needed to solve this new equation in order to solve the given equation. Note the examples given in the model problems. This section serves as a review of equation-solving techniques learned to date.

In the equation $ab = c$, we solve for b by dividing both members of the equation by a so that $b = \dfrac{c}{a}$. Even though it is true that $a \neq 0$ in this example, such a restriction will not be mentioned with each problem in the exercises. It should be understood that each variable used as a divisor is not equal to zero.

10-8 TRANSFORMING FORMULAS

Show how a formula, such as $D = RT$, can be transformed so that each variable becomes the subject of the formula:

$$D = RT \quad\left|\quad \dfrac{D}{R} = \dfrac{RT}{R} \quad\right|\quad \dfrac{D}{T} = \dfrac{RT}{T}$$
$$\dfrac{D}{R} = T \quad\left|\quad \dfrac{D}{T} = R\right.$$

Thus, $D = RT$ or $T = \dfrac{D}{R}$ or $R = \dfrac{D}{T}$.

Demonstrate similar procedures for formulas involving addition and subtraction, such as $P = 2L + 2W$.

You may wish to mention the applications of some of the formulas given in the examples and exercises. Students will already be familiar with some of them:

Distance = rate $\times$ time

Area$_{\text{Rectangle}}$ = length $\times$ width

Area$_{\text{Triangle}}$ = $\dfrac{1}{2}$(base)(height)

Interest = principal $\times$ rate $\times$ time

10-9 PROPERTIES OF INEQUALITY

The Order Property of Numbers (also called the Trichotomy Property) and the Transitive Property of Inequality are illustrated by points on a number line. Since the number line and the ordering of numbers were introduced in Section 1-7, these properties should be easily understood.

The addition and multiplication properties of inequality will take more time to illustrate. After some investigation, it becomes clear that adding (or subtracting) the same number to (or from) both members of an inequality leaves the order of the inequality unchanged.

When asked if multiplying (or dividing) both members of an inequality by the same number (other than 0) will leave the order of the inequality unchanged, most students will think that this is the case. If asked to choose a number to demonstrate with, they invariably choose a positive number. However, when

81

the multiplier is a negative number, the inequality is reversed. You might show some numerical illustrations in addition to those given in the text, so that students can see various other cases. For example, multiply the following first by $+3$ and then by -3: $-9 < 2$, $-9 < -2$, and $9 > -2$.

10-10 FINDING AND GRAPHING THE SOLUTION SETS OF INEQUALITIES

Since a number is a member of the solution set of $2x < 6$ if and only if it is a member of the solution set of $x < 3$, we refer to $2x < 6$ and $x < 3$ as equivalent inequalities. In this section, each given inequality is to be transformed into a simpler equivalent inequality whose solution set is evident. Thus, $x < 3$ is more desirable than $2x < 6$.

The domain of all variables in the exercises is the set of signed numbers. Stress that the solution $\{x \,|\, x < 3\}$ is not the same as the set of integers less than 3 by comparing their graphs:

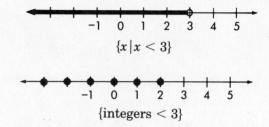

$$\{x \,|\, x < 3\}$$

$$\{\text{integers} < 3\}$$

Procedures for finding the solution set of an inequality parallel those methods used to solve equations. Stress the one exception to this rule: When we multiply or divide each member of the inequality by a negative number, the order of the inequality is reversed.

Computer Activity (10-10)   The following program will allow students to check their solutions to inequalities such as those in Exercises 1–51 on pages 303 and 304, or to solve similar inequalities of their own choosing. The program points out the need to reverse the order of the inequality when dividing by a negative number.

```
100    REM      THIS PROGRAM WILL SOLVE A
110    REM      FIRST-DEGREE INEQUALITY
120    REM      AFTER PARENTHESES HAVE BEEN
130    REM      REMOVED.
140    PRINT "THE COMPUTER WILL SOLVE A FIRST-DEGREE"
150    PRINT "INEQUALITY FOR YOU BUT FIRST YOU MUST"
160    PRINT "USE THE DISTRIBUTIVE PROPERTY TO REMOVE"
170    PRINT "PARENTHESES."
180    PRINT
190    PRINT "ENTER THE SYMBOL FOR THE INEQUALITY:"
200    PRINT "FOR LESS THAN, ENTER <"
210    PRINT "FOR GREATER THAN, ENTER >"
220    PRINT "FOR LESS THAN OR EQUAL TO, ENTER <="
230    PRINT "FOR GREATER THAN OR EQUAL TO, ENTER >="
240    INPUT D$
250    IF D$ = "<" THEN E$ = ">"
260    IF D$ = ">" THEN E$ = "<"
270    IF D$ = "<=" THEN E$ = ">="
280    IF D$ = ">=" THEN E$ = "<="
290    PRINT "WHAT IS THE VARIABLE IN THE INEQUALITY?"
300    INPUT V$
310    PRINT "HOW MANY TERMS IN ";V$;" ARE IN THE LEFT"
320    PRINT "MEMBER OF THE INEQUALITY?"
330    INPUT N
```

```
340    LET S = 0
350    IF N = 0 THEN 430
360    PRINT "ENTER THE COEFFICIENTS OF ";V$;" FROM THE"
370    PRINT "LEFT MEMBER, PRESSING THE RETURN KEY"
380    PRINT "AFTER EACH ENTRY."
390    FOR I = 1 TO N
400    INPUT A
410    LET S = S + A
420    NEXT I
430    PRINT "HOW MANY CONSTANTS ARE IN THE LEFT"
440    PRINT "MEMBER OF THE INEQUALITY?"
450    INPUT N
460    LET C = 0
470    IF N = 0 THEN 550
480    PRINT "ENTER THE CONSTANTS FROM THE LEFT"
490    PRINT "MEMBER, PRESSING THE RETURN KEY AFTER"
500    PRINT "EACH ENTRY."
510    FOR I = 1 TO N
520    INPUT B
530    LET C = C - B
540    NEXT I
550    PRINT "HOW MANY TERMS IN ";V$;" ARE IN THE RIGHT"
560    PRINT "MEMBER OF THE INEQUALITY?"
570    INPUT N
580    IF N = 0 THEN 660
590    PRINT "ENTER THE COEFFICIENTS OF ";V$;" FROM THE"
600    PRINT "RIGHT MEMBER, PRESSING THE RETURN KEY"
610    PRINT "AFTER EACH ENTRY."
620    FOR I = 1 TO N
630    INPUT A
640    LET S = S - A
650    NEXT I
660    PRINT "HOW MANY CONSTANTS ARE IN THE RIGHT"
670    PRINT "MEMBER OF THE INEQUALITY?"
680    INPUT N
690    IF N = 0 THEN 770
700    PRINT "ENTER THE CONSTANTS FROM THE RIGHT"
710    PRINT "MEMBER, PRESSING THE RETURN KEY AFTER"
720    PRINT "EACH ENTRY."
730    FOR I = 1 TO N
740    INPUT B
750    LET C = C + B
760    NEXT I
770    PRINT
780    IF S = 0 THEN 900
790    IF S < 0 THEN 830
800    PRINT V$;D$;C / S
810    PRINT
820    GOTO 980
830    PRINT V$;E$;C / S
840    PRINT
850    PRINT "NOTICE THAT THE ORDER OF THE INEQUALITY"
```

```
860    PRINT "HAS BEEN REVERSED BECAUSE BOTH MEMBERS"
870    PRINT "OF THE INEQUALITY WERE DIVIDED BY A"
880    PRINT "NEGATIVE NUMBER."
890    GOTO 980
900    IF C = 0 THEN 940
910    IF C > 0 THEN 660
920    IF D$ = "<" OR D$ = "<=" THEN 970
930    GOTO 950
940    IF D$ = ">" OR D$ = ">=" THEN 970
950    PRINT "SOLUTION SET = ALL NUMBERS IN DOMAIN"
960    GOTO 980
970    PRINT "SOLUTION SET = THE EMPTY SET"
980    PRINT
990    PRINT "DO YOU WANT TO SOLVE ANOTHER? (Y OR N)"
1000   INPUT R$
1010   IF R$ = "Y" OR R$ = "YES" THEN 190
1020   END
```

10-11 SOLVING VERBAL PROBLEMS BY USING INEQUALITIES

Students must be familiar with the algebraic representation of sentences involving relationships of inequality. Sentences containing expressions such as "is at least," "is at most," "is less than" "is more than," "the minimum value of," "the maximum value of," and so forth should be understood, both in light of their meanings and in their algebraic representations.

Once the appropriate inequality symbol is chosen and the algebraic sentence is written, the solution of the inequality follows the same basic procedure used to solve equations in one variable. (The exception occurs when multiplying or dividing by a negative value.)

SAT PREPARATION EXERCISES (Chapter 10)

Questions 1–7 each consist of two quantities, one in Column A and one in Column B. You are to compare the two quantities and choose:

A if the quantity in Column A is greater;
B if the quantity in Column B is greater;
C if the two quantities are equal;
D if the relationship cannot be determined from the information given.

Notes

1. In certain questions, information concerning one or both of the quantities to be compared is centered above the two columns.
2. In a given question, a symbol that appears in both columns represents the same thing in Column A as it does in Column B.
3. Letters such as x, n, and k stand for real numbers.

Column A	Column B
1. The solution of $4x + 9 = 5$	The solution of $4y + 9 = 3$

$$P = (2x - 1)(3x - 2)$$

Column A	Column B
2. The value of P when $x = \frac{1}{2}$	The value of P when $x = \frac{2}{3}$

$$y < -3$$

3. $4 - 3y$	13

$$x > 2y$$

4. $2x + 2y$	$6y$

$$x = 2$$

5. $x^3 + 3x^2 + 2x$	$2x^2 + 6x + 4$

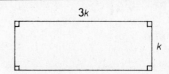

A rectangle has a length that is 3 times its width.

6. The area of the rectangle when its length is doubled	The area of the rectangle when its width is doubled

x is an integer, and $x > 1$.

7. $(x)(x + 2)$	$2(x + 1)$

In 8–17, select the letter of the correct answer.

8. The solution of $3x + k = 9$ is zero when k is
   (A) 3 (B) -3 (C) 9 (D) -9

9. Solve: $7(x + 3) + 9(x + 3) - 4(x + 3) = 48$
   (A) 1 (B) 3.5 (C) 4 (D) 7

10. If $8(x + 4) = 16$, and $y(x + 4) = 24$, then y is
    (A) -2 (B) -4 (C) 4 (D) 12

11. If $5(y + 3) = 20$, and $y = x - 3$, then x is
    (A) 1 (B) 4 (C) -1 (D) -4

12. If $3(2x - 1) = 30$, then $2x + 1$ equals
    (A) $4\frac{1}{2}$ (B) $5\frac{1}{2}$ (C) 10 (D) 12

13. If $x > 1$ and $y > z$, then which of the following is not necessarily true?
    (A) $xy > z$
    (B) $xy > xz$
    (C) $x + y > z + 1$
    (D) $x^2 > x$

14. If p represents $x + 1 < 4$ and q represents $x - 1 > -4$, then the graph of the disjunction $p \lor q$ is

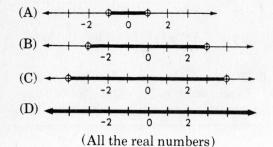

(All the real numbers)

15. If $3(2x - 1) < 5$, then which of the following is not necessarily true?
(A) $6x - 3 < 6$ (B) $2x - 1 < 2$
(C) $3 - 6x > -5$ (D) $1 - 2x > -1$

16. If the sum of two integers is even, and the product of these integers is odd, then the integers
(A) are both odd   (B) are consecutive
(C) are both even   (D) are never equal

17. If the average of two consecutive odd integers is 44, what is the product of their sum and difference?
(A) 176   (B) 88   (C) 45   (D) 43

SUGGESTED TEST ITEMS (Chapter 10)

In 1–12, solve and check:

1. $3a - 7 = 5$ **2.** $11 - x = 2$ **3.** $7(y - 1) - y = 23$ **4.** $4(3 - d) = 6d + 2$

5. $\frac{3}{8}b + 2 = 50$ **6.** $.4c + 1.1 = .3c + 7.8$ **7.** $6 - 2x = 10x$ **8.** $8(x + 2) = 4x$

9. $5(2r - 3) = 9(r - 1)$ **10.** $x + 5 = 1 - 7x$ **11.** $2(s + 3) = 6$ **12.** $\frac{1}{2}y + 3 = \frac{1}{3}y + 2$

13. Solve for h in terms of A and V: $V = \frac{1}{3}Ah$

14. a. Solve for C in terms of F: $F = \frac{9}{5}C + 32$

    b. Using the formula obtained in part **a,** find the Celsius temperature C when the Fahrenheit temperature F is 14°.

15. When Marcy bought some postcards for 40 cents each, she paid a tax of 20 cents. How many postcards did she buy if the total cost of cards and tax was 3 dollars?

In 16–20, find and graph the solution set.

16. $3x < 9$ **17.** $2x - 1 \geq 5$ **18.** $1 - 7x < 15$

19. $(2x > 4) \vee (3x < -6)$ **20.** $(x + 1 \leq 7) \wedge (x - 1 \geq 0)$

21.

The above graph shows the solution of which inequality?
(1) $-1 \leq x < 3$ (2) $-1 < x \leq 3$ (3) $-1 \leq x \leq 3$ (4) $-1 < x < 3$

22.

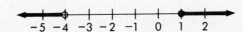

The above graph shows the solution of which inequality?
(1) $(x < -4) \vee (x \geq 1)$ (2) $(x < -4) \wedge (x \geq 1)$ (3) $-4 < x \leq 1$ (4) $(x \leq 1) \vee (x > -4)$

23. Use an algebraic strategy to solve the following problem.

    At the auto repair shop, Mrs. Angiers was given an estimate of at most \$165 to repair her car. This estimate included \$20 an hour for labor and \$75 for parts. What is the maximum number of hours that the mechanic expected to spend on the job?

BONUS: Elaine was making favors for a party. She made $\frac{1}{3}$ on Monday, $\frac{1}{2}$ of the remainder on Tuesday, $\frac{1}{2}$ of those still remaining on Wednesday, and she finished on Thursday by making 12. How many favors did she make?

CHAPTER **11**

Geometry

Aims

- To formulate good mathematical definitions.
- To use algebra in the solution of geometric problems.
- To introduce transformation geometry.

Students are already familiar with the common geometric figures and with the relationships of size and shape that follow from the definitions of these figures. Many of these relationships will be generalized by using algebraic representation. One of the goals of this course is to prepare students to begin the study of formal proof in Course II with a sense of familiarity concerning most of the theorems to be proved.

From the outset, it is important to use proper symbolism. The difference between $AB = CD$ and $\overline{AB} \cong \overline{CD}$, or between $\angle ABC \cong \angle DEF$ and $m\angle ABC = m\angle DEF$ should be made clear.

Arithmetic as well as algebraic strands are woven together with the geometry throughout this chapter. There are many places for applications of logic.

This chapter presents an introduction to transformations through an informal study of symmetries, line and point reflections, rotations, and translations.

11-1 POINTS, LINES, AND PLANES

This opening section begins to lay the groundwork for the study of geometry. Many terms will already be familiar to students, but time should be spent so that precise meanings replace vague concepts.

The exercises anticipate some confusion that students might have in using the correct notation. You may wish to do some of these exercises orally with the class, and invite such elementary questions as "When is it acceptable to omit dots for points in a diagram?"

11-2 ANGLES, ANGLE MEASURES, AND PERPENDICULARITY

In this section, angles are classified according to their measures. Establish that in this course angle measure will always be in degrees. Remind students that the **m** notation is understood to refer to degrees. Thus, in an expression such as $m\angle A = 50$, the degree symbol is omitted.

Encourage students to make use of a protractor both to measure angles and to draw them. Have students use a protractor to measure a reflex angle, and discuss the related measures $x°$ and $(360 - x)°$.

The discussion of angles should include the concept of an angle being formed by a counterclockwise rotation. The diagram shown on page 313 of the text can be reinforced by a simple classroom demonstration using two erasers or rulers to represent the sides of the opening angle. Counterclockwise rotations are common in the study of trigonometry and transformation geometry.

Note that the traditional study of the trigonometry of the right triangle is omitted from Course I. A brief unit on right triangle trigonometry is studied as an optional topic in Course II, as an application of similar triangles. The unit circle is studied in Course III.

Point out that the biconditional statement is applicable to basic definitions in mathematics. For example: "Two lines are perpendicular if and only if the two lines or parts of the lines intersect to form right angles."

Computer Activity (11-2) The following program will provide practice in classifying angles as acute, right, obtuse, or straight.

Note: On some computers, RND (1) may have to changed to RND (0).

```
100   REM     THIS PROGRAM WILL PROVIDE
110   REM     PRACTICE IN CLASSIFYING
120   REM     ANGLES.
130   LET C = 0
140   LET D = 0
150   LET M =   INT ( RND (1) * 180) + 1
160   IF M / 8 =   INT (M / 8) THEN M = 180
170   IF M / 7 =   INT (M / 7) THEN M = 90
180   LET T = 0
190   IF M < 90 THEN R$ = "ACUTE"
200   IF M = 90 THEN R$ = "RIGHT"
210   IF M > 90 AND M < 180 THEN R$ = "OBTUSE"
220   IF M = 180 THEN R$ = "STRAIGHT"
230   PRINT "IDENTIFY THE ANGLE WHOSE"
240   PRINT "MEASURE IS ";M;" AS BEING"
250   PRINT "ACUTE, RIGHT, OBTUSE, OR STRAIGHT."
260   PRINT
270   LET D = D + 1
280   INPUT A$
290   PRINT
300   IF A$ = R$ THEN 450
310   IF A$ = "ACUTE" THEN   PRINT "THE MEASURE OF AN";
320   IF A$ = "ACUTE" THEN   PRINT "ACUTE ANGLE < 90."
330   IF A$ = "RIGHT" THEN   PRINT "THE MEASURE OF A RIGHT";
340   IF A$ = "RIGHT" THEN   PRINT "ANGLE IS 90."
350   IF A$ = "STRAIGHT" THEN   PRINT "THE MEASURE OF A";
360   IF A$ = "STRAIGHT" THEN   PRINT "STRAIGHT ANGLE IS 180."
370   IF A$ = "OBTUSE" THEN   PRINT "THE MEASURE OF AN OBTUSE";
380   IF A$ = "OBTUSE" THEN   PRINT "ANGLE IS MORE THAN";
390   IF A$ = "OBTUSE" THEN   PRINT "90 BUT LESS THAN 180."
400   LET T = T + 1
410   IF T < 3 THEN   PRINT "TRY AGAIN.": GOTO 230
420   PRINT
430   PRINT "AN ANGLE OF ";M;" DEGREES IS ";R$;"."
440   GOTO 480
450   PRINT "THAT'S RIGHT."
```

```
460    LET C = C + 1
470    PRINT
480    PRINT "DO YOU WANT TO TRY ANOTHER ANGLE?"
490    INPUT B$
500    IF B$ = "Y" OR B$ = "YES" THEN 150
510    PRINT
520    PRINT "YOU ANSWERED ";C;" OUT OF ";D;" CORRECTLY."
530    END
```

11-3 PAIRS OF ANGLES

In addition to the definitions and explanations offered in the text, you may wish to enrich your discussions by considering the following.

Adjacent Angles

The definition given in the text specifies three conditions:

1. The two angles must have a common vertex.
2. The two angles must have a common side.
3. The two angles may not have any interior points in common.

Offer some diagrams in which only one or two of the conditions are satisfied. For example,

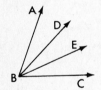

∠ *ABE* and ∠ *DBC* are not adjacent angles because conditions 2 and 3 fail.

∠ *ABD* and ∠ *ABC* are not adjacent angles because condition 3 fails.

∠ *ABC* and ∠ *BCD* are not adjacent angles because conditions 1 and 2 fail. ($\overrightarrow{BC}$ is not $\overrightarrow{CB}$).

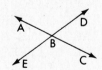

∠ *ABE* and ∠ *DBC* are not adjacent angles because condition 2 fails.

Complementary and Supplementary Angles

We use the same method to find the complement of a given angle, no matter how the original angle is expressed. Consider the following chalkboard arrangement:

Measure of Original Angle	Manner in Which the Complement Is Found	Measure of Complement
$40°$	$90° - 40°$	$50°$
$x°$	$90° - x°$	$(90 - x)°$
$(2x + 10)°$	$90° - (2x + 10)°$	$(80 - 2x)°$

Emphasize a check based upon the definition of complementary angles (that is, the sum of the measures of the original angle and its complement is $90°$).

A similar discussion is applicable to supplementary angles.

Mention that the definitions of complementary and supplementary angles limit the number of angles to two. Thus, in the following diagram, angles 1, 2, and 3 are not supplementary even though the sum of their measures is $180°$.

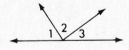

Linear Pair

A linear pair can also be described as two adjacent angles that are supplementary.

The hidden conditional and its converse, formed from this definition, require the use of a conjunction:

$L \to (A \land S)$: If two angles form a linear pair, then they are adjacent and supplementary.

$(A \land S) \to L$: If two angles are adjacent and supplementary, then they form a linear pair.

Students often overlook the conjunction and form conclusions that are false. Ask for the truth value of the following statements:

$L \to S$: If two angles form a linear pair, then they are supplementary. (True)

$S \to L$: If two angles are supplementary, then they form a linear pair. (False)

$L \to A$: If two angles form a linear pair, then they are adjacent. (True)

$A \to L$: If two angles are adjacent, then they form a linear pair. (False)

Vertical Angles

Have students measure several pairs of vertical angles to verify that if two straight lines intersect, the vertical angles formed are equal in measure. Mention that as a pair of scissors opens and closes, it forms vertical angles.

At this point, the text states that two angles equal in measure are also congruent. Elicit that the converse of this statement is also true.

Computer Activities (11-3) The following program will provide practice in finding the measures of the complement and supplement of an angle.

Note: On some computers, RND (1) may have to be changed to RND (0).

```
100    REM     THIS PROGRAM WILL PROVIDE
110    REM     PRACTICE WITH COMPLEMENTARY
120    REM     AND SUPPLEMENTARY ANGLES.
130    LET C = 0
140    LET D = 0
150    LET Y =  INT ( RND (1) * 2)
160    LET T = 0
170    IF Y = 0 THEN 390
180    LET X =  INT ( RND (1) * 89) + 1
190    PRINT "WHAT IS THE MEASURE OF THE COMPLEMENT"
200    PRINT "OF AN ANGLE OF ";X;" DEGREES?"
210    LET T = T + 1
220    LET D = D + 1
230    INPUT A
240    IF A = 90 - X THEN 620
250    IF T > 1 THEN 350
260    PRINT "TWO ANGLES ARE COMPLEMENTS IF THE SUM"
270    PRINT "OF THEIR MEASURES IS 90."
280    PRINT
290    PRINT "THE MEASURE OF THE COMPLEMENT OF AN"
300    PRINT "ANGLE OF ";X;" DEGREES IS 90 - ";X
310    PRINT
320    PRINT "TRY AGAIN."
330    PRINT
340    GOTO 190
350    PRINT "THE MEASURE OF THE COMPLEMENT OF AN"
360    PRINT "ANGLE OF ";X;" DEGREES IS ";90 - X
370    PRINT
380    GOTO 650
```

```
390    LET X =  INT ( RND (1) * 179) + 1
400    PRINT
410    PRINT "WHAT IS THE MEASURE OF THE SUPPLEMENT"
420    PRINT "OF AN ANGLE OF ";X;" DEGREES?"
430    LET T = T + 1
440    LET D = D + 1
450    INPUT A
460    IF A = 180 - X THEN 620
470    IF T > 1 THEN 580
480    PRINT
490    PRINT "TWO ANGLES ARE SUPPLEMENTS IF THE SUM"
500    PRINT "OF THEIR MEASURES IS 180."
510    PRINT
520    PRINT "THE MEASURE OF THE SUPPLEMENT OF AN"
530    PRINT "ANGLE OF ";X;" DEGREES IS 180 - ";X
540    PRINT
550    PRINT "TRY AGAIN."
560    PRINT
570    GOTO 410
580    PRINT "THE MEASURE OF THE SUPPLEMENT OF AN"
590    PRINT "ANGLE OF ";X;" DEGREES IS ";180 - X
600    PRINT
610    GOTO 650
620    PRINT "THAT'S RIGHT."
630    LET C = C + 1
640    PRINT
650    PRINT "WOULD YOU LIKE TO TRY ANOTHER? (Y OR N)"
660    INPUT A$
670    IF A$ = "YES" OR A$ = "Y" THEN 150
680    PRINT
690    PRINT "YOU ANSWERED ";C;" OUT OF ";D;" CORRECTLY."
700    END
```

Students with an introductory understanding of programming should be able to write the following programs, which are simpler in nature but still deal with the same concept.

This program finds the measure of the complement of a given angle:

```
10    REM   THIS PROGRAM WILL FIND THE
20    REM   MEASURE OF THE COMPLEMENT
30    REM   OF ANY ANGLE.
40    PRINT "ENTER THE MEASURE OF AN ANGLE."
50    INPUT A
60    LET C = 90 - A
70    PRINT "THE MEASURE OF THE COMPLEMENT IS ";C
80    END
```

If you wish to find the supplement of an angle, the following changes must be made:

```
60    LET S = 180 - A
70    PRINT "THE MEASURE OF THE SUPPLEMENT IS ";S
```

11-4 ANGLES AND PARALLEL LINES

Although a line is in fact parallel to itself, the concept of parallelism is limited here to two or more distinct lines in a plane. Segments and rays are parallel if the lines that contain them are parallel.

When two lines are cut by a transversal, various angles are formed. Alternate interior, alternate exterior, and corresponding angles are pairs of angles that are congruent if and only if the two lines cut by the transversal are parallel.

Make a point that in a problem accompanied by a diagram, it is the *given* (the facts that are stated) that become the conditions of the problem. We do not make assumptions based on the appearance of the diagram. Thus, unless lines in a diagram are given as parallel, we cannot assume that they are.

Offer the following as a visual aid to help students identify alternate interior angles and corresponding angles:

1. Look for the letter **N** or the letter **Z** in different positions to identify alternate interior angles.
2. Look for the letter **F** in different positions to identify corresponding angles.

Note that alternate interior angles and corresponding angles exist whether the lines that form them are parallel or not.

In this course, the statement about alternate interior angles of parallel lines is treated as a postulate. Simple algebraic proofs concerning other pairs of angles of parallel lines are offered in the text. These proofs help to prepare students for Course II.

11-5 GEOMETRIC FIGURES

Following the discussion in the text about plane geometric figures, curves, and polygons, you may wish to ask questions such as: Why can't a polygon have fewer than three sides? Why isn't a circle an example of a polygon? How can a square be an example of a simple closed curve?

To enrich the discussion about polygons, ask for commonly used real-life examples such as the octagonal stop sign. Have students look around the classroom and identify different shapes. Pictures of architectural designs and other art forms are rich in geometric shapes.

11-6 THE TRIANGLE

In this section, triangles are classified according to their angles and according to their sides. Once the students intuitively accept the fact that the sum of the measures of the angles of a triangle is 180° (they should use a protractor to verify this statement), you may ask them to sketch a triangle that is:

1. both right and isosceles
2. both scalene and obtuse
3. both isosceles and acute

Ask questions such as the following:

1. Can a triangle contain two right angles? one right angle and one obtuse angle? two obtuse angles?
2. Can a right triangle be equilateral? isosceles?
3. Can an obtuse triangle be equilateral? isosceles?

The terms *equilateral* and *equiangular* are introduced. Establish the biconditional: equilateral triangle ↔ equiangular triangle. Go on to establish that each angle of an equilateral (equiangular) triangle contains 60°.

Elicit the fact that the sum of the measures of the two acute angles of a right triangle is 90°. That is, the acute angles of a right triangle are complementary. Students should also determine that each acute angle of an isosceles right triangle contains 45°.

An exterior angle of a triangle is defined in terms of the linear pair it forms with one of the interior angles of the triangle. Ask the students to describe another method for determining the measure of an exterior angle of a triangle. After several problems, they should realize that the measure of any exterior angle of a triangle is equal to the sum of the measures of the two remote interior angles of the triangle.

An interesting problem touched upon in the exercises deals with the sum of the measures of the three exterior angles of a triangle whose three interior angle measures are given. (See Exercise 19 on page 339.) After several triangles of different angle measures are investigated, students will see that the sum of the measures of the exterior angles of any triangle is always 360°. For homework, you may wish to ask for an explanation. One possible solution to this problem is:

The measure of each exterior angle is 180° minus the measure of the interior angle of the triangle that is adjacent to it.

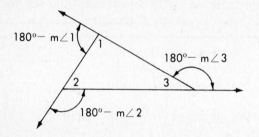

The sum of the measures of these three exterior angles is:

$(180° - m\angle 1) + (180° - m\angle 2) + (180° - m\angle 3)$
$= 540° - m\angle 1 - m\angle 2 - m\angle 3$
$= 540° - (m\angle 1 + m\angle 2 + m\angle 3)$
$= 540° - 180°$
$= 360°$

Allow sufficient time for treating the properties of an isosceles triangle. When you draw an isosceles triangle on the chalkboard, do not always locate the vertex angle at the top of the diagram and the base angles at the bottom. In the following diagram, $\angle B$ is the vertex angle and $\angle A$ and $\angle C$ are the base angles.

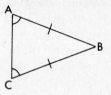

Exterior angles of isosceles triangles provide good exercise material. Using the diagram below, in which $m\angle A = 54$ and $\overline{AB} \cong \overline{BC}$, students should be able to find: (1) $m\angle ACB = 54$, (2) $m\angle ABC = 72$, and (3) $m\angle ACD = 126$.

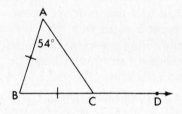

Remember that the properties of triangles discussed in this section are not addressed formally. Once you feel that the students have grasped the relationships, verbal problems should then be provided to reinforce their understanding. Angle measures are now determined algebraically rather than by the use of a protractor.

Computer Activities (11-6) The following program determines if three angles of given measures can be the angles of a triangle:

```
10   REM    THIS PROGRAM WILL DETERMINE IF
20   REM    THREE GIVEN ANGLES CAN BE THE
30   REM    ANGLES OF A TRIANGLE.
40   PRINT "ENTER THE MEASURES OF THREE ANGLES"
45   PRINT "SEPARATED BY COMMAS."
50   INPUT A,B,C
60   LET S = A + B + C
70   IF S = 180 THEN 100
80   PRINT "THESE ANGLES CANNOT BE THE ANGLES"
85   PRINT "OF A TRIANGLE."
90   GOTO 110
100  PRINT "THESE ANGLES CAN BE THE ANGLES OF"
105  PRINT "A TRIANGLE."
110  END
```

The following program can be used to find the measure of the third angle needed to create a triangle when the measures of two angles are given:

```
10   REM    THIS PROGRAM WILL FIND THE
20   REM    MEASURE OF THE THIRD ANGLE
30   REM    OF A TRIANGLE.
40   PRINT "ENTER THE MEASURES OF TWO ANGLES"
45   PRINT "SEPARATED BY A COMMA."
50   INPUT A,B
60   IF A + B >= 180 THEN 110
70   LET C = 180 - (A + B)
80   PRINT "THE MEASURE OF THE THIRD ANGLE"
90   PRINT "OF THE TRIANGLE IS ";C
100   GOTO 120
110   PRINT "A TRIANGLE CANNOT BE FORMED."
120   END
```

The following program finds the measure of the vertex angle of an isosceles triangle when the measure of a base angle is given:

```
10   REM    THIS PROGRAM WILL FIND THE
20   REM    MEASURE OF A VERTEX ANGLE
30   REM    OF AN ISOSCELES TRIANGLE.
40   PRINT "ENTER THE MEASURE OF A BASE ANGLE."
50   INPUT B
60   IF 2 * B >= 180 THEN 100
70   LET V = 180 - (2 * B)
80   PRINT "THE MEASURE OF THE VERTEX ANGLE IS ";V
90   GOTO 110
100   PRINT "A TRIANGLE CANNOT BE FORMED."
110   END
```

To find the measure of a base angle of an isosceles triangle given the measure of the vertex angle, we can use a program similar to the preceding one.

```
10   REM    THIS PROGRAM WILL FIND THE
20   REM    MEASURE OF A BASE ANGLE
30   REM    OF AN ISOSCELES TRIANGLE.
40   PRINT "ENTER THE MEASURE OF THE VERTEX ANGLE."
50   INPUT V
60   LET B = (180 - V) / 2
70   PRINT "EACH BASE ANGLE MEASURES ";B
80   END
```

11-7 CONGRUENT TRIANGLES

Before you discuss the concept of congruent triangles, establish the conditions necessary for any two polygons to be congruent. Since two polygons are congruent if and only if all pairs of corresponding sides are congruent and all pairs of corresponding angles are congruent, the same conditions must hold true for any two triangles. However, the text shows that not all six pairs of corresponding parts of the triangles need to be shown congruent. To determine congruence in triangles, it is sufficient to show congruence of only three selected pairs of corresponding parts.

Time should be provided for discovery of some of the basic conditions for congruence of triangles by experimentation with rulers and protractors, either in class or as a homework assignment prior to this lesson.

The text shows procedures for drawing a triangle congruent to a given triangle by s.a.s. ≅ s.a.s. and by a.s.a. ≅ a.s.a. If students go through a similar procedure for drawing a triangle congruent to a given triangle by s.s.s. ≅ s.s.s., they will find that since they are not using any angle measure, they will have to keep trying until they can get the second and third sides of the given lengths to meet at a common endpoint.

You may wish to mention that although triangle congruence cannot generally be established using two pairs of sides and a pair of nonincluded angles (s.s.a. ≅ s.s.a.), these conditions do establish congruence in two right triangles (hy. leg ≅ hy. leg).

Also, you might point out that when two pairs of angles are congruent, the third pair of angles must also be congruent. Thus, any side is an included side between two angles congruent to the corresponding angles in the other triangle.

Note that only drawing tools (rulers and protractors) are used in Course I. Formal constructions with straightedge and compasses will be studied in Course II.

11-8   THE QUADRILATERAL

It is important, especially in this section, that students realize what constitutes a good mathematical definition. For example, a rectangle is defined as a parallelogram in which all four angles are right angles. What does it mean to say that a rectangle is a parallelogram? This statement means that a rectangle must have all the properties of a parallelogram.

A rectangle must also have some distinguishing feature(s) that separates it from the rest of the broader set of parallelograms.

A rectangle has four right angles. Can we define a rectangle as a parallelogram with one right angle? Elicit the properties of a parallelogram that lead to an answer of yes.

A diagram is helpful in understanding basic definitions.

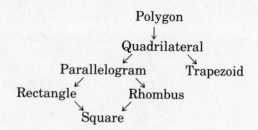

Note how each figure is defined from the figure listed above it.

In Course I, the properties of the family of parallelograms are limited to those mentioned in the text. Properties concerning diagonals will be studied in Course II.

In the exercises, conditional statements are given concerning the special quadrilaterals. The students are asked to determine the truth values of each statement and its converse, inverse, and contrapositive. A background in logic helps students to a greater understanding of the relationships that exist among the quadrilaterals.

The sum of the measures of the angles of any quadrilateral is 360°. Students will see that a quadrilateral can be divided into two triangles, each of whose angle measures has a sum of 180°. How many degrees are in the sum of the measures of the angles of a pentagon? a hexagon? After considering a number of examples, students can arrive at a general formula for the sum of the measures of the angles of any n-sided polygon, namely $(n - 2)180°$.

11-9   TRANSFORMATIONS

Traditionally, transformations had been reserved for higher-level mathematics courses. However, even at this early stage, students are receptive to an informal presentation of transformations and symmetries. To promote informality, you may wish, for example, to refer to a reflection as a *flip,* and to a translation as a *slide.*

Since each of the transformations, reflection, translation, and rotation, preserves distance and angle measure, a figure is congruent to its image under all of these transformations. A discussion of dilation, a transformation that preserves angle measure but not distance, is presented in Chapter 12 as an application of similarity.

The study of transformations is helpful in developing an intuitive understanding of congruence and similarity, as well as of the properties of certain plane figures. For example, in a discussion of the isosceles triangle, it can be neatly demonstrated that the bisector of the vertex angle, the median from the vertex angle, and the altitude from the vertex angle are one and the same segment. Since these segments in a triangle are not required Course I study, the approach should be informal. Students can discover for themselves that the symmetry about the bisector of the vertex angle does not exist with respect to the bisector of a base angle. Extend the discussion to a scalene triangle and to an equilateral triangle.

A rectangle is offered as an example of a figure that has more than one axis of symmetry. Ask about other quadrilaterals. Students generally expect a parallelogram to be symmetric about its diagonals. To complement the text explanation that such is not the case, demonstrate with a paper cutout of a parallelogram, folded along a diagonal. Although the parallelogram is thus shown not to have line symmetry, students will see later that it does have point symmetry.

Students should have fun looking at letters and words for symmetry, and finding symmetries in mirror reflections, in prisms, in advertising logos, and in examples from nature and architecture. They also enjoy hands-on experience in drawing symmetric figures by paperfolding or by using a ruler. They should see that when a ruler is laid perpendicular to the line of reflection, the preimage and image points are equidistant from that line.

An overhead projector is helpful in discussing transformations. Rotational symmetry, in particular, can be clearly demonstrated by using matching overlays to show what rotation is needed for a figure to coincide with itself. Overlays can also be used to demonstrate that a rotation of 180 degrees about a point P is equivalent to a point reflection in P.

You may wish to copy and distribute the page that follows. When the chords are carefully drawn, the result is a sketch of a cardioid, or heart-shaped curve. Ask students to locate the axis of symmetry. Note the integration of arithmetic, geometry, and algebra in this exercise.

Feb. 14th

A Valentine's Day Gift From Your Math Teacher

The circumference of a circle is divided into 36 equal parts, each arc measuring 10° (geometry). Starting at a point and going in a clockwise direction, the points are numbered from 1 to 36 and then again from 37 to 72 (arithmetic).

Using a ruler, draw chords that are line segments (geometry) to connect the points according to the rule $n \rightarrow 2n$ (algebra). For example, $1 \rightarrow 2$, $2 \rightarrow 4$, $3 \rightarrow 6$, . . . , up to $35 \rightarrow 70$.

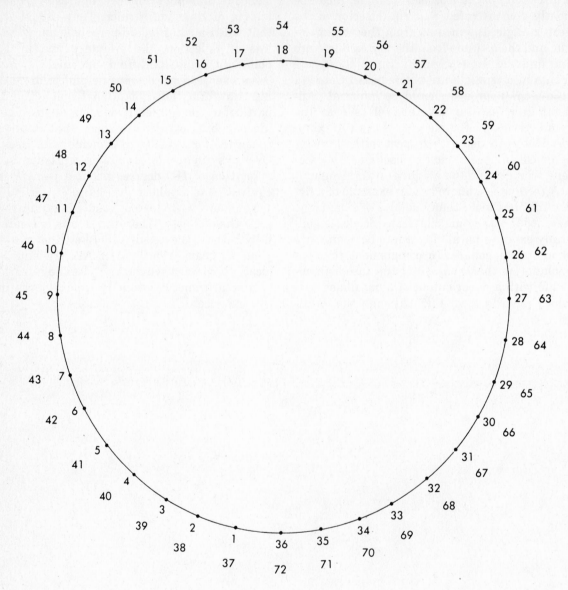

SAT PREPARATION EXERCISES (Chapter 11)

Questions 1–9 each consist of two quantities, one in Column A and one in Column B. You are to compare the two quantities and choose:

A if the quantity in Column A is greater;
B if the quantity in Column B is greater;
C if the two quantities are equal;
D if the relationship cannot be determined from the information given.

Notes

1. In certain questions, information concerning one or both of the quantities to be compared is centered above the two columns.
2. In a given question, a symbol that appears in both columns represents the same thing in Column A as it does in Column B.
3. Letters such as x, n, and k stand for real numbers.

Column A	*Column B*

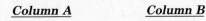

1. $m\angle P + m\angle Q$ $m\angle R + m\angle S$

$\overline{PQ} \perp \overline{RS}$ and $\overline{RS} \cap \overline{TV} = Q$

2. $m\angle RQV + m\angle PQT$ $m\angle SQP$

Triangle ABC is an acute triangle.

3. $m\angle A + m\angle B$ $m\angle C$

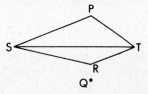

4. The average of   The sum of
a, b, and c x, y, and z

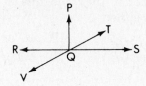

5. $m\angle P + m\angle Q + m\angle R$ The sum of the measures of an exterior angle at P and an exterior angle at R

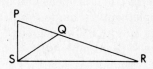

Point Q is the reflection of point P with respect to line segment $\overline{ST}$.

6. $m\angle P$ $m\angle R$

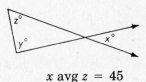

Angle PQS is acute.

7. $m\angle P + m\angle PSQ$ $m\angle R + m\angle RSQ$

x avg $z = 45$

8. y $x + z$

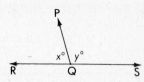

Angle *PQR* is larger than its complement.

9.

$\dfrac{x}{y}$ $\dfrac{1}{3}$

In 10–17, select the letter of the correct answer.

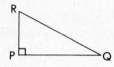

10. How many points, *T*, can be found so that $\triangle PQT$ and the above triangle are congruent?
(A) 1   (B) 2   (C) 3   (D) 4

11. If $\angle X$ and $\angle Y$ are complementary, and $\angle X$ and $\angle Z$ are supplementary, which of the following is true?
(A) $m\angle X + m\angle Y + m\angle Z = 270$
(B) $2(m\angle X) = m\angle Y + m\angle Z$
(C) $m\angle Z - m\angle X = 90$
(D) $m\angle Z - m\angle Y = 90$

12. The average of the measures of angle *X*, its complementary angle, and its supplementary angle is 80 degrees. Then the measure of the complement of angle *X* is
(A) 30°   (B) 60°   (C) 90°   (D) 120°

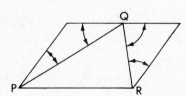

13. In the figure above, triangle *PQR* shares a side of the parallelogram. What is the sum of the marked angles?
(A) 135°   (B) 180°   (C) 270°   (D) 360°

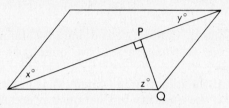

14. $\overline{PQ}$ is perpendicular to a diagonal of the parallelogram. Which of the following is true?
(A) $x + y + z = 180$ (C) $x + z = 90$
(B) $x + y + 2z = 180$ (D) $y + z = 90$

15. Of the symmetries below, the letter S has
   I point symmetry
   II line symmetry
   III rotational symmetry
(A) I and II only   (B) II and III only
(C) I and III only   (D) I, II, and III

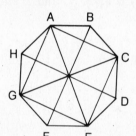

16. The regular octagon shown has several lines of symmetry. If the image of $\overline{AE}$ is $\overline{GC}$ under a reflection in one of these lines of symmetry, then the line of reflection could be either
(A) $\overleftrightarrow{AG}$ or $\overleftrightarrow{AC}$ (B) $\overleftrightarrow{AG}$ or $\overleftrightarrow{CE}$
(C) $\overleftrightarrow{AE}$ or $\overleftrightarrow{GC}$ (D) $\overleftrightarrow{HD}$ or $\overleftrightarrow{FB}$

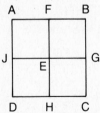

17. Under a 90-degree counterclockwise rotation about point *E*, followed by a translation, the image of $\overline{EG}$ is $\overline{HE}$. Under the same transformations, the image of $\overline{BG}$ is

(A) $\overline{BF}$ (B) $\overline{JE}$ (C) $\overline{AJ}$ (D) $\overline{FE}$

SUGGESTED TEST ITEMS (Chapter 11)

1. In the diagram, $\overleftrightarrow{AB} \perp \overleftrightarrow{CD}$, E is the midpoint of $\overline{AB}$, and $\overline{BC} \cong \overline{AC}$.

   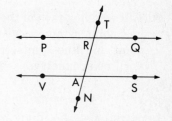

   a. Name the opposite ray of $\overrightarrow{EA}$.
   b. Name a right angle.
   c. Name an acute angle.
   d. Name an obtuse angle.
   e. Name a line segment congruent to $\overline{BE}$.
   f. Name an angle congruent to $\angle CBE$.
   g. Name the image of A under a reflection in $\overleftrightarrow{CD}$.
   h. Name a line of symmetry for $\triangle ABC$.
   i. Which of the following cannot be used to prove $\triangle BEC \cong \triangle AEC$?
      (1) a.s.a. $\cong$ a.s.a.   (2) s.a.s. $\cong$ s.a.s.   (3) a.a.a. $\cong$ a.a.a.   (4) s.s.s. $\cong$ s.s.s.

2. In the diagram, $\overleftrightarrow{PQ} \parallel \overleftrightarrow{VS}$, and $\overleftrightarrow{TN}$ intersects $\overleftrightarrow{PQ}$ at R and $\overleftrightarrow{VS}$ at A. If $m\angle VAN = 85$, find:

   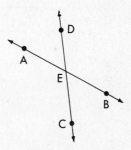

   a. $m\angle SAN$ b. $m\angle SAR$
   c. $m\angle PRA$ d. $m\angle QRA$

3. In $\triangle ABC$, $m\angle A$ is 20 degrees more than $m\angle B$, and $m\angle C$ is 8 degrees less than $m\angle B$. Find the measure of each angle of the triangle.

4. In the diagram, $\overleftrightarrow{AB}$ intersects $\overleftrightarrow{CD}$ at E.
   If the measure of $\angle AEC$ is represented by $5x - 12$, and $m\angle BED$ is represented by $3x + 40$, find:
   a. $m\angle AEC$ b. $m\angle BED$ c. $m\angle AED$ d. $m\angle CEB$

5. In $\triangle PQR$, the measure of the exterior angle at P is 28 degrees less than the measure of $\angle QPR$. Find the measure of the exterior angle at P.

6. The measure of an angle is $\frac{4}{5}$ of the measure of its supplement. Find the measure of the angle and of its supplement.

7. In the figure, $ABCD$ is a rectangle.
   If $AB = x + 12$ and $DC = 2x - 8$, find x.

   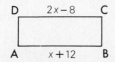

8. Copy the following and draw as many lines of symmetry for each of the figures as possible.

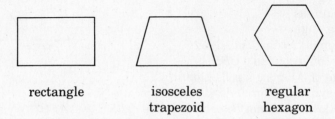

rectangle   isosceles   regular
            trapezoid   hexagon

9. Tell whether each of the letters at the right has point symmetry, line symmetry, both point and line symmetry, or neither point nor line symmetry.

H E A R T S

BONUS: A person hiking close to a river sees a campfire that was left burning. He runs to the river to get some water and then runs to put out the fire. Copy the sketch and draw in the shortest path the hiker can take to the river and then to the campfire.

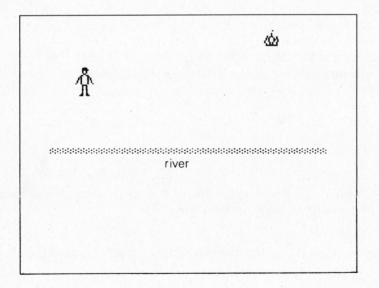

river

CHAPTER **12**

Ratio and Proportion

Aims

- To establish the concepts of ratio, proportion, and direct variation.

- To use ratio and proportion in solving verbal problems.

- To introduce similarity of geometric figures.

- To use ratio in comparing perimeters and areas of similar figures.

12-1 RATIO

Since a ratio is a comparison of two numbers expressed as an ordered pair, present the topic of finding a ratio as an example of a binary operation ($a * b = c$). Stress that the terms of a ratio must be expressed in the same unit of measure before the quotient is found. To show that the ratio of terms expressed in the same unit of measure is independent of

the unit of measure used, present the following example.

The ratio of 36 inches to 2 yards may be written as $36:72$ using inches, as $3:6$ using feet, or as $1:2$ using yards. Each of these ratios in lowest terms is $1:2$. An understanding that the terms must be in the same unit of measure can be reinforced by a demonstration of "cancellation," which can occur only when the units are the same. For example,

$$\frac{36 \text{ inches}}{2 \text{ yards}} = \frac{36 \text{ ~~inches~~}}{72 \text{ ~~inches~~}} = \frac{36}{72} = \frac{1}{2}$$

Some students may reduce the ratio $\frac{36}{72}$ to $\frac{18}{36}$ and stop. They must be reminded to continue reducing until the simplest form (in this case, $\frac{1}{2}$) is reached.

Computer Activity (12-1) The following program could be used by students to solve problems such as Exercises 6, 10, 15, and 16 on pages 371 and 372, or to solve similar problems of their own choosing. In Exercises 15 and 16, remind students that quantities must be expressed in the same unit of measure.

```
100    REM    THIS PROGRAM WILL EXPRESS A
110    REM    RATIO IN LOWEST TERMS.
120    PRINT "ENTER THE FIRST NUMBER OF THE RATIO."
130    INPUT A
140    PRINT
150    PRINT "ENTER THE SECOND NUMBER OF THE RATIO."
```

```
160   INPUT B
170   PRINT
180   LET A1 = A
190   LET B1 = B
200   IF A > B THEN   GOSUB 330
210   LET R = B -   INT (B / A) * A
220   IF R = 0 THEN 260
230   LET B = A
240   LET A = R
250   GOTO 210
260   PRINT "IN LOWEST TERMS THE RATIO IS ";A1 / A;"/";B1 / A
270   PRINT
280   PRINT "DO YOU WANT TO DO ANOTHER? (Y OR N)"
290   INPUT R$
300   PRINT
310   IF R$ = "Y" OR R$ = "YES" THEN 120
320   GOTO 370
330   LET T = A
340   LET A = B
350   LET B = T
360   RETURN
370   END
```

12-2   USING A RATIO TO EXPRESS A RATE

A ratio comparing two quantities is not limited to quantities of the same unit. A comparison of quantities of different types is common and leads to the concept of rate. For example, the ratio of 12 cookies to 4 persons becomes 3 cookies per person. Use comparison shopping as an application. For example:

Which is a better buy?
a. 8 oz. @ $.80   **b.** 12 oz. @ $1.08

The better buy is choice **b,** since it yields a cost of 9¢ per ounce, while the cost in **a** is 10¢ per ounce.

To show that the ratio of terms comparing quantities expressed in different units is not independent of the units of measure, present the following example.

If a car travels 30 miles in 1 hour, it travels 158,400 feet in 3,600 seconds. Therefore, the rate can be expressed as 30:1 or 30 miles per hour. The same rate can be expressed as 158,400:3,600 or 44:1 or 44 feet per second. Therefore, the units of measure are an important part of the rates.

12-3   SOLVING VERBAL PROBLEMS INVOLVING RATIOS

Students have been using an algebraic strategy to solve verbal problems. The procedure established in Section 4-5 lists one step as identifying the unknown (that is, presenting a legend). When the ratio of two or more numbers is given, that ratio determines the legend. For example, if two numbers are in the ratio 2:3, the legend is written:

Let $2x$ = the smaller number.
Then $3x$ = the larger number.

A common student error is to stop after solving an equation to find the value of x. Remind them to refer to the legend and to find the solution to the problem.

The text provides a variety of mathematical and nonmathematical examples involving ratios in realistic settings.

12-4   PROPORTION

In this section, the fundamental principle of proportion is developed: *In any proportion, the product of the means is equal to the product of the extremes.* This is often called **cross multiplication.** If this shorter expression is used, be sure students understand that it only applies to proportions. They sometimes incorrectly apply cross multiplication to expressions such as the sum of two fractions.

Students will use cross multiplication to solve the equations given in the exercises. In these exercises, no proportion will yield a second-degree equation. Such quadratic equations are dealt with in Chapter 20.

Computer Activity (12-4) To determine whether two given ratios form a proportion, the following program may be used:

```
10   REM   THIS PROGRAM WILL DETERMINE
20   REM   WHETHER TWO RATIOS FORM A
30   REM   PROPORTION.
40   PRINT "ENTER THE NUMBERS OF THE FIRST RATIO"
45   PRINT "SEPARATED BY A COMMA."
50   INPUT A,B
60   PRINT "ENTER THE NUMBERS OF THE SECOND RATIO"
65   PRINT "SEPARATED BY A COMMA."
70   INPUT C,D
80   LET E = A * D
90   LET M = B * C
100  IF E = M THEN 130
110  PRINT "THE NUMBERS DO NOT FORM A PROPORTION."
120  GOTO 140
130  PRINT "THE NUMBERS FORM A PROPORTION."
140  END
```

12-5 DIRECT VARIATION

Direct variation is a familiar concept even if the terms introduced in this section are unfamiliar. Direct variation occurs when there is a *constant rate.*

Use Model Problem 3 to elicit that, in certain situations, we expect a constant rate. In this case, the calories per gram are constant at 4.5, or $\frac{9}{2}$. Point out that the constant rate is the basis for the check. That is, we verify that 315 calories is the correct number for 70 grams because the ratio $\frac{315}{70}$ yields the ratio $\frac{9}{2}$, the constant determined from the original condition, $\frac{90}{20}$.

12-6 PERCENT AND PERCENTAGE PROBLEMS

When the base and the rate are given, it is convenient to multiply the base by the rate expressed as a decimal fraction to find the percentage. However, when the percentage is given and either the base or the rate is to be found, the use of a proportion is recommended.

The text shows an algebraic solution for Model Problem 2 that involves proportion. An alternate algebraic solution relies on translating the words of the problem into an equation.

Let n = the number.

$\underbrace{25\% \text{ of a number}}\ \underbrace{\text{is}}\ \underbrace{80}.$

$.25n \qquad = 80$

Students have seen this treatment before, in Section 4-6, where percent problems were first introduced.

Computer Activities (12-6) The following program will express a fraction as a percent:

```
10 REM  THIS PROGRAM WILL EXPRESS
20 REM  A FRACTION AS A PERCENT.
30 PRINT "ENTER THE NUMERATOR."
40 INPUT N
50 PRINT "ENTER THE DENOMINATOR."
60 INPUT D
70 LET P = (N / D) * 100
80 PRINT N; " / "; D; " = "; P; "%"
90 END
```

To find the percentage of any given number, you can use the following program:

```
10 REM  THIS PROGRAM WILL FIND THE
20 REM   PERCENTAGE WHEN THE RATE AND
30 REM  BASE ARE ENTERED.
40 PRINT "ENTER THE RATE WITHOUT THE % SYMBOL."
50 INPUT R
60 PRINT "ENTER THE BASE."
70 INPUT B
80 LET P = B * (R / 100)
90 PRINT "THE PERCENTAGE IS "; P; "."
100 END
```

12-7 SIMILAR POLYGONS

When a picture is enlarged, we want the enlargement to be proportional to the original so that the figures will not be distorted. Pictures that have been enlarged or reduced in size are familiar examples of similar polygons.

Remind students of the notational difference between $\overline{AB}$ (a line segment) and AB (the measure of the line segment). Note that when we write ratios or proportions, we are dealing with measures.

In the exercises, students are asked if two rectangles must be similar. They are also asked about other types of quadrilaterals. After discussing these figures, ask students to explain why two equilateral triangles must be similar. Elicit a statement concerning the similarity of any two polygons with the same number of sides. (Any two *regular* polygons with the same number of sides are similar.)

Continue to encourage students to draw diagrams for problems involving geometric figures. Similar triangles or other polygons need not be drawn exactly to a given ratio, but a reasonably accurate sketch can often help to avoid errors.

12-8 SIMILAR TRIANGLES; DILATION

After establishing a.a. ≅ a.a. as a condition for similarity of two triangles, a fourth type of transformation, dilation, is introduced as an application.

Ask students for other examples of dilation. You might begin by mentioning that a doctor dilates (enlarges) the pupils of the eyes during a detailed eye examination.

Proportions are used to solve for the unknown lengths of sides in similar triangles. Using the model problem on page 397, you might show students that reducing a ratio can simplify the arithmetic.

$$\frac{x}{18} = \frac{16}{24}$$

$$\frac{x}{18} = \frac{2}{3}$$

$$3x = 36$$

$$x = 12$$

Students may write an incorrect proportion because they mistakenly use only a part of a side of a triangle. You might have them look again at the diagram for Model Problem 2, as shown below, after the answer to part **a** has been obtained.

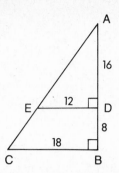

Emphasize that, for example, $\frac{16}{12} \neq \frac{8}{18}$. Since segment $\overline{BD}$ is not a side of either triangle, its measure, 8, cannot be a term of any correct ratio.

Students frequently have difficulty setting up a correct proportion because they are not paying attention to which angles correspond or to the fact that corresponding sides are found opposite congruent angles. Exercises 1-4 are intended to help students develop this sense. You might have students mark their diagrams to show congruent angles. For example, the diagram for Exercise 19 could be marked as shown below.

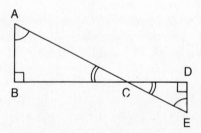

In this exercise, angles B and D are given as right angles. The intersecting line segments $\overline{AE}$ and $\overline{BD}$ should lead students to recognize a pair of vertical angles. Encourage students to write the vertices of the triangles in order of their correspondence ($\triangle ABC \sim \triangle EDC$ or $\triangle CAB \sim \triangle CED$). Corresponding sides can thus be easily identified.

In problems relating to physical situations, such as finding the height of a tree, students should be sure to write the unit of measure in the answer. Even when the unit is unspecified, as in Exercise 12, students may write an answer in the form "$DF = 8$ units," and should understand that this refers to linear units.

Writing an informal proof, as is asked for in Exercise 22, is an introduction to a skill that will be required in Course II, where formal proof is emphasized. You should spend some time letting students feel the importance of order in a proof. Elicit that it does not matter which is the first pair of angles focused on, but that it does matter that two pairs of congruent angles are established before we can state that two triangles are similar.

12-9 RATIOS OF PERIMETERS AND OF AREAS OF SIMILAR POLYGONS

After a numerical development of the relationship between the ratio of the perimeters of similar triangles and the ratio of the measures of the corresponding sides, you might wish to show students an algebraic proof.

The key to the proof that follows is in the setup. We set up two similar triangles so that the ratio of the measures of the corresponding sides, which is known to be constant, can be specified.

Given: $\triangle ABC \sim \triangle A'B'C'$
   Let the measures of the sides of $\triangle ABC$ be called as_1, as_2, and as_3.
   Let the measures of the sides of $\triangle A'B'C'$ be called bs_1, bs_2, and bs_3.

Show: The ratio of the perimeters is equal to the ratio of the measures of the corresponding sides.

Proof

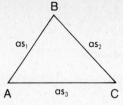
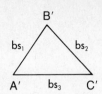

1. $\dfrac{\text{sides of } \triangle ABC}{\text{sides of } \triangle A'B'C'} = \dfrac{as_1}{bs_1} = \dfrac{as_2}{bs_2} = \dfrac{as_3}{bs_3} = \dfrac{a}{b}$

2. perimeter of $\triangle ABC = as_1 + as_2 + as_3$
$$= a(s_1 + s_2 + s_3)$$

3. perimeter of $\triangle A'B'C' = bs_1 + bs_2 + bs_3$
$$= b(s_1 + s_2 + s_3)$$

4. $\dfrac{\text{perimeter of } \triangle ABC}{\text{perimeter of } \triangle A'B'C'} = \dfrac{a(s_1 + s_2 + s_3)}{b(s_1 + s_2 + s_3)} = \dfrac{a}{b}$

5. Therefore, from steps 1 and 4, $\dfrac{\text{perimeter of } \triangle ABC}{\text{perimeter of } \triangle A'B'C'} = \dfrac{\text{sides of } \triangle ABC}{\text{sides of } \triangle A'B'C'}$

In Model Problem 2 on page 404, note how helpful a diagram is to show the relationship between a change in the side of the square and the corresponding change in the perimeter. Encourage students to draw diagrams as they do the exercises.

As with Model Problem 1, an alternate solution to Model Problem 2 would begin with determining the perimeters of the old and new squares. Note how the new perimeter can be obtained by substitution into the perimeter formula.

$$\text{old perimeter} = 4s$$
$$\text{new perimeter} = 4(3s) = 12s$$
$$\frac{\text{new perimeter}}{\text{old perimeter}} = \frac{12s}{4s} = \frac{3}{1}$$

You might wish to offer an algebraic proof for the statement that the ratio of the areas of similar triangles is the square of the ratio of the measures of the corresponding sides.

As with the proof offered earlier for perimeter, the key to the area proof that follows is in the setup. Again, we set up two similar triangles so that the ratio of the measures of corresponding sides, which is known to be constant, can be specified. We begin by establishing that the corresponding altitudes have the same ratio as the corresponding sides.

Given: $\triangle ABC \sim \triangle A'B'C'$ with altitudes $\overline{BD}$ and $\overline{B'D'}$.
 Let the ratio of corresponding sides be $a\!:\!b$.

Show: The ratio of the areas is equal to the square of the ratio of the corresponding sides.

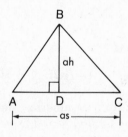

Proof

1. To establish that corresponding altitudes of similar triangles have the same ratio as the corresponding sides, first consider triangles ABD and $A'B'D'$, for which the altitudes of triangles ABC and $A'B'C'$ are sides.
 Since $\triangle ABD \sim \triangle A'B'D'$ (a.a. $\cong$ a.a.),

 $\dfrac{BD}{B'D'} = \dfrac{AB}{A'B'}$ where $\dfrac{AB}{A'B'}$ represents the ratio of the corresponding sides of the original similar triangles.

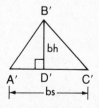

2. In the original triangles, let the measures of the bases and the altitudes to these bases be as follows:

base $AC = as$ base $A'C' = bs$

altitude $BD = ah$ altitude $B'D' = bh$

3. Substitute into the formula for the area of a triangle.

$$\text{area of } \triangle = \tfrac{1}{2}(\text{base} \times \text{altitude})$$

$$\text{area of } \triangle ABC = \tfrac{1}{2}(as)(ah)$$

$$= \tfrac{1}{2}a^2(sh)$$

$$\text{area of } \triangle A'B'C' = \tfrac{1}{2}(bs)(bh)$$

$$= \tfrac{1}{2}b^2(sh)$$

4. $$\frac{\text{area of } \triangle ABC}{\text{area of } \triangle A'B'C'} = \frac{\tfrac{1}{2}a^2(sh)}{\tfrac{1}{2}b^2(sh)} = \frac{a^2}{b^2}$$

5. Therefore, $\dfrac{\text{area of } \triangle ABC}{\text{area of } \triangle A'B'C'} = \dfrac{a^2}{b^2} = \left(\dfrac{a}{b}\right)^2 = \left(\dfrac{\text{sides of } \triangle ABC}{\text{sides of } \triangle A'B'C'}\right)^2$

If you have previously mentioned to students that reducing a ratio can simplify the arithmetic in the solution of a proportion, you must remind them now to be careful as they reduce ratios that are perfect squares. For example, demonstrate with the ratio $16:36$ from Model Problem 2 on page 407. The simplest form of $\dfrac{16}{36}$ is $\dfrac{4}{9}$, not $\dfrac{2}{3}$.

$$\frac{16 \div 4}{36 \div 4} = \frac{4}{9} \qquad \sqrt{\frac{16}{36}} = \frac{4}{6} = \frac{2}{3}$$

Note that the exercises for perimeter required students to work on either side of the proportion. That is, they were asked, sometimes, to find a perimeter and, sometimes, to find a side. The exercises for area, however, are limited to one side of the proportion, finding area. This is because finding a side, as in the following example, leads to a simple *quadratic* equation if a straightforward algebraic solution is pursued.

You may wish to suggest the following example as a challenge question. Even if students cannot solve the equation, they may find an answer by guessing and checking.

Example: The areas of two similar triangles are in the ratio $16:25$. If the length of a side of the smaller triangle is 8 cm, find the length of the corresponding side of the larger triangle.

Algebraic Solution

Let $x = $ the length of the side of the larger triangle.

$$\frac{\text{area of small } \triangle}{\text{area of large } \triangle} = \left(\frac{\text{side of small } \triangle}{\text{side of large } \triangle}\right)^2$$

$$\frac{16}{25} = \left(\frac{8}{x}\right)^2$$

$$\frac{16}{25} = \frac{64}{x^2}$$

$$16x^2 = 1{,}600$$

$$x^2 = 100$$

$$x = \pm 10$$

Answer: The side of the larger triangle measures 10 cm.

Note that in the previous solution, we took the square root of each member of the equation as a final step. It is also possible to simplify the equation by taking the square root of each member as an initial step.

$$\frac{16}{25} = \left(\frac{8}{x}\right)^2$$

$$\pm\frac{4}{5} = \frac{8}{x}$$

$$\pm 4x = 40$$

$$x = \pm 10$$

In considering ratios of perimeters and areas, there are several reasons for paying particular attention to units of measure.

For example:

(1) as in Model Problem **1b** on page 403, the solution goes from a ratio (no unit) to a length (linear unit).

(2) in working with areas, an additional distinction must be made: ratio of areas (no unit), measures of areas (square units), and measures of sides (linear units).

SAT PREPARATION EXERCISES (Chapter 12)

In 1–15, select the letter of the correct answer.

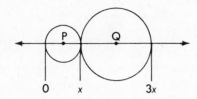

1. What is the ratio of the circumference of circle P to that of circle Q?

(A) $\frac{1}{2}$ (B) $\frac{x}{2}$ (C) $\frac{1}{4}$ (D) $\frac{x}{4}$

2. The ratio of the length of a rectangle to its width is $4:1$. What percent of the perimeter is the width?

(A) $33\frac{1}{3}\%$ (B) 25% (C) 20% (D) 10%

3. The area of a circle is 9π and the perimeter of a square is 12. Which of the following drawings correctly shows the relative sizes of the circle and the square?

(A) 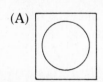 (B)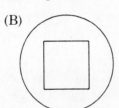

(C) 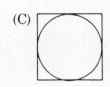 (D)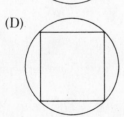

4. If $ax = 6$ and $bx = 8$, then x^2 equals

(A) $48ab$ (B) $\frac{48}{ab}$ (C) $\frac{ab}{48}$ (D) $\frac{6b}{8a}$

5. If $5(x + 5) = 2(x + 1)$, then $\frac{x + 5}{3x + 3}$ equals

(A) $\frac{2}{5}$ (B) $\frac{2}{15}$ (C) $\frac{6}{5}$ (D) $\frac{5}{2}$

$$1x^{100}y^4,\ 3x^{97}y^6,\ 5x^{94}y^8,\ 7x^{91}y^{10},\ \dots$$

6. If the pattern above is continued, what would be the 21st term?

(A) $41x^{40}y^{44}$ (B) $41x^{37}y^{44}$
(C) $43x^{40}y^{44}$ (D) $43x^{37}y^{44}$

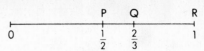

7. What is the ratio of PQ to QR?

(A) $\frac{1}{2}$ (B) $\frac{2}{3}$ (C) $\frac{3}{4}$ (D) $\frac{5}{6}$

8. If $2x + 7 = 12$, then the ratio of $2x$ to $2x + 5$ is

(A) $\frac{1}{2}$ (B) $\frac{2}{3}$ (C) $\frac{3}{4}$ (D) $\frac{4}{5}$

9. If the continued ratio $x:y:z$ is $2:3:k$, and y is 75% of z, then x is what percent of z?

(A) 75% (B) $66\frac{2}{3}\%$ (C) 50% (D) $33\frac{1}{3}\%$

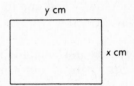

10. If the ratio of x to y is $2:3$, then twice the area of the rectangle is

(A) $\frac{x^2}{3}$ cm^2 (B) $3x^2$ cm^2

(C) $6x^2$ cm^2 (D) $9x^2$ cm^2

11. What is the ratio of the average of 3, 5, and x to the sum of 3, 5, and x?

(A) $\frac{1}{3}$ (B) $\frac{8 + x}{15x}$ (C) $\frac{8 + x}{3}$ (D) $\frac{3x}{8 + x}$

12. What is the ratio of $2(2^{200})$ to $(2^{200})^2$?

(A) $\frac{1}{2}$ (B) $\frac{1}{2^{100}}$ (C) $\frac{1}{2^{199}}$ (D) $\frac{1}{2^{200}}$

13. In a certain class, $\frac{4}{5}$ of the students have pencils and $\frac{3}{4}$ of them have pens. If there are 20 students in the class, what is the smallest number of them who might have both pens and pencils?

(A) 15 (B) 11 (C) 5 (D) 4

14. In a triangle, side x is $\frac{1}{2}$ of side y and side z is $\frac{3}{4}$ of side y. Then side y is what fractional part of the perimeter of the triangle?

(A) $\frac{2}{3}$ (B) $\frac{1}{3}$ (C) $\frac{3}{8}$ (D) $\frac{4}{9}$

15. How many more squares must be shaded so that the ratio of the shaded squares to the unshaded squares is the same as the ratio of the length of the shorter side of the rectangle to the length of the longer side?
    (A) 4 (B) 3 (C) 2 (D) 1

Questions 16–26 each consist of two quantities, one in Column A and one in Column B. You are to compare the two quantities and choose:

  A if the quantity in Column A is greater;
  B if the quantity in Column B is greater;
  C if the two quantities are equal;
  D if the relationship cannot be determined from the information given.

Notes

1. In certain questions, information concerning one or both of the quantities to be compared is centered above the two columns.
2. In a given question, a symbol that appears in both columns represents the same thing in Column A as it does in Column B.
3. Letters such as x, n, and k stand for real numbers.

Column A	Column B

16. $\dfrac{1 \text{ millimeter}}{1 \text{ centimeter}}$ $\dfrac{1 \text{ centimeter}}{1 \text{ meter}}$

$$x > 0; y < 0$$

17. $\dfrac{x}{y}$ $\dfrac{y}{x}$

18. $2 + \dfrac{1}{2 + \frac{1}{2}}$ $2\frac{1}{2}$

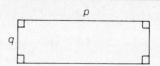

A rectangle with length p and width q

19. One-fourth the perimeter of the rectangle   The average of p and q

20. The distance traveled in one hour at a rate of 10 km in 15 minutes   The distance traveled in one hour at a rate of 12 km in 20 minutes

$$x > y > 0$$

21. $\dfrac{x + y}{x}$ $\dfrac{x + y}{y}$

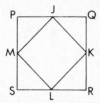

Square *JKLM* is formed by joining the midpoints of the sides of square *PQRS*.

22. Area of *PQRS*   Area of *JKLM* when its length and width are doubled

X and Y are consecutive even integers $(0 < X < Y)$.

23. $X + 50\%$ of Y $Y + 50\%$ of X

24. The largest side of a given triangle   50% of the perimeter of a given triangle

X, Y, and Z are consecutive positive odd integers, in order.

25. 50% of Y 20% of $(X + Y)$

X, Y, and Z are the measures of the sides of a triangle, in descending order of length.

26. X 50% of $(Y + Z)$

SUGGESTED TEST ITEMS (Chapter 12)

In 1–4, express each ratio in simplest form.

1. $15:45$ 2. $18:3$ 3. $\dfrac{1}{3}:\dfrac{5}{12}$ 4. 10 g to 4 kg

5. It takes a machine 5 minutes to fill 360 cereal boxes. Express the rate at which the machine works in boxes per second.

6. If a car used 16 gallons of gasoline to travel 512 miles, how far can the car travel on 12 gallons of gasoline?

In 7–10, solve and check.

7. $\dfrac{2}{9} = \dfrac{x}{36}$ 8. $\dfrac{a+1}{7} = \dfrac{a-1}{5}$ 9. $\dfrac{y}{y-3} = \dfrac{6}{5}$ 10. $\dfrac{1}{3} = \dfrac{2x-3}{5x}$

11. Lemonade is made by mixing frozen lemonade concentrate with water in the ratio of $1:3$. How many cups of concentrate are needed to prepare 12 cups of lemonade?

12. The measures of the angles of a triangle are in the ratio $2:2:5$. What is the measure of each angle of the triangle?

13. A baseball team won 30 games and lost 10. What percent of the games that they had played did they lose?

14. Find the missing value for x in the table if y varies directly as x.

x	12	15	?
y	8	10	14

15. Mr. Carter found that 32% of the persons who work in his office come to work by bus. How many persons work in Mr. Carter's office if 8 come to work by bus?

16. In the diagram, $\triangle ABC \sim \triangle ADE$, $DE = 7$, $BC = 10$, and $DB = 6$. Find AD.

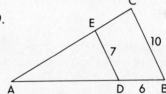

17. The perimeters of two triangles are in the ratio $3:8$. The lengths of the sides of the smaller triangle are 12 cm, 15 cm and 21 cm. Find the lengths of the sides of the larger triangle.

BONUS I: If 20 typists can type 20 pages in 20 minutes, how many typists are needed to type 40 pages in 40 minutes? How many pages can 10 typists type in 10 minutes?

BONUS II: Separate the polygon in the diagram into four congruent polygons that are each similar to the original.

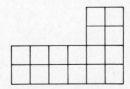

CHAPTER **13**

Special Products and Factoring

Aims

- To consider special products such as the squares of monomials, the product of the sum and difference of two terms, and the product of two binomials.

- To factor polynomial expressions completely by reversing the procedures used to find special products.

13-1 UNDERSTANDING THE MEANING OF FACTORING

Since the *unit* 1 is neither prime nor composite, we consider positive integers greater than 1 as we factor into primes. Technically, the integers 2 and 3 also do not factor into primes because, again, the unit 1 is not a prime ($2 = 2 \times 1$ and $3 = 3 \times 1$). Thus, the statement in the text reads "*In general,* a positive integer can be expressed as the product of prime numbers." The prime factorization of a prime is the prime itself even though there are no factors involved. The prime factorization of 3 is 3.

Note that every nonzero rational number is a factor of every other nonzero rational number. For example, 6 is a factor of 5 since $6\left(\dfrac{5}{6}\right) = 5$. However, in this section, when we factor an integer, we deal only with factors that are integers.

To find the greatest common factor (GCF) of two or more given integers, such as 32 and 60, alternate approaches may be shown.

Method 1

List all the factors of 32 and 60.
32: 1, 2, 4, 8, 16, 32
60: 1, 2, 3, 4, 5, 6, 10, 12, 15, 20, 30, 60
Common factors = 1, 2, 4
        GCF = 4

Method 2

Express 32 and 60 as products of primes.
$$32 = 2 \cdot 2 \cdot 2 \cdot 2 \cdot 2 \text{ or } 2^5$$
$$\downarrow \ \downarrow$$
$$60 = 2 \cdot 2 \cdot 3 \cdot 5 \quad \text{ or } 2^2 \cdot 3 \cdot 5$$
$$\downarrow \ \downarrow$$
$$\text{GCF} = 2 \cdot 2 \qquad\qquad = 2^2 \text{ or } 4$$

When two numbers have no common factor other than 1, the numbers are *relatively prime*. When considering the GCF of two monomials, we work with both the numerical coefficients and the powers of the variable bases. Model Problem 2 shows how both of these are broken down to obtain the GCF. As students become skilled, they will be able to do much of this work mentally.

Note that the GCF of one positive and one negative coefficient is positive. Later, when students use factoring in solutions of equations, there may be a particular reason to use the negative of the GCF when writing a monomial factor.

Be sure students understand that for parts c and e of Exercise 27, the second factors must be negative since the first factors are negative and the original numbers are positive.

Computer Activities (13-1) The three programs that follow will find all the factors of an integer, determine if an integer is a prime, and find the greatest common factor of two integers. These programs could be used by students to check their results for exercises from this section.

```
100   REM   THIS PROGRAM WILL FIND ALL
110   REM   OF THE FACTORS OF ANY POSITIVE
120   REM   INTEGER.
130   REM   IT DISPLAYS THE PAIRS OF
140   REM   FACTORS IN TWO COLUMNS.
150   PRINT "FOR WHAT POSITIVE INTEGER WOULD YOU"
160   PRINT "LIKE TO FIND THE FACTORS?"
170   PRINT "ENTER A POSITIVE INTEGER."
180   INPUT N
190   IF N < 1 THEN 170
200   IF N > < INT (N) THEN 170
210   PRINT
220   LET L =  INT ( SQR (N))
230   PRINT "THE FACTORS OF ";N;" ARE:"
240   FOR I = 1 TO L
250   IF N / I > < INT (N / I) THEN 270
260   PRINT I,N / I
270   NEXT I
280   PRINT
290   PRINT "DO YOU HAVE ANOTHER POSITIVE INTEGER"
300   PRINT "FOR WHICH YOU WOULD LIKE TO FIND"
310   PRINT "THE FACTORS? (Y OR N)"
320   INPUT A$
330   IF A$ = "Y" OR A$ = "YES" THEN 170
340   END
```

```
100   REM   THIS PROGRAM WILL DETERMINE IF
110   REM   A POSITIVE INTEGER IS A PRIME.
120   PRINT "WHAT POSITIVE INTEGER WOULD YOU LIKE TO"
130   PRINT "TEST TO SEE IF IT IS A PRIME?"
140   PRINT "ENTER A POSITIVE INTEGER."
150   INPUT N
160   IF N < 1 THEN 140
170   IF N > < INT (N) THEN 140
180   PRINT
190   IF N = 1 THEN 280
200   LET F = 0
210   LET L =  INT ( SQR (N))
220   FOR I = 1 TO L
230   IF N / I = INT (N / I) THEN F = F + 1
240   IF F = 2 THEN 280
```

```
250    NEXT I
260    PRINT N;" IS A PRIME."
270    GOTO 290
280    PRINT N;" IS NOT A PRIME."
290    PRINT
300    PRINT "DO YOU HAVE ANOTHER POSITIVE INTEGER"
310    PRINT "WHICH YOU WOULD LIKE TO TEST TO SEE IF"
320    PRINT "IT IS A PRIME? (Y OR N)"
330    INPUT A$
340    IF A$ = "Y" OR A$ = "YES" THEN 140
350    END




100    REM    THIS PROGRAM WILL FIND THE
110    REM    GREATEST COMMON FACTOR OF
120    REM    TWO INTEGERS.
130    PRINT "TO FIND THE GREATEST COMMON FACTOR OF"
140    PRINT "TWO INTEGERS, ENTER THE INTEGERS"
150    PRINT "SEPARATED BY A COMMA."
160    INPUT A,B
170    PRINT
180    LET A1 = A
190    LET B1 = B
200    IF A > B THEN  GOSUB 330
210    LET R = B -  INT (B / A) * A
220    IF R = 0 THEN 260
230    LET B = A
240    LET A = R
250    GOTO 210
260    PRINT "THE GREATEST COMMON FACTOR OF"
270    PRINT A1;" AND ";B1;" IS ";A
280    PRINT
290    PRINT "DO YOU WANT TO DO ANOTHER? (Y OR N)"
300    INPUT R$
310    IF R$ = "Y" OR R$ = "YES" THEN 130
320    GOTO 370
330    LET T = A
340    LET A = B
350    LET B = T
360    RETURN
370    END
```

The use of programs such as these will enable students and teachers to perform the necessary computations for larger numbers than are usually assigned.

13-2 FACTORING POLYNOMIALS WHOSE TERMS HAVE A COMMON MONOMIAL FACTOR

When factoring a polynomial whose terms have a common monomial factor, remind students to check their work by multiplying the factors, to see that the product is the original polynomial. Impress upon students that the *greatest* monomial factor is to be found. For example:

$$12x^2y + 24xy^3 = 6xy(2x + 4y^2)$$

But, note that $2x + 4y^2$ can be factored further. Thus:

$$\begin{aligned} 12x^2y + 24xy^3 &= 6xy(2x + 4y^2) \\ &= 6xy \cdot 2(x + 2y^2) \\ &= 12xy(x + 2y^2) \quad Ans. \end{aligned}$$

In doing this type of factoring, students sometimes find it easier to think in terms of multiplying rather than dividing. An alternate approach to the Model Problem is:

$3cd$ is the GCF of $6c^3d$, $12c^2d^2$, and $3cd$.

To find the other factor, write the GCF

$$3cd(\qquad\qquad)$$

and ask "By what must I multiply $3cd$ to get *each* of the original terms?"

By what must I
multiply $3cd$ to get $6c^3d$? $3cd(2c^2 \qquad\qquad)$

By what must I
multiply $3cd$ to get $-12c^2d^2$? $3cd(2c^2 - 4cd \qquad)$

By what must I
multiply $3cd$ to get $3cd$? $3cd(2c^2 - 4cd + 1)$ *Ans.*

Note that this method may help students to remember the final term of 1, which many tend to omit.

13-3 SQUARING A MONOMIAL

Squaring a monomial means to use that monomial as a factor two times. Give several examples and ask students what they have noticed in each case:

Step 1	*Step 2*
$(2x)^2 = (2x)(2x)$	$= (2)(2)(x)(x)$
Step 3	*Step 4*
$= 2^2 \cdot x^2$	$= 4x^2$

Step 1	*Step 2*
$(-3y^3)^2 = (-3y^3)(-3y^3)$	$= (-3)(-3)(y^3)(y^3)$
Step 3	*Step 4*
$= (-3)^2(y^3)^2$	$= 9y^6$

Step 2 should be eliminated once students understand the method.

Observations:

1. The operation of squaring is distributed over each factor of the product. In general, when a and b are signed numbers and m and n are positive integers:

$$(a^m b^n)^2 = a^{2m} b^{2n}$$

2. When a monomial is a square, its numerical coefficient is a square.

3. When a monomial is a square, the exponent of each variable is an even number, as seen by $(a^m)^2 = a^{2m}$.

Squaring a monomial can be applied geometrically. For example:

Find the area of a square whose side is represented by $3x^2y$.

$$\begin{aligned} \text{Since } A = s^2, \text{ then } A &= (3x^2y)^2 \\ &= (3x^2y)(3x^2y) \\ &= 9x^4y^2 \end{aligned}$$

13-4 MULTIPLYING THE SUM AND DIFFERENCE OF TWO TERMS

When we multiply the sum of two terms by the difference of the same two terms, the sum of the "middle terms" is zero, so that the product is the square of the first term minus the square of the second term. For example:

$$(x + y)(x - y) = x^2 - xy + xy - y^2 = x^2 - y^2$$

Students should be able to find these products mentally. Fractions and decimals are contained in the exercises, reinforcing skills in these areas.

An interesting arithmetic application of these special algebraic products is to calculate the product of two numbers by writing them as the same amount above and below their average. For example:

$$\begin{aligned} (21)(19) &= (20 + 1)(20 - 1) \\ &= 20^2 - 1^2 = 400 - 1 = 399 \end{aligned}$$

$$\begin{aligned} (56)(64) &= (60 - 4)(60 + 4) \\ &= 60^2 - 4^2 = 3{,}600 - 16 = 3{,}584 \end{aligned}$$

As they become adept, you can extend the calculations to include fractions and decimals. For example:

$$\left(3\tfrac{1}{4}\right)\left(2\tfrac{3}{4}\right) = \left(3 + \tfrac{1}{4}\right)\left(3 - \tfrac{1}{4}\right)$$

$$= 3^2 - \left(\tfrac{1}{4}\right)^2 = 9 - \tfrac{1}{16} = 8\tfrac{15}{16}$$

$$\begin{aligned} (9.8)(10.2) &= (10 - .2)(10 + .2) \\ &= 10^2 - (.2)^2 = 100 - .04 = 99.96 \end{aligned}$$

13-5 FACTORING THE DIFFERENCE OF TWO SQUARES

By reversing the thought process established in the previous section, students should recognize how to factor the difference of two squares.

Some students may factor $25 - x^2$ as $(x + 5)(x - 5)$, instead of $(5 + x)(5 - x)$, because of the tendency to place the variable first when writing each binomial factor. If students develop the habit of checking their answers by mentally multiplying the factors obtained, these errors could be avoided.

Students should also be familiar with the perfect squares from $1^2 = 1$ to $12^2 = 144$ before factoring the binomials found in the exercises. In this way, the factors of $x^2 - 1.21$, namely $(x + 1.1)(x - 1.1)$, may not seem difficult. Note the need for an even number of decimal places in order that a decimal numeral be a square. For example, 1.21 and .0121 are the squares of 1.1 and .11 respectively, but .121 is not a square.

13-6 FINDING THE PRODUCT OF TWO BINOMIALS

Multiplication of two binomials was introduced in Section 9-5. Now, students are asked to find the product of two binomials mentally. When presented with an example such as $(x + 5)^2$, some students will immediately answer $x^2 + 25$, disregarding the "middle term." Emphasize the point that:

$$\begin{aligned} (x + 5)^2 &= (x + 5)(x + 5) \\ &= x^2 + 5x + 5x + 25 \\ &= x^2 + 10x + 25 \end{aligned}$$

Here is a good place to reintroduce geometric interpretations of these products, such as were presented in Chapters 8 and 9. For example, to demonstrate the value of $(x + 5)^2$:

Begin with a square of side x and area x^2.

Increase the length of side x to $x + 5$.

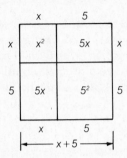

Note that this new square contains *four* parts of area (x^2, $5x$, $5x$, and 5^2), not just the two parts x^2 and 5^2.

13-7 FACTORING TRINOMIALS OF THE FORM $ax^2 + bx + c$

As students learn the procedure for factoring trinomials of the form $ax^2 + bx + c$, certain relationships become apparent:

1. If the leading coefficient is 1 ($a = 1$), then the coefficient of the first term of each binomial is 1.
2. If the sign of the third term is negative ($c < 0$), then the sign of the last term of one binomial is positive, while the sign of the last term of the other binomial is negative.
3. If the sign of the third term is positive ($c > 0$), consider the middle term, bx:
   a. If b is positive, then the sign of the last term in each binomial factor must be positive.
   b. If b is negative, then the sign of the last term in each binomial factor must be negative.

Note: Knowing these relationships will reduce the number of possible pairs of factors to list and to test.

When factoring trinomials where the coefficient of the x^2 term is a number other than 1, students should list the possible pairs of factors. Once students become familiar with factoring techniques, however, certain possible pairs of factors can be eliminated immediately. For example:

Factor $2x^2 - x - 6$.

Some possible pairs of factors are:

$$(2x + 6)(x - 1) \qquad (2x - 6)(x + 1)$$
$$(2x + 2)(x - 3) \qquad (2x - 2)(x + 3)$$

In each case, the first binomial factor is not prime. Disregard such factors.

Two other possible pairs are:

$$(2x + 1)(x - 6) \qquad (2x - 1)(x + 6)$$

The coefficient of the middle term is either too high or too low. Disregard these factors. Consider:

$$(2x + 3)(x - 2) \qquad (2x - 3)(x + 2)$$

In actuality, these two pairs should be tested first. After multiplying the factors, the student will see that the correct answer is $(2x + 3)(x - 2)$.

Every expression that is the product of two factors is also the product of the opposites of these factors. For example, $2x^2 - x - 6 = (2x + 3)(x - 2) = (-2x - 3)(-x + 2)$. However, the factors with positive coefficients of the first terms are commonly used.

13-8 FACTORING COMPLETELY

When the instruction is to factor a polynomial *completely*, the process of factoring continues until all factors other than monomial factors are prime. Students should look first for the existence of the greatest common factor so that any remaining factoring may be made easier.

Two types of errors in this area are:

1. Students find binomial factors that are not prime because they have forgotten to first

factor the greatest common monomial term. For example:

$$100x^2 - 36y^2 = (10x + 6y)(10x - 6y)$$
$$\text{not prime}$$

This can be corrected by additional factoring:

$$= 2(5x + 3y) \cdot 2(5x - 3y)$$
$$= 4(5x + 3y)(5x - 3y)$$

2. Students correctly find the greatest common monomial factor and/or one pair of binomial factors, but they forget to check each binomial to see if it is factored completely. For example:

$$64x^2 - 4x^2y^4$$
$$= 4x^2(16 - y^4) \quad \text{still factorable}$$
$$= 4x^2(4 + y^2)(4 - y^2) \quad \text{still factorable}$$
$$= 4x^2(4 + y^2)(2 + y)(2 - y)$$

To test understanding of this section, ask for the factors of $x^2 + 36$. Some responses may be $(x + 6)(x - 6)$ or $(x + 6)(x + 6)$, but these factors do not have a product equal to $x^2 + 36$. At this level, $x^2 + 36$ cannot be factored.

SAT PREPARATION EXERCISES (Chapter 13)

Questions 1–6 each consist of two quantities, one in Column A and one in Column B. You are to compare the two quantities and choose:

  A if the quantity in Column A is greater;
  B if the quantity in Column B is greater;
  C if the two quantities are equal;
  D if the relationship cannot be determined from the information given.

Notes

1. In certain questions, information concerning one or both of the quantities to be compared is centered above the two columns.
2. In a given question, a symbol that appears in both columns represents the same thing in Column A as it does in Column B.
3. Letters such as x, n, and k stand for real numbers.

Column A	*Column B*
1. $(a - b)^2$	$(b - a)^2$

x is an integer.

2. $x(x + 2)$	$(x + 1)(x - 1)$
3. $(x^2 - y^2)(x + y)$	$(x - y)(x^2 + 2xy + y^2)$

$k \neq 0$

4. $x^2 + k^2$	$(x + k)(x - k)$

$h > 0, g > 0$

5. $h^2 + g^2$	$(h + g)^2$

$y = x + 2$

6. $y^2 - 8y + 15$	$x^2 - 4x + 3$

In 7–19, select the letter of the correct answer.

7. $(6 + 2)(2)(5) - (2)(4)(12 - 2)$ equals
(A) 0 (B) 40 (C) 80 (D) 160

8. $(95)(83)$ equals
(A) $(90)(80) + (5)(3)$
(B) $(90)(80) + (5)(80) + (3)(90)$
(C) $90^2 - (2)(90) - (5)(7)$
(D) $90^2 - (5)(7)$

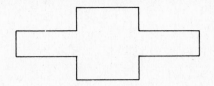

9. If each vertical segment is of length y, and each horizontal segment is of length x, then the perimeter is
(A) $2(3x + 3y)$ (B) $(3x)(3y)$
(C) $5(xy)$ (D) $12(x + y)$

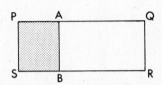

10. In rectangle $PQRS$, the areas of the shaded and unshaded regions are $x^2 + 3x$ and $6x + 18$, respectively. If $PS > PA$ and $PS \neq AQ$, then for all values of $x > 0$ the perimeter of the rectangle is
(A) $2x + 9$ (B) $4x + 18$
(C) $2x^2 + 9x$ (D) $4x^2 + 18x$

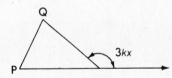

11. If $m\angle P = (3x^2)$, $m\angle Q = (6x)$, and the measure of the exterior angle is $(3kx)$, then an expression for k is
(A) $x + 2$ (B) $x^2 + 3x$
(C) $3x^2 + 3x$ (D) $9x^4 + 18x^2$

12. If $4x^2 = (2)(6)$, and $3y^2 = (3)(6)$, then $(x + y)(x - y)$ equals
(A) 3 (B) 0 (C) -3 (D) 6

13. If $x = y + 5$, then $x^2 - 2xy + y^2$ is
(A) 100 (B) 50 (C) 25 (D) 10

14. If $x^2 + y^2 = xy = 5$, then $(x + y)^2$ equals
(A) 15 (B) 20 (C) 25 (D) 50

Rectangular Box

15. If, for all values of $x > 1$, the area of face I is $x^2 - 1$, and the area of face II is $x^2 + 3x + 2$, then the area of face III can be represented by
(A) $x^2 + 3x + 1$ (B) $x^2 - 3x + 2$
(C) $2x^2 + 3x + 1$ (D) $x^2 + x - 2$

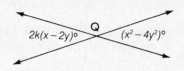

18. Two lines intersect above at Q. Use the degree measures shown in the diagram to find an expression for k.
(A) $x + 2y$ (B) $x - 2y$
(C) $\dfrac{x + 2y}{2}$ (D) $\dfrac{x - 2y}{2}$

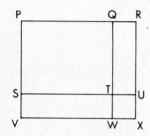

16. If $PQ = PV = y$ and $UX = XW = 2$, which of the rectangles above has an area of $y^2 - 4$?
(A) $PQTS$ (B) $PRUS$
(C) $PQWV$ (D) $PRXV$

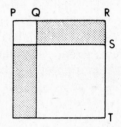

19. If $PR = RT = x$ and $QR = ST = y$, then what is the sum of the areas of the shaded rectangles?
(A) $x^2 - y^2$ (B) $2xy - y^2$
(C) $2xy - 2y^2$ (D) $x^2 - xy$

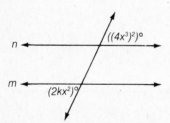

17. The lines m and n are parallel. Use the degree measures shown in the diagram to find an expression for k.
(A) $4x^2$ (B) $4x^4$ (C) $8x^2$ (D) $8x^4$

SUGGESTED TEST ITEMS (Chapter 13)

1. Write the prime factorization of 495.
2. List all of the whole numbers that are factors of 90.
3. What is the greatest common factor of $12a^2b$ and $42ab^2$?

In 4–7, write an equivalent expression without parentheses.

4. $(5ab^2)^2$ 5. $(2x - 1)^2$ 6. $(x + 3)(2x - 3)$ 7. $(y - 7)(y + 7)$

In 8–19, factor completely.

8. $12a^2 - 6ab$ 9. $a^2 - 5a + 6$ 10. $s^2 - 25$ 11. $8r^3 - 2r^2$

12. $x^2 + 8x - 20$ 13. $y^2 + 6y + 9$ 14. $2x^2 - x - 6$ 15. $4b^2 + 15b + 9$

16. $4c^2 + 16$ 17. $9b^2 - 16$ 18. $5y^2 - 20$ 19. $5x^2 - 10x + 5$

20. Express as a binomial, the area of a rectangle if the length is represented by $(3x - 1)$ and the width by $(2x + 1)$.

21. Express in terms of s, the length of one side of a square if the area of the square is represented by $4s^2 - 12s + 9$.

BONUS: Show that the product of two consecutive odd integers is always 1 less than the square of their average. Is this also true for consecutive even integers?

BONUS: Show that any integer that is one less than a perfect square can be factored into two consecutive even or two consecutive odd integers.

CHAPTER 14

Fractions, and First-Degree Equations and Inequalities Involving Fractions

Aims

- To teach the fundamental operations with algebraic fractions, including reducing to lowest terms.

- To solve equations containing fractional coefficients, as well as fractional equations.

- To extend these processes to the solution of literal equations.

Throughout this chapter, the operations on algebraic fractions are related to the corresponding operations on arithmetic fractions.

The work of this chapter may be limited to fractions with monomial denominators. It is important that you do not spend an inordinate amount of time to achieve mastery of all of the material in this chapter. Students should review their work with arithmetic fractions and apply those principles to algebraic fractions. All of the work with fractions, equations involving fractions, and fractional equations will be considered again in Courses II and III.

14-1 THE MEANING OF AN ALGEBRAIC FRACTION

An algebraic fraction, or rational expression, is a quotient of polynomials. Every rational expression, such as $\frac{8}{2}$, corresponds to a division problem, $8 \div 2$. Since division by zero is not possible, a rational expression is undefined (has no meaning) when its denominator equals 0. Thus, the expression $\frac{x+8}{x+2}$ is undefined if $x + 2 = 0$, or $x = -2$.

1. Recall that when $\frac{a}{b} = c$, $bc = a$. Substituting -2 for x in $\frac{x+8}{x+2}$, the expression becomes $\frac{-2+8}{-2+2}$, or $\frac{6}{0}$.

If $\frac{6}{0} = c$, then $0 \cdot c = 6$. But, there is no value of c for which $0 \cdot c = 6$. Therefore, $\frac{6}{0}$ has no value, or is undefined.

2. Substituting -8 for x in $\frac{x+8}{x+2}$, the expression becomes $\frac{-8+8}{-8+2} = \frac{0}{-6} = 0$.

If $\frac{0}{-6} = c$, then $-6c = 0$. This equation is true when $c = 0$. Therefore, $\frac{0}{-6} = 0$, a defined value.

Computer Activity (14-1) The following program provides practice in determining the values for which a fraction is undefined.

Note: On some computers, RND (1) may have to be changed to RND (0).

```
100   REM     THIS PROGRAM WILL TEST THE USER
110   REM     ON THE VALUES FOR WHICH A
120   REM     FRACTION IS UNDEFINED.
130   PRINT "A FRACTION IS UNDEFINED IF THE VALUE OF"
140   PRINT "ITS DENOMINATOR IS ZERO."
150   PRINT
160   PRINT "FIND THE VALUE OF X FOR WHICH THE"
170   PRINT "GIVEN FRACTIONS ARE UNDEFINED."
180   PRINT "WRITE FRACTIONAL VALUES AS DECIMALS."
190   PRINT "THAT IS, IF THE DENOMINATOR IS 2X - 3,"
200   PRINT "AND X IS UNDEFINED FOR 3 / 2, ENTER 1.5."
210   LET A =  INT ( RND (1) * 2) + 1
220   LET B =  INT ( RND (1) * 11) - 5
230   LET C =  INT ( RND (1) * 10) - 3
240   IF C = 0 THEN 230
250   LET T = 0
260   PRINT  TAB( 8);C
270   PRINT  TAB( 7);"-----"
280   PRINT  TAB( 7);
290   IF A = 2 THEN PRINT "2";
300   PRINT "X";
310   IF B > 0 THEN PRINT "+";
320   IF B = 0 THEN 340
330   PRINT B
340   PRINT
350   INPUT D
360   LET T = T + 1
370   IF D = ( - B / A) THEN 490
380   PRINT
390   PRINT "FOR THE VALUE OF X THAT YOU GAVE,"
400   PRINT "THE DENOMINATOR EQUALS ";A * D + B
410   PRINT
420   IF T = 3 THEN 470
430   PRINT "THE FRACTION IS UNDEFINED WHEN THE"
440   PRINT "DENOMINATOR EQUALS ZERO."
450   PRINT "TRY AGAIN."
460   GOTO 260
470   PRINT "THE FRACTION IS UNDEFINED WHEN X = "; - B / A
480   GOTO 500
490   PRINT "THAT'S RIGHT!"
500   PRINT
510   PRINT "DO YOU WANT TO DO ANOTHER?(Y OR N)"
520   INPUT R$
530   IF R$ = "Y" OR R$ = "YES" THEN 210
540   END
```

14-2 REDUCING FRACTIONS TO LOWEST TERMS

A fraction, whether arithmetic or algebraic, is said to be reduced to lowest terms when its numerator and denominator have no common factor other than 1 or -1. In this section, we show alternate ways to reduce fractions to lowest terms. One method uses the division property of a fraction, whereas another method, which is the one preferred by most students, uses factoring techniques and cancellation.

Help students to remember that cancellation of factors is division by writing the quotient 1 when a factor is divided by itself. This will aid students in avoiding the following error:

$$\frac{3x + 6}{6x + 12} = \frac{\cancel{3}(x + 2)}{\underset{2}{\cancel{6}(x + 2)}} = 2$$

At this point, you may consider some situations where cancellation is not possible. For example, in the expression $\frac{x + 2}{x}$, the x terms cannot be cancelled since x is not a factor in the numerator. Suppose the x terms were cancelled. The fraction would become $\frac{1 + 2}{1}$ or $\frac{3}{1}$. Show that this is not equal to the value of $\frac{x + 2}{x}$ by substituting a numerical value for x.

Letting $x = 3$, $\frac{3 + 2}{3} = \frac{5}{3} \neq \frac{3}{1}$.

Emphasize that cancellation is valid only by a factor of the *entire* numerator and denominator.

Students are amused to see that sometimes a correct answer can be stumbled upon even when performing invalid cancellations. In the following example, invalid cancellations of a and 2, with an additional murky thought like "$-$ divided by $+$ equals $-$" can lead to the correct answer.

$$\frac{a^2 - 4}{a + 2} = \frac{\overset{a}{\cancel{a^2}} - \overset{2}{\cancel{4}}}{\underset{1}{\cancel{a}} + \underset{1}{\cancel{2}}} = a - 2$$

invalid cancellations
correct answer

14-3 MULTIPLYING FRACTIONS

When multiplying fractions, it is preferable to use the cancellation method first to reduce the form of the product before applying the general rule, thus simplifying the arithmetic.

For example, it is easier to treat $\frac{14}{15} \cdot \frac{5}{21}$ as $\frac{\cancel{7} \cdot 2}{3 \cdot \cancel{5}} \cdot \frac{\cancel{5}}{\cancel{7} \cdot 3} = \frac{2}{9}$ than to multiply first.

These same procedures are used when multiplying algebraic fractions. Emphasize the need to factor binomial and trinomial numerators and denominators. Also, remind students that they must have one factor in the numerator and the identical factor in the denominator before they can cancel. Thus, in the following example, it is not valid to cancel the factor $(x + 1)$, which appears only in the numerator of each fraction.

$$\frac{2x + 2}{x + 3} \cdot \frac{x^2 + 4x + 3}{4}$$

$$= \frac{\overset{1}{\cancel{2}}(x + 1)}{\cancel{x + 3}} \cdot \frac{(x + 1)\overset{1}{\cancel{(x + 3)}}}{\underset{2}{\cancel{4}}}$$

$$= \frac{(x + 1)^2}{2} \quad Ans.$$

Note that the factored form $\frac{(x + 1)^2}{2}$ and the expanded form $\frac{x^2 + 2x + 1}{2}$ are both acceptable answers. Unless there is a particular reason not to, answers can be left in factored form.

14-4 DIVIDING FRACTIONS

To perform the operation of division, we multiply the dividend of a quotient by the reciprocal of the divisor. At times, students will cancel before taking the reciprocal of the divisor. These errors can be avoided by suggesting that students follow a definite procedure such as:

1. Write the division problem.

$$\frac{4x + 8}{3} \div \frac{4}{9}$$

2. Write an equivalent problem using multiplication.

$$= \frac{4x + 8}{3} \cdot \frac{9}{4}$$

3. Factor and cancel common factors.

$$= \frac{\overset{1}{\cancel{4}}(x + 2)}{\underset{1}{\cancel{3}}} \cdot \frac{\overset{3}{\cancel{9}}}{\underset{1}{\cancel{4}}}$$

4. Write the final product.

$$= 3(x + 2) \quad Ans.$$

14-5 ADDING OR SUBTRACTING FRACTIONS THAT HAVE THE SAME DENOMINATOR

A comparison between the rules for addition and subtraction of simple arithmetic fractions and of algebraic fractions is again helpful. Students seem to have more difficulty with subtraction than they do with addition. For example, a common error is to write:

$$\frac{3x + 2}{4} - \frac{2x + 5}{4} = \frac{3x + 2 - 2x + 5}{4}$$

Stress the use of parentheses as a means of showing that the entire numerator, $2x + 5$, is being subtracted:

$$\frac{3x + 2}{4} - \frac{2x + 5}{4} = \frac{(3x + 2) - (2x + 5)}{4}$$

$$= \frac{3x + 2 - 2x - 5}{4}$$

$$= \frac{x - 3}{4}$$

14-6 ADDING OR SUBTRACTING FRACTIONS THAT HAVE DIFFERENT DENOMINATORS

To add or subtract fractions with different denominators, we must first transform the fractions into equivalent fractions that have a common denominator. We use the lowest common denominator (L.C.D.) to do this.

Methods for finding the L.C.D. have been presented in previous mathematics courses. One such method involves prime factorization. For example, we may find the L.C.D. of the denominators $8x^2y$ and $10xy^2$ in the following manner:

$$8x^2y = 2 \cdot 2 \cdot 2 \quad \cdot x \cdot x \cdot y \quad = \boxed{2^3} \quad \cdot \boxed{x^2} \cdot y$$
$$10xy^2 = 2 \quad \cdot 5 \cdot x \cdot y \cdot y = \left(2 \cdot \boxed{5} \cdot x \cdot \boxed{y^2}\right)$$
$$\text{L.C.D.} = 2 \cdot 2 \cdot 2 \cdot 5 \cdot x \cdot x \cdot y \cdot y = 2^3 \cdot 5 \cdot x^2 \cdot y^2$$
$$= 40x^2y^2 \quad Ans.$$

Note that the L.C.D. is the least common multiple of the algebraic expressions.

For each prime factor, we find the highest power of that factor to appear in any of the denominators. The L.C.D. is the product of these highest powers.

Encourage students to determine mentally the L.C.D. in the exercises. Remind them to reduce answers to lowest terms.

14-7 SOLVING EQUATIONS CONTAINING FRACTIONAL COEFFICIENTS

In Chapter 10, some of the first-degree equations studied contained fractional coefficients. At that point, both the additive and multiplicative inverses were used to solve the equations. Now that students are familiar with finding the L.C.D., equations that contain fractional coefficients can be solved by multiplying both members of the equation by the L.C.D. Thus, an equivalent equation without fractional coefficients is formed. For example, solve for x:

Method 1	*Method 2*
$\dfrac{2x}{3} - 4 = \dfrac{x}{2}$	$\dfrac{2x}{3} - \dfrac{4}{1} = \dfrac{x}{2}$
$\dfrac{2}{3}x - 4 = \dfrac{1}{2}x$	$6\left(\dfrac{2x}{3} - \dfrac{4}{1}\right) = 6\left(\dfrac{x}{2}\right)$
$-\dfrac{2}{3}x = -\dfrac{2}{3}x$	$2(2x) - 6(4) = 3(x)$
	$4x - 24 = 3x$
$-4 = -\dfrac{1}{6}x$	$-4x = -4x$
	$-24 = -x$
$-6(-4) = -6\left(-\dfrac{1}{6}x\right)$	$24 = x$
$24 = x$	

In problems such as $\dfrac{3x - 5}{7} - \dfrac{2x + 4}{5} = 4$, it should become obvious that Method 2 is preferred.

For equations that are in the form of a proportion, a third method, using the products of the means and extremes, can be used. Point out that this method is the same as multiplying both sides of the equation by the product of the denominators, which is the L.C.D., or a multiple of the L.C.D. Stress that in order to cross multiply, there can be only one term in each member of the equation. Thus, only Exercises 1–6 and 13–18 can be solved by this method.

After learning to solve equations by multiplying both members by the L.C.D. to obtain an equivalent equation, students often confuse the process with that of finding the sum or difference of two algebraic fractions. Show the difference between the following exercises:

Add: $\frac{x}{3} + \frac{x}{4}$

$$\frac{x \cdot 4}{3 \cdot 4} + \frac{x \cdot 3}{4 \cdot 3} = \frac{4x}{12} + \frac{3x}{12}$$
$$= \frac{7x}{12} \quad Ans.$$

Solve: $\frac{x}{3} + \frac{x}{4} = 21$

$$12\left(\frac{x}{3} + \frac{x}{4}\right) = 12(21)$$
$$4x + 3x = 252$$
$$7x = 252$$
$$x = 36 \quad Ans.$$

Ask students to list some differences between the two procedures, their justifications, and their results. For example:

(1) When adding two fractions, we use the L.C.D. to change the fractions to equivalent fractions with like denominators so we can add the fractions.
(2) The sum of two fractions is a fraction (even if later reducible to one with a denominator of 1).
(3) When solving an equation with fractional coefficients, we use the L.C.D. to write an equivalent equation that does not contain fractions.
(4) The equivalent equation we show in our work is actually the result of applying the multiplication property of equality to an equation, all of whose terms have like denominators.

$$\frac{x}{3} + \frac{x}{4} = 21$$
$$\frac{4x}{12} + \frac{3x}{12} = \frac{252}{12}$$
$$12\left(\frac{4x}{12} + \frac{3x}{12}\right) = 12\left(\frac{252}{12}\right)$$
$$4x + 3x = 252$$

Each member of the equation $4x + 3x = 252$ is 12 times each member of the equation $\frac{x}{3} + \frac{x}{4} = 21$.

The text offers a variety of settings in which a verbal problem can lead to an equation involving fractions. In keeping with the problem-solving philosophy established at the beginning of the text, these problems are offered primarily as a resource that should not be presented in its entirety on consecutive days.

Model Problem 5 establishes that the procedure for clearing an equation of fractions is applicable to clearing an equation of decimals. You might suggest that students show their work as follows:

$$.05x + .25(3x) + .10(x + 5) = 3.20$$
$$.05\,x + .25\,(3x) + .10\,(x + 5) = 3.20$$

When there are different numbers of decimal places among the terms of an equation, thinking of an L.C.D. can help remind students that the number of places they must move the decimal point in every term is determined by the greatest number of decimal places in any term. Thus, in Exercise 31, for example, we move the decimal point two places to the right because the L.C.D. is 100:

$$.03y - 1.2 = 8.7$$
$$.03\,y - 1.20 = 8.70$$

14-8 SOLVING INEQUALITIES CONTAINING FRACTIONAL COEFFICIENTS

Students generally feel comfortable repeating for inequalities the procedure they learned for equations. Ask students to recall what operations change the order of an inequality and what operations leave the order of an inequality unchanged.

Graphing the solution set for an inequality reminds students of the difference between an infinite solution set, which they will often obtain when they solve an inequality, and a finite solution set, which they usually obtain when they solve an equation. Then, each verbal problem in this section requires that students select, from the infinite solution set for the inequality set up to solve the problem, the particular value that satisfies all the conditions of the problem.

Many of the verbal problems in this section parallel the settings of the verbal problems from the last section on equalities. Thus, students have another opportunity to start from a familiar experience and accept a new challenge. The major difference, of course, is now in the relationship of inequality.

14-9 SOLVING FRACTIONAL EQUATIONS

The text distinguishes between an equation with fractional coefficients and a fractional equation, in which the variable appears in a denominator. The procedure for solution in both types of equations involves using the L.C.D. to clear of fractions.

Stress that for an expression or equation involving a variable in a denominator, the domain of definition is limited to those values of the variable that do not yield a denominator of 0.

When both members of an equation are multiplied by some number, that number must be nonzero in order that the resulting equation be equivalent to the original equation. When a fractional equation is multiplied by the L.C.D., which contains a variable, we must exclude all values of the variable that would make the denominators, and therefore the L.C.D., equal to 0. The solution set of the equation cannot contain values of the variable that make one or more of the denominators equal to 0. To emphasize this requirement, you might ask students to tell, before they try to solve a fractional equation, for which values of the variable a particular equation is not defined. Model Problem 2 shows that when the only possible candidate for solution of a fractional equation is a value of the variable for which the equation is not defined, the solution set is empty.

It is necessary that students check the possible candidates for an answer before they write a solution set. Some of the fractional equations in the exercises have no solution.

Students will be aware of this in Exercises 19–21, when the direction asks them to explain why there is no solution. But, they must continue to check their results to spot other equations for which there are no solutions.

Emphasize that the check is to be done in the original equation, and that the method of solution is not repeated in the check. Instead, we separately work out the arithmetic for the left and right members of the equation. (See Model Problems 1 and 2.)

Some of the fractional equations in the exercises can be solved as proportions, obtaining the products of the means and extremes. Ask students to recall the definition of a proportion as an equation in which each member is a ratio.

Exercises 31 and 32 appear to lead to second-degree equations. However, if the equations are solved correctly, the square terms cancel.

Note that fractional inequalities are not included in this course. You may want to mention to students the complexities of solving a fractional inequality. That is, because the L.C.D. contains a variable, we must consider separate cases in the solution to a fractional inequality: when we are multiplying by a positive number (and the order of the inequality remains unchanged), and when we are multiplying by a negative number (and the order of the inequality changes).

14-10 EQUATIONS AND FORMULAS INVOLVING SEVERAL VARIABLES

Literal equations, including formulas, can be solved for any indicated variable. At the outset, it is helpful to relate the solution of a literal equation to the solution of a corresponding equation containing numbers in the places of all but the indicated variable. This procedure is shown in the model problem on page 461.

SAT PREPARATION EXERCISES (Chapter 14)

Questions 1–8 each consist of two quantities, one in Column A and one in Column B. You are to compare the two quantities and choose:

A if the quantity in Column A is greater;
B if the quantity in Column B is greater;
C if the two quantities are equal;
D if the relationship cannot be determined from the information given.

Notes

1. In certain questions, information concerning one or both of the quantities to be compared is centered above the two columns.
2. In a given question, a symbol that appears in both columns represents the same thing in Column A as it does in Column B.
3. Letters such as x, n, and k stand for real numbers.

Column A	*Column B*
1. $\dfrac{10}{20} - \dfrac{2}{4}$	$\dfrac{10-2}{20-4}$

$$1 < \frac{x}{y} < 2$$

2. x	y

$$0 < x < y < 1$$

3. $x + y$	xy

The lengths of three sides of a triangle are consecutive integers.

4. The average of the lengths of all sides of the triangle	The average of the lengths of the smallest and largest sides of the triangle

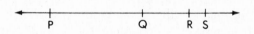

5. The area of rectangle I	The area of parallelogram II

6. The positive difference between $\dfrac{1}{6}$ and $\dfrac{1}{12}$ / The positive difference between $\dfrac{1}{5}$ and $\dfrac{1}{10}$

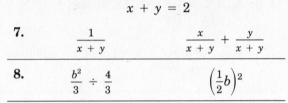

$$x + y = 2$$

7. $\dfrac{1}{x+y}$ / $\dfrac{x}{x+y} + \dfrac{y}{x+y}$

8. $\dfrac{b^2}{3} \div \dfrac{4}{3}$ / $\left(\dfrac{1}{2}b\right)^2$

In 9–14, select the letter of the correct answer.

9. If $\dfrac{x}{3} + \dfrac{y}{4} = 10$ and y is twice x, then the average of $\dfrac{x}{3}$ and $\dfrac{y}{4}$ is

(A) 18 (B) 12 (C) 10 (D) 5

10. If $\dfrac{x}{3} + \dfrac{y}{4} + \dfrac{z}{5} = 1\dfrac{1}{4}$, then $20x + 15y + 12z$ is

(A) 30 (B) 45 (C) 75 (D) 105

11. PQ is $\dfrac{2}{3}$ of PR and QR is $\dfrac{3}{4}$ of QS. PR is what fraction of PS?

(A) $\dfrac{6}{7}$ (B) $\dfrac{7}{8}$ (C) $\dfrac{8}{9}$ (D) $\dfrac{9}{10}$

12. If $\dfrac{2x+1}{3} = \dfrac{3x+2}{4}$, then

(A) $\dfrac{2x}{3} = \dfrac{3x}{4}$ (B) $\dfrac{2x+2}{3} = \dfrac{3x+3}{4}$

(C) $\dfrac{2x+4}{3} = \dfrac{3x+6}{4}$ (D) $\dfrac{6x+3}{3} = \dfrac{12x+8}{4}$

13. If $\dfrac{(2)(3)(4)}{(5)(6)(7)} = \dfrac{x}{y}$ and $\dfrac{(3)(4)(5)}{(6)(7)(8)} = \dfrac{ax}{by}$, then $\dfrac{a}{b}$ is

(A) $\dfrac{1}{49}$ (B) $\dfrac{49}{16}$ (C) $\dfrac{25}{29}$ (D) $\dfrac{25}{16}$

14. If $\dfrac{1}{xy} + \dfrac{1}{yz} + \dfrac{1}{xz} = P$, and twice the reciprocal of P is xyz, then $x + y + z$ is

(A) 1 (B) 2 (C) $\dfrac{1}{2}$ (D) 0

SUGGESTED TEST ITEMS (Chapter 14)

1. For what value of x is the fraction $\dfrac{2x - 5}{x + 4}$ undefined?

In 2–5, express the fraction as an equivalent fraction in lowest terms.

2. $\dfrac{9x^2y}{27xy^2}$ 3. $\dfrac{3a + 3b}{6}$ 4. $\dfrac{9c^3 - 3c^2}{9c^4}$ 5. $\dfrac{4xy + 2y}{20xy}$

In 6–14, perform the indicated operations and express the answer in lowest terms.

6. $\dfrac{5x^2}{6} \cdot \dfrac{12}{25x}$ 7. $\dfrac{6y - 12}{8} \cdot \dfrac{4y}{3y^2}$ 8. $12x^2 \div \dfrac{4x}{3}$

9. $3x \cdot \dfrac{1}{5x}$ 10. $3x + \dfrac{1}{5x}$ 11. $\dfrac{x - 5}{3} + \dfrac{2x + 3}{5}$

12. $\dfrac{2}{3x} \div \dfrac{6}{4x}$ 13. $\dfrac{a + 2}{5a} - \dfrac{a + 5}{2a}$ 14. $\dfrac{a}{6} \div \dfrac{7a}{12}$

15. If the length of a rectangle is represented by $\dfrac{3b}{4}$ and the width is represented by $\dfrac{2b}{5}$, represent the perimeter of the rectangle in lowest terms.

In 16–21, solve and check:

16. $\dfrac{3x - 7}{5x} = \dfrac{1}{4}$ 17. $\dfrac{1}{2}a - \dfrac{1}{3}a = \dfrac{5}{6}$ 18. $\dfrac{y}{3} + 12 = \dfrac{5y}{9}$

19. $\dfrac{x - 3}{2} = \dfrac{x + 5}{3}$ 20. $\dfrac{3b}{4} - \dfrac{b + 4}{6} = \dfrac{5}{3}$ 21. $.2d + 1 = .24d$

In 22 and 23, use an algebraic solution to solve the problem.

22. When 9 is added to $\dfrac{2}{3}$ of a number, the result is $\dfrac{7}{6}$ of the number. Find the number.

23. A child's bank contains 22 coins. There are twice as many dimes as nickels and the rest are quarters. Find the largest possible number of quarters in the bank if the value of the coins is at most $3.50.

BONUS: Of a group of persons questioned, two-thirds said that they read the newspaper and three-fourths said that they listened to the news on television. One-tenth said that they neither read the newspaper nor listened to the news on television. What fractional part of the group questioned both read the newspaper and listened to the news on television? What is the smallest number of persons that could have been surveyed?

CHAPTER **15**

Probability

Aims

- To introduce empirical and theoretical probability.

- To evaluate simple probabilities applied to fair objects by the theoretical rule.

- To determine the probabilities of compound events by using the counting principle, tree diagrams, listings of ordered elements, and graphs.

- To define and evaluate permutations, using factorial notation and formula.

- To solve probability problems in which items are chosen at random either without replacement or with replacement.

Originally developed to answer questions that arose in games of chance, the principles of probability have been applied to important questions that arise in education, science, industry, and the social sciences. Encourage students to research some of these uses.

From the outset, the text establishes a link between the topics of probability and statistics. Empirical probability requires the collection of data. Thus, some vocabulary of statistics is introduced in this chapter. The text then uses empirical probability to lead into theoretical probability, reserving further discussion of the presentation of data for Chapter 16.

Probability and permutations are topics that may have been introduced to and investigated by students in earlier grades. However, a more thorough presentation should be made at this time. Students, although able to obtain correct answers to simple probability problems, often lack a true understanding of the meaning of the answers and an appreciation of when certain rules do or do not apply.

In addition to standard types of probability problems, some problems that use an algebraic solution are included in this chapter.

15-1   EMPIRICAL PROBABILITY

It is important that students perform an empirical study in probability before they are introduced to the rule for theoretical probability. For one reason, the theoretical rule can be applied only to fair objects, that is, objects for which each singleton outcome is equally likely to occur. Too often, students will want to treat every situation as if this is the case, but the differences between biased and fair objects must be recognized.

Perform an experiment in class. Collect the data, organize the data in a table that includes cumulative relative frequency, and construct a graph of the cumulative relative frequency as the number of trials increases. Students may toss coins, as outlined in the text, or roll dice. By starting with a fair object, students will see why we assign certain probabilities such as P (head on a coin) $= \frac{1}{2}$ and P (4 on a die) $= \frac{1}{6}$. They will also be able to compare their guess for the probability of an event with the cumulative relative frequency found by the experiment. Once the experiment is performed, the definition of empirical probability will make sense: probability is a guess of the cumulative relative frequency of an event, but the guess is based on the careful and accurate gathering of data in a scientific experiment.

The text introduces a folded index card as an example of a biased object. After performing an experiment with a fair coin or a fair die, ask what probability might be assigned to each of the three outcomes obtained by tossing the biased folded card. Is the probability of each outcome $\frac{1}{3}$? The answer is no. Some students might say that there are 2 ways for the card to fall on its side, 2 ways for the card to fall on its edge, and only 1 way for the card to land as a tent. Can we say P (side) $= \frac{2}{5}$, P (edge) $= \frac{2}{5}$, and P (tent) $= \frac{1}{5}$? Again, the

answer is no. The fallacy in reasoning lies in an attempt to apply the rule for theoretical probability to a biased object, for which each singleton outcome is not equally likely to occur. There is only one way to determine the probabilities: perform an empirical study. Let the students toss the cards at home and collect the data in class the following day. The results will show that no particular probability can be assigned since the likelihood of achieving a certain outcome depends on other factors such as the size of the card used and the manner in which the card was tossed.

Compare the result of generating random integers within some range on a computer with the result of asking a group of people to each select an integer within the same range. Is each number equally likely to occur in both cases? Studies have shown that, in large numbers of trials, a computer will produce the integers within the selected range with equal frequencies. People, however, evidencing natural human biases, will not.

The exercises offer suggestions for other experiments, using both fair and biased objects. As students answer questions dealing with probability, a sense of theoretical probability should emerge.

Computer Activities (15-1) The following program uses the function that generates numbers randomly. Recall that on some machines RND (1) must be written RND (0).

```
10   REM    THIS PROGRAM PRINTS TWENTY
15   REM    RANDOM NUMBERS BETWEEN
20   REM    ZERO AND ONE.
30   FOR N = 1 TO 20
40   PRINT  RND (1)
50   NEXT N
60   END
```

The following program uses the greatest integer function, INT (X). If X is an integer, then INT (X) = X, as in INT (8) = 8. However, if X is not an integer, then INT (X) equals the largest integer that is less than X. For example, INT (4.9) = 4, INT $\left(\frac{3}{4}\right)$ = 0, and INT (−1.3) = −2.

```
10   REM    THIS PROGRAM PRINTS TWENTY
15   REM    INTEGERS SELECTED AT RANDOM
20   REM    FROM ZERO THROUGH NINE.
30   FOR N = 1 TO 20
40   PRINT  INT (10 *  RND (1)),
50   NEXT N
60   END
```

To print integers randomly selected from 1 through 10, alter the previous program as follows:

```
40   PRINT  INT (10 *  RND (1) + 1),
```

To print only the digits 1 through 6 selected at random (to simulate the faces of a die), alter the previous program as follows:

```
40   PRINT  INT (6 *  RND (1) + 1),
```

To print only the digits 0 or 1 selected at random (to simulate a head and a tail on a coin), alter the previous program as follows:

```
40   PRINT  INT (2 *  RND (1)),
```

The following program records the occurrence of heads or tails in a given number of tosses of a coin.

```
100   REM    THIS PROGRAM SIMULATES TOSSING
110   REM    A COIN ANY GIVEN NUMBER
120   REM    OF TIMES, AND RECORDS THE
130   REM    PROBABILITY FOR HEADS AND THE
140   REM    PROBABILITY FOR TAILS.
150   LET H = 0
160   LET T = 0
170   PRINT "HOW MANY TOSSES?"
180   INPUT N
190   FOR K = 1 TO N
200   LET X =  INT (2 *  RND (1))
210   IF X = 0 THEN 240
220   LET T = T + 1
230   GOTO 250
240   LET H = H + 1
250   NEXT K
260   PRINT "TOSS";"  # OF TIMES";"  % OF TIME"
270   PRINT
280   PRINT "HEADS";"      ";H;"        ";
290   PRINT (H / N) * 100
300   PRINT "TAILS";"      ";T;"        ";
310   PRINT (T / N) * 100
320   END
```

15-2 THEORETICAL PROBABILITY

After introducing terms such as *outcome, sample space,* and *event,* we define the theoretical probability of an event as the number of ways that the event can occur divided by the total number of possibilities, or $P(E) = \frac{n(E)}{n(S)}$. In other words, theoretical probability is a ra-

tio that can be written without performing an experiment. Why then did we do the experiments in the last section? We did them because the rule for theoretical probability can be applied only to fair objects, while the empirical approach can be used with any object—fair or biased.

If each outcome of a sample space has an equal chance of occurring, this sample space is said to have *uniform probability*. Ask if a weighted coin or loaded dice have uniform probability.

Any selection of objects made without looking or without being able to influence the result is referred to as a *random selection*. Imagine that you could select any one of twenty sealed envelopes. Each envelope has a single dollar bill, except one that contains a hundred-dollar bill. The probability of selecting the $100 bill is $\frac{1}{20}$. Would the probability change if a selection that is not random were used? Suppose the bills were not in envelopes, but they were openly displayed on a table. You can select any one bill. Is the probability of selecting the $100 bill still $\frac{1}{20}$?

Exercise 11 on page 478 uses geometric figures in a probability problem to review some important properties of polygons.

15-3 EVALUATING SIMPLE PROBABILITIES

To write any simple probability, it is necessary to determine the number of ways the specific event can occur, where the set of outcomes in the event is a subset of the sample space. Emphasize that the probability of any event E must be equal to or greater than zero (the impossible case) and less than or equal to one (the certain case).

In rolling a fair die, the probability that an even number will appear is $\frac{3}{6}$, or $\frac{1}{2}$. Since $\frac{1}{2} = .5$, or 50%, we can say that $P(\text{even number}) = \frac{1}{2}$, or .5, or 50%. Thus, the probability of an event can be expressed as a fraction, as a decimal, or as a percent. Probabilities are usually stated in fractional form. Although the text shows fractions also reduced to simplest form, there is no need to require that students do this. You might even prefer that students leave their fractional answers to reflect the way they thought about the problems.

An algebraic solution to a simple probability problem is presented in Model Problem 2 on page 482.

15-4 THE PROBABILITY OF *A AND B*

Suppose we agree to meet at Main Street *and* Second Avenue. How exact is that location? What word would you use to describe our meeting place? It is the *intersection* of two streets.

Where else have we used the word *and* in our study of mathematics this year? More than one student should recall the study of logic.

There is a natural integration of probability, logic, and sets within this section. In addition to discussing the concept from many viewpoints, note the similarities in the symbols used:

In sets, *A and B* is written as $A \cap B$.
In logic, *p and q* is written as $p \wedge q$.

15-5 THE PROBABILITY OF *A OR B*

Suppose we agree to meet at Main Street *or* Second Avenue. How exact is that location? Not very exact; we could easily miss each other by being anywhere on Main Street or anywhere on Second Avenue. In terms of sets, students will recognize the *union*. Their study of *or* in logic will help them understand the use of this connective in probability. Again, note the similarities in the symbols used:

In sets, *A or B* is written as $A \cup B$.
In logic, *p or q* is written as $p \vee q$.

The use of a Venn diagram (page 492) is an important aid in understanding the meaning of the rule:

$P(A \text{ or } B) = P(A) + P(B) - P(A \text{ and } B)$
$P(A \cup B) = P(A) + P(B) - P(A \cap B)$

Once this rule is understood, you may wish to study the probability of a union from a different viewpoint, by considering three disjoint sets. For example:

If $P(A) = .8$, $P(B) = .4$, and $P(A \cap B) = .3$, find $P(A \cup B)$.

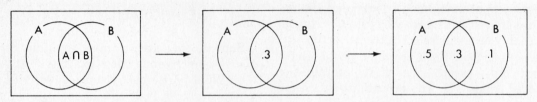

Draw a Venn diagram and write .3 in the intersection to represent $P(A \cap B)$. Since $P(A) = .8$ and $P(A \cap B) = .3$, what probability can be assigned to the crescent-shaped region of A that does not include the intersection? Students will see that $.8 - .3 = .5$, or, by addition, that $.3 + .5 = .8$. [This region, which need not be formally defined, is called *A less B*, written symbolically as A/B. Thus, $P(A/B) = .5$.] In a similar manner, the crescent-shaped region of B is $.4 - .3 = .1$. [More formally, the region is *B less A*, written symbolically as B/A, and $P(B/A) = .1$.]

The probability of the union is the sum of the probabilities of the three disjoint sets, that is: $P(A \cup B) = .5 + .3 + .1 = .9$

Compare this answer to one found by the more familiar approach:

$$P(A \cup B) = P(A) + P(B) - P(A \cap B)$$
$$= .8 + .4 - .3 = .9$$

15-6 THE PROBABILITY OF *NOT A*; PROBABILITY AS A SUM

Working with the probability that an event does occur to determine the probability that the event does not occur is an indirect approach, and, in complex situations, can be more efficient than a direct approach. Acknowledge with students, however, that a direct approach for many of these simple situations is not only possible, but is sometimes more efficient. In Model Problem 1, for example, we can go directly to the required event; there are two ways to roll a number that is not less than 5, namely, 5 and 6. Therefore,

$P(\text{not less than 5}) = \frac{2}{6}$.

Take advantage of any opportunity to apply the rules of probability to real-life situations. For example, in Exercise 2 explore what it means to say that there is a 30% chance of rain. Elicit that past experience has shown that given certain atmospheric conditions, rain has occurred on about 30 of 100 such days. Elicit also that fixing a probability for rain is complex, taking into account an array of variable factors, and is not simply either it will rain or it will not rain.

The general exercises at the end of this section present a summary of all probability concepts presented to this point.

15-7 THE COUNTING PRINCIPLE AND SAMPLE SPACES

When problems involve two or more activities, the number of outcomes can be obtained by actually displaying and counting the possibilities. A tree diagram, a set of ordered pairs, or a graph are ways of displaying the outcomes of two activities. If three or more activities are involved, a graph is not feasible. A tree diagram is recommended for most problems.

When preparing a tree diagram, students sometimes mistakenly include the number of trials, for example, for 3 tosses of a coin, they may start the tree with 1, 2, 3. Emphasize that only outcomes appear in a tree diagram.

The counting principle is a multiplication

procedure that gives the number of outcomes without displaying them. It can be applied to any sample space, including those that result from three or more activities. The counting principle should be used to check the number of outcomes displayed when a tree diagram is used, as well as being used when the number of possible outcomes makes the tree diagram impractical.

15-8 PROBABILITIES AND THE COUNTING PRINCIPLE; PREDICTING OUTCOMES

If two dice are rolled, students can accept the fact that the outcomes on these dice are *independent* of each other. However, if a single die is rolled twice, some students erroneously believe that the outcome of the first toss has some influence on the outcome of the second toss. Elicit that this is not so; the outcome of the second toss is still independent of the first.

Note with the class that the counting principle allows us to determine only the number of ways in which two or more activities can occur. A tree diagram, a listing, or a graph allow us to see the actual outcomes. In this section, we have stated a counting principle for probability, thus providing a method for determining a probability ratio for independent compound events without reference to the particular outcomes. In the next section, we will again illustrate the sample space, thus seeing the actual outcomes, and we will use these outcomes to determine probabilities for compound events. Unlike the counting principle, which is limited to compound events that are independent, the illustrations will allow us to determine probabilities for any compound events.

The text also presents the use of a proportion as a way of obtaining a relatively meaningful expectation based on past records. Note that in some of the given situations, the compound events are clearly independent, as in consecutive tosses of a coin or in consecutive rolls of a die. However, in Exercise 11, for example, although the radios are individual items, the manufacturing process consists of a series of related events. Elicit reasons for the

occurrence of a defect, such as the longer an operator works without rest the more prone he or she is to error. Elicit also that, as with any theoretical probability, a prediction becomes more reliable as the number of trials increases. Thus, although we may not find exactly 1 defective radio in the first set of 400, or exactly 2 in the first set of 800, we are likely to find about 25 defective radios in the total set of 10,000.

15-9 PROBABILITIES WITH TWO OR MORE ACTIVITIES

In this section, a sample space, listed as a set of ordered elements or shown as a tree diagram, should be established before probabilities of compound events are found. In many instances, students prefer a tree diagram. Note that a tree diagram also helps students to write a listing of ordered elements.

Point out the relationship to logic here. Show how the listings in a truth table correspond to the branches of a tree diagram and to a listing of ordered elements. Use two variables and three variables.

Emphasize that a tree diagram depicts a definite pattern that makes it easier to list the elements in the sample space.

For larger sample spaces, such as the 36 elements obtained from rolling two dice, a tree diagram is awkward to draw. Nevertheless, you might wish students to experience drawing one such diagram and, therefore, will assign Exercise 7a. Even if you don't ask students to complete the diagram, they should be encouraged to draw a few parts so that they can see how the diagram is related to the listing of ordered pairs. You should assign Exercise 7b, which requires a listing for this sample space, so that students will have a handy reference when working out other dice problems.

For this same sample space, you might ask students what they observe about the graph shown in Model Problem 3. Their responses may include some of the following facts:

(1) All the points representing a sum of 8 fall on a straight line.
(2) If a point is on that line, then that point represents a way to obtain a sum of 8.

(3) If a point is not on that line, then that point does not represent a way to obtain a sum of 8.

(4) All the points "above" that line represent sums greater than 8.

(5) All the points "below" that line represent sums less than 8.

Note how such observations prepare students for graph work with linear open sentences in the coordinate plane, which will be presented in Chapter 17.

As enrichment now, you might have students try to write these observations symbolically. For example:

Let x represent a possible outcome for the first die.

Let y represent a possible outcome for the second die.

Then, (x, y) represents a possible outcome for the two dice.

(1) $\{(x, y) \mid x + y = 8\}$ falls on a straight line.

(2) If a point is on that line, then for that point $x + y = 8$.

(3) If a point is not on that line, then for that point $x + y \neq 8$.

(4) For all the points "above" that line, $x + y > 8$.

(5) For all the points "below" that line, $x + y < 8$.

Note that since the domains for these variables x and y are each limited to the set $\{1, 2, 3, 4, 5, 6\}$, the set of ordered pairs (x, y) has exactly 36 elements, or points. Within this limited portion of the coordinate plane, called a *lattice of points,* we are considering the line $x + y = 8$ with only 5 discrete points on it. Later, when the line $x + y = 8$ is presented in the full coordinate plane, the line will have an infinite number of points, and these points will not be discrete (there will be an infinite number of points between any two points on the line).

Students will welcome another opportunity to review those aspects of probability previously presented through sets and Venn diagrams. You can do this with sets and a lattice of points. For example, to demonstrate the relationship between $P(A)$ and $P(not\ A)$, use a lattice of 36 points that produce 25 squares when connected. Let a point be selected at random from the region enclosed by the squares whose vertices are the corner points of the lattice. Let $P(A)$ be the probability of selecting a point in the shaded region. To begin, use the following lattice in which students can count squares to determine that $P(A) = \frac{7}{25}$ and $P(not\ A) = \frac{18}{25}$.

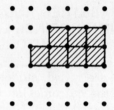

You can use different configurations of A, including half squares. The following lattice still results in $P(A) = \frac{7}{25}$ and $P(not\ A) = \frac{18}{25}$.

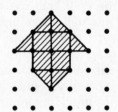

The following lattices will demonstrate the meanings of $P(A\ and\ B)$ and $P(A\ or\ B)$ under different relationships that could exist between A and B. For all three situations, $P(A) = \frac{8}{25}$ and $P(B) = \frac{4}{25}$.

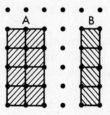

A and B are disjoint.
$$P(A\ and\ B) = 0$$
$$P(A\ or\ B) = \frac{12}{25} = P(A) + P(B)$$

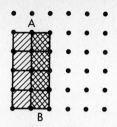

B is a subset of A.

$$P(A \text{ and } B) = \frac{4}{25} = P(B)$$

$$P(A \text{ or } B) = \frac{8}{25} = P(A)$$

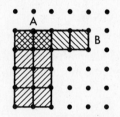

A and B intersect.

$$P(A \text{ and } B) = \frac{2}{25} = P(A \cap B)$$

$$P(A \text{ or } B) = \frac{10}{25} = P(A) + P(B) - P(A \cap B)$$

15-10 PERMUTATIONS

In this section, students learn how to count the number of ways arrangements can be ordered. The factorial notation, introduced as representing the permutation of n objects taken n at a time where n is a natural number, serves as a simple notation for the factors of this product. Allow students to leave all but the simpler answers in factored form.

At this point, students may not yet realize just how large some of these numbers can become. For example, 9 persons can be seated in a row 9! ways. Ask: "If a new arrangement were achieved every second, how long would it take to represent every possible arrangement?" Since $9! = 9 \cdot 8 \cdot 7 \cdot 6 \cdot 5 \cdot 4 \cdot 3 \cdot 2 \cdot 1 = 362{,}880$, it would take 362,880 seconds. Since there are 86,400 seconds in a day, it would take exactly 4.2 days (4 days, 4 hours, 48 minutes) to rearrange just 9 persons in a row in every possible order. How long would it take to rearrange 13 persons in a row? (72,072 days, or almost 200 years.)

Take the time to show why: $2! + 4! \neq 6!$
$\frac{4!}{2!} \neq 2!$ $8! - 6! \neq 2!$ $2! \cdot 3! \neq 6!$

Demonstrate also how to simplify a division containing factorials. For example:

$$\frac{100!}{98!} = \frac{100 \cdot 99 \cdot \cancel{98!}}{\cancel{98!}} = 100 \cdot 99 = 9{,}900$$

This is a technique that can be used in the next section when determining the permutation of n things taken r at a time.

As an alternate approach to the solution of many permutation problems, you may wish to introduce a diagramming technique. For example, reconsider Model Problem 2, which asks for the number of possible arrangements of the letters in {**N, O, W**}.

Solution:
(1) There are 3 spaces to be filled: ___ ___ ___
(2) Any of the 3 letters can be used to fill the first space: _3_ ___ ___
(3) After the first space has been filled, there are 2 choices remaining for the second space: _3_ · _2_ ___
(4) After the second space has been filled, there is only 1 choice remaining for the third space: _3_ · _2_ · _1_

Answer: There are $3 \cdot 2 \cdot 1$, or 6, ways.

You may also wish to introduce a challenge by asking students to consider this same problem with the additional condition that the first letter must be a vowel.

Solution:
(1) There are 3 spaces to be filled: ___ ___ ___
(2) Since there is only 1 vowel, **O**, there is only 1 way to fill the first space: _1_ ___ ___
(3) After **O** has been used, there are 2 choices remaining for the second space, **N** or **W**:   _1_ · _2_ ___

(4) After a letter has been used in the second space, there is only 1 letter remaining for the third space:

$$\underline{1} \; \cdot \; \underline{2} \; \cdot \; \underline{1}$$

Answer: There are $1 \cdot 2 \cdot 1$, or 2, ways: **ONW; OWN.**

Note that students can check this by referring to part **b** of the model solution where all possible arrangements are listed.

You can continue with the original problem and different additional conditions. For example, in how many arrangements will the last letter be a consonant?

Solution:

(1) Beginning with the particular condition, there are 2 ways to fill the last space, either with **N** or **W**:

$$\underline{} \; \underline{} \; \underline{2}$$

(2) After the last space has been filled, return to the first space. There are 2 choices remaining for this space, **O** and one consonant:

$$\underline{2} \; \underline{} \; \underline{2}$$

(3) After the first space has been filled, there is 1 choice remaining for the second space:

$$\underline{2} \; \cdot \; \underline{1} \; \cdot \; \underline{2}$$

Answer: There are $2 \cdot 1 \cdot 2$, or 4, ways: **OWN; WON; NOW; ONW.**

Computer Activity (15-10) The following program will find the value of $n!$. For values of n that are larger than 13, the result is usually written in scientific notation. Values of $n!$ for $n > 34$ exceed the capabilities of most microcomputers.

```
100  REM  THIS PROGRAM WILL FIND THE VALUE
110  REM  OF N FACTORIAL FOR ANY INTEGER
120  REM  LESS THAN 34.
130  PRINT "FOR WHAT INTEGER, N, DO YOU WANT TO"
140  PRINT "FIND N FACTORIAL? ( 0 < N < 34 )"
150  PRINT "ENTER A WHOLE NUMBER BETWEEN 1 AND 33."
160  INPUT N
170  IF N < 1 OR N > 33 THEN 150
180  LET P = 1
190  IF N = 1 THEN 230
200  FOR I = 2 TO N
210  LET P = P * I
220  NEXT I
230  PRINT N;"! = ";P
240  PRINT
250  PRINT "DO YOU WANT TO DO ANOTHER? (Y OR N)"
260  INPUT R$
270  IF R$ = "Y" OR R$ = "YES" THEN 130
280  END
```

15-11 MORE ABOUT PERMUTATIONS

In considering arrangements, we do not always include all of the given objects every time. In such cases, when n objects are taken r at a time ($r \le n$), the counting principle is also applicable. For example, in how many ways can 2 students be chosen for president and vice president from a class of 30 students?

By the counting principle, there are $30 \cdot 29$ or 870 possible selections. This can also be written as $_{30}P_2$.

In the text, the general formula for arranging n things r at a time is written:

$$_nP_r = \underbrace{n(n-1)(n-2)\ldots}_{r \text{ factors}}$$

The general formula for $_nP_r$ can also be written $_nP_r = \dfrac{n!}{(n-r)!}$. Thus, an alternate way of evaluating $_{30}P_2$ is:

$$_{30}P_2 = \frac{30!}{(30-2)!} = \frac{30!}{28!} = \frac{30 \cdot 29 \cdot \cancel{28!}}{\cancel{28!}}$$
$$= 30 \cdot 29 = 870$$

Although this notation is not used in this text, reference to alternate formulas appears in subsequent textbooks in this series.

Some mention of the term *combination* might be made at this point, only to show the difference between a combination and a permutation. An in-depth study of combinations occurs in Course II.

15-12 PROBABILITY WITHOUT REPLACEMENT; PROBABILITY WITH REPLACEMENT

Some problems found in this section specifically mention *without* replacement or *with* replacement. In some instances, however, no mention is made about replacement. If this is the case, as in Exercise 9, common sense should prevail. Students should be able to determine whether or not replacement occurs in a problem even though it is not specified.

The evaluation of probabilities with two or more activities is handled in the same manner in these exercises as it was in Sections 15-8 and 15-9, when the concept was introduced.

Computer Activity (15-12) The computation involved in evaluating $_nP_r$ for large values of n and r is often tedious. The following program makes it possible to demonstrate how rapidly the number of arrangements increases as n and r increase.

```
100   REM   THIS PROGRAM WILL EVALUATE THE
110   REM   NUMBER OF PERMUTATIONS OF N
120   REM   THINGS TAKEN R AT A TIME.
130   PRINT "THIS PROGRAM WILL FIND THE NUMBER OF"
140   PRINT "POSSIBLE ARRANGEMENTS OF THINGS CHOSEN"
150   PRINT "FROM A SET WITHOUT REPLACEMENT."
160   PRINT
170   PRINT "ENTER THE NUMBER OF ELEMENTS IN THE SET."
180   INPUT N
190   PRINT
200   PRINT "ENTER THE NUMBER OF ELEMENTS CHOSEN."
210   INPUT R
220   IF R <= N THEN 290
230   PRINT
240   PRINT "THE NUMBER OF THINGS CHOSEN FROM A SET"
250   PRINT "CANNOT BE GREATER THAN THE NUMBER OF"
260   PRINT "THINGS IN THE SET."
270   PRINT "TRY AGAIN."
280   GOTO 160
290   LET P = 1
300   FOR I = 0 TO R - 1
310   LET P = P * (N - I)
320   NEXT I
330   PRINT
340   PRINT "THERE ARE ";P;" ARRANGEMENTS OF ";N
350   PRINT "THINGS TAKEN ";R;" AT A TIME."
360   PRINT
370   PRINT "DO YOU WANT TO DO ANOTHER? (Y OR N)"
380   INPUT R$
390   IF R$ = "Y" OR R$ = "YES" THEN 160
400   END
```

SAT PREPARATION EXERCISES (Chapter 15)

Questions 1–7 each consist of two quantities, one in Column A and one in Column B. You are to compare the two quantities and choose:

A if the quantity in Column A is greater;
B if the quantity in Column B is greater;
C if the two quantities are equal;
D if the relationship cannot be determined from the information given.

Notes

1. In certain questions, information concerning one or both of the quantities to be compared is centered above the two columns.
2. In a given question, a symbol that appears in both columns represents the same thing in Column A as it does in Column B.
3. Letters such as x, n, and k stand for real numbers.

<u>**Column A**</u>	<u>**Column B**</u>

A single card is selected at random from a standard deck of cards.

1. Probability of a king | Probability of a heart

A standard six-sided die

2. If tossed once, probability of obtaining a 4 | If tossed twice, probability that the numbers are the same

3. P(both heads), if two fair coins are tossed | P(all heads), if three fair coins are tossed

A bank containing only quarters and nickels is shaken until a coin falls out.

4. Probability of a 25¢ coin | Probability of a 5¢ coin

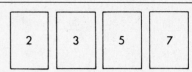

At random, 2 of the 4 cards are selected. The product of the numbers is recorded.

5. P(product is even) P(product is odd)

The spinner has three equal regions: 1, 2, 3. The arrow is spun *twice* and the sum of the numbers is recorded.

6. P(sum is even) P(sum is odd)

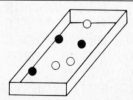

7. The probability of drawing a black marble after one black marble has been removed | The probability of drawing a white marble after one black marble has been added

In 8–20, select the letter of the correct answer.

8. In Central High, there is one administrator for 10 teachers and one teacher for 25 students. If k represents the number of students, which of the following represents the number of administrators?

(A) $\frac{25k}{10}$ (B) $250k$ (C) $\frac{k}{250}$ (D) $\frac{10k}{25}$

9. A bowl contains only red and black marbles. There are x red marbles, with 2 more black marbles than red. If a marble is selected at random, the probability that it will be black is

(A) $\frac{2}{x}$ (B) $\frac{x}{x+2}$ (C) $\frac{x}{2x+2}$ (D) $\frac{x+2}{2x+2}$

10. Set P is {2, 3, 5} and set Q is {6, 10, 15}. If one element is selected at random from set P and another from set Q, what is the probability that the P element is a divisor of the Q element?

    (A) 1 (B) $\frac{1}{3}$ (C) $\frac{1}{2}$ (D) $\frac{2}{3}$

11. A student answers 3 multiple-choice questions by random guessing. Each question has 1 correct answer and 3 incorrect answers. The probability that he will get all three wrong is

    (A) $3\left(\frac{1}{4}\right)$ (B) $\left(\frac{1}{4}\right)^3$ (C) $3\left(\frac{3}{4}\right)$ (D) $\left(\frac{3}{4}\right)^3$

12. There are 3 black marbles in a bowl containing a total of x marbles. If one marble is drawn at random, not replaced, and another is drawn at random, what is the probability that both are black?

    (A) $\dfrac{6}{x^2 - x}$ (B) $\dfrac{3x}{x^2 - x}$

    (C) $\dfrac{x}{3x - 3}$ (D) $\dfrac{2x}{3x - 3}$

13. If each operation is performed at random in evaluating the numerical expression $3 + (5)(10) - 4$, what is the probability of obtaining the correct value?

    (A) $\frac{1}{6}$ (B) $\frac{1}{3}$ (C) $\frac{1}{2}$ (D) $\frac{2}{3}$

14. A red spinner has consecutive integers from x to $x + 3$ inclusive, and a blue spinner has consecutive integers from y to $y + 4$. How many elements are in the sample space representing the number pairs possible using one number from each spinner?
    (A) 12 (B) 15
    (C) 20 (D) $(x + 3)(y + 4)$

15. A car travels a distance of 60 miles, the first half at 30 mph and the second half at 60 mph. If a headlight could burn out at any time, picked at random, during the trip, what is the probability, if the light burns out during the trip, it would burn out during the first 30 miles?

    (A) $\frac{1}{2}$ (B) $\frac{1}{3}$ (C) $\frac{2}{3}$ (D) 1

16. The three regions on the spinner are *unequal* in size. Let x represent the number of the region on which the arrow lands in a single spin. $P(x$ is a multiple of 3$) = \frac{4}{5}$, and $P(x$ is a multiple of 5$) = \frac{3}{5}$. Then, $P(x$ is a multiple of 2$) =$
    (A) $\frac{2}{5}$ (B) $\frac{3}{5}$ (C) $\frac{4}{5}$ (D) $\frac{7}{5}$

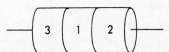

17. The wheels above rotate independently on an axis, and each wheel is divided into three equal sections labeled with the digits 1, 2, and 3. If the spinning wheels are stopped at random to form a 3-digit number, what is the probability that the number is a multiple of 3?

    (A) $\frac{1}{9}$ (B) $\frac{2}{9}$ (C) $\frac{3}{9}$ (D) $\frac{4}{9}$

18. If a number P is selected from {4, 5, 6} and another number Q is selected from the remaining numbers in the set, what is the probability that $x^2 + Px + Q$ can be factored into two binomials?

    (A) $\frac{1}{2}$ (B) $\frac{1}{3}$ (C) $\frac{1}{4}$ (D) $\frac{1}{6}$

19. A number x is selected at random from:
    {2, 3, 4, 5, 6, 8, 9, 10, 11, 12}
    $P(x$ is a multiple of 3$)$ is twice as great as
    (A) $P(x$ is even$)$ (B) $P(x$ is odd$)$
    (C) $P(x$ is prime$)$ (D) $P(x$ is square$)$

20. Let $P(x)$ equal the probability that x is drawn, at random, from the set {0, $\frac{1}{4}$, $\frac{1}{2}$, $\frac{3}{4}$}. Then $P(P(\frac{1}{2}) + P(\frac{1}{4}))$ is *not* equal to
    (A) $\frac{1}{4}$ (B) $P(\frac{3}{4})$ (C) $P(\frac{1}{2})$ (D) $\frac{1}{2}$

SUGGESTED TEST ITEMS (Chapter 15)

1. Evaluate each of the following:

   a. $4!$ **b.** $7!$ **c.** $_5P_5$ **d.** $_5P_3$ **e.** $\dfrac{9!}{8!}$

2. If the probability that it will snow tomorrow is 30%, what is the probability that it will not snow?

3. Two students from a class of 12 boys and 8 girls are chosen at random. What is the probability that the students chosen are:

   a. both boys? **b.** both girls? **c.** a boy and a girl?

4. In how many different orders can 6 persons line up to board a bus?

5. Marcy has a reading list of 12 books. In how many different orders can she choose 3 of the books?

6. Marcy has a reading list of 12 biographies and 5 historical novels. In how many different ways can she choose 1 biography and 1 historical novel from the list?

7. Two cards are drawn at random from a standard deck of 52 cards. What is the probability that the cards are both aces?

8. In how many ways can the letters of the word EQUALITY be arranged?

9. If $P(A) = .7$, $P(B) = .5$, and $P(A \cap B) = .3$, find $P(A \cup B)$.

10. If 2 fair 6-sided dice are tossed, what is the probability that the faces that turn up show a sum of 9?

11. Four fair coins are tossed simultaneously.

    a. Show the sample space by a tree diagram or by listing.
    b. What is the total number of outcomes in the sample space?
    c. What is the probability of the coins showing 2 heads and 2 tails?
    d. What is the probability of the coins showing at least 1 head?

12. The probability of drawing a red marble from a sack that contains only red and green marbles is $\dfrac{1}{4}$. After 10 red marbles are removed from the sack, the probability of drawing a red marble from the sack is $\dfrac{1}{6}$. How many red and how many green marbles were in the sack before the red marbles were removed?

13. Adam, Bert, Clara, Doris, Elaine, and Flora are members of the school choir. One will be chosen at random to sing the opening solo and a second will be chosen to sing the closing solo at the Spring Concert. Each is equally likely to be chosen for the solos.

    a. Draw a tree diagram or write the sample space of possible pairs of choir members who could be chosen.
    b. What is the probability that 2 boys are chosen?
    c. What is the probability that 1 boy and 1 girl are chosen?
    d. What is the probability that Bert is not chosen?

14. The letters of the word BEGIN are arranged at random.

    a. How many arrangements are possible?
    b. How many arrangements that begin with a vowel are possible?
    c. What is the probability that an arrangement chosen at random begins with a vowel?

BONUS: Grace is playing a game in which she needs to advance exactly 15 spaces in order to win. The number of spaces that she may advance is determined by rolling a die. What is the probability that she will win in 3 turns?

CHAPTER 16

Statistics

Aims

- To introduce the steps necessary to describe, analyze, and summarize a set of data.

- To discuss some statistical graphs.

- To present measures of central tendency and other measures of location.

Use newspapers and magazines to show how often statistical studies and graphs are used in daily life. Have students conduct one or more statistical studies of their own. While learning standard procedures, students should recognize when a sample is biased, and should discuss which measure(s) of central tendency applies to a study.

Cumulative frequency histograms are constructed so that percentiles, quartiles, and the median scores can be determined. While the use of data to predict trends and future events may be discussed, such analysis is not studied at this course level.

16-1 THE COLLECTION OF DATA

In this section, students are introduced to the first step of any statistical study, the collection of data. Ask students if they have ever taken part in a survey. Was the data collected carefully and accurately? Can we trust statistical reports in which no mention is made of the collection of data? In the exercises, the difference between fair and biased sampling is highlighted. A discussion of these exercises should lead to an understanding of the reliability of data.

For an assignment, ask students to prepare some questions for a statistical study, to determine how the data is to be collected, and to establish a sampling method to be used. By actually attempting to initiate a survey, students will begin to understand the difficulties involved in collecting reliable data.

16-2 THE ORGANIZATION OF DATA INTO TABLES

Once the data of a statistical study has been carefully collected, it must be organized into tables. Discuss the rules for grouping data and explain that there are many ways to set up tables for the same set of scores.

Students seem to have difficulty in determining the intervals to use in grouping data. Let students suggest ways to group a set of data, and write these on the chalkboard. Let the class examine these suggestions by applying such criteria as: Has the range been covered? Does it matter whether we arrange the intervals in ascending or descending order? Are there too many intervals? Too few? Which of the suggestions display the data most effectively?

Computer Activity (16-2) The following program makes a frequency table for a set of data with any number of numbers.

```
100    REM   THIS PROGRAM WILL MAKE A
110    REM   FREQUENCY TABLE FOR A SET OF
120    REM   NUMBERS WITH A RANGE LESS THAN
130    REM   ONE HUNDRED.
140    DIM C(100)
150    PRINT "THIS IS A PROGRAM THAT WILL HELP YOU TO"
160    PRINT "MAKE A FREQUENCY TABLE FOR A SET OF"
170    PRINT "NUMBERS IF THE DIFFERENCE BETWEEN THE"
180    PRINT "LARGEST AND SMALLEST NUMBER IS"
190    PRINT "NOT MORE THAN 100."
200    PRINT
210    PRINT "EACH TIME I ASK A QUESTION,"
220    PRINT "TYPE THE ANSWER AND PRESS THE"
230    PRINT "RETURN KEY."
240    PRINT
250    FOR I = 0 TO 100
260    LET C(I) = 0
270    NEXT I
280    PRINT "HOW MANY NUMBERS ARE IN YOUR SET"
290    PRINT "OF DATA?"
300    INPUT N
310    PRINT "WHAT IS THE LARGEST NUMBER?"
320    INPUT L
330    PRINT "WHAT IS YOUR SMALLEST NUMBER?"
340    INPUT S
350    IF L - S > 100 THEN 510
360    PRINT "EACH TIME I WRITE '?', TYPE ONE OF THE"
370    PRINT "NUMBERS AND PRESS THE RETURN KEY."
380    PRINT "YOU MUST ENTER ";N;" NUMBERS BEFORE"
390    PRINT "I WILL PRINT THE FREQUENCY TABLE."
400    FOR I = 1 TO N
410    INPUT X
420    LET C(X - S) = C(X - S) + 1
430    NEXT I
440    PRINT
450    PRINT "NUMBER","FREQUENCY"
460    FOR I = 100 TO 0 STEP  - 1
470    IF C(I) = 0 THEN 490
480    PRINT I + S,C(I)
490    NEXT I
500    GOTO 540
510    PRINT "YOUR SET OF NUMBERS IS TOO BIG FOR ME"
520    PRINT "TO HANDLE USING THIS PROGRAM."
530    PRINT
540    PRINT "DO YOU WANT TO DO ANOTHER? (Y OR N)"
550    INPUT R$
560    IF R$ = "Y" OR R$ = "YES" THEN 150
570    END
```

16-3 USING GRAPHS TO PRESENT ORGANIZED DATA

Citing the popular saying, "One picture is sometimes worth a thousand words," point out that it is common to see organized data pictured graphically. Students will respond with a sense of familiarity, realizing that they have had some experience with statistical graphs. Establish that we use the bar graph and the picture graph to show the comparison of different items, and the line graph to show changes in the same item.

Have students find examples of bar graphs, line graphs, and picture graphs in newspapers or magazines. Ask them to list observations that can be made from the numerical facts presented in each graph.

16-4 THE HISTOGRAM

The histogram is introduced as a bar graph with adjoining bars. Unlike the previous bar graph, a histogram is used to display data relating to successive intervals, such as 0–9, 10–19, 20–29, etc.

For purposes of consistency, be sure students designate and label the left side of the histogram "frequency" and the base "intervals." Note that the questions asked about the histogram may include problems concerning percents and simple probabilities.

You may wish to introduce another grouping technique that is useful in determining the distribution of a data set. The plot called a ***stem-leaf diagram*** will display the distribution pattern formed by the data. This diagram can also be related to a histogram.

Model Problem

Construct a stem-leaf diagram for the following data set, which consists of grades (in percents) on a test earned by 32 students.

93, 85, 50, 98, 65, 62, 99, 95, 77, 82, 74, 83, 77, 90, 73, 72,
86, 66, 45, 99, 50, 89, 78, 70, 75, 95, 80, 78, 83, 81, 72, 75.

Procedure:

1. Choose convenient numbers to serve as *stems*.

   a. Determine the lowest grade and the highest grade.

   lowest grade = 45   highest grade = 99

   b. Since all the grades are two-digit numbers that fall between 45 and 99, we will choose the stems to be the tens' digits of these numbers.

   The stems are the digits 4, 5, 6, 7, 8, and 9.

2. Think of each two-digit grade in two parts, called the *stem* and the *leaf*.

   the stem = the tens digit   the leaf = the units digit

   For example, the grade 93 has a stem (tens digit) of 9 and a leaf (units digit) of 3.

147

3. Construct the stem-leaf diagram.

    a. Write the stems vertically with a line to the right.

```
4 |
5 |
6 |
7 |
8 |
9 |
```

    b. Enter each grade onto the diagram by writing its leaf value on the row with its stem.

        Enter the first grade, 93, with stem 9 and leaf 3.

```
4 |
5 |
6 |
7 |
8 |
9 | 3
```

        Enter the second and third grades (85, with stem 8 and leaf 5; 50, with stem 5 and leaf 0).

```
4 |
5 | 0
6 |
7 |
8 | 5
9 | 3
```

        Note how the leaf value of the fourth grade (98, with stem 9 and leaf 8) must occupy the next available space in its row.

```
4 |
5 | 0
6 |
7 |
8 | 5
9 | 38
```

        Continue in this way until all 32 grades are entered.

```
4 | 5
5 | 00
6 | 526
7 | 74732805825
8 | 52369031
9 | 3895095
```

Stem-Leaf Diagram

See the distribution:

If you rotate the stem-leaf diagram 90° counterclockwise, you will see the distribution of the grades.

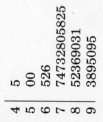

Use straight "borders" to obtain the form of a histogram.

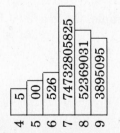

Note:

1. A stem-leaf diagram is quicker to construct than a histogram.
2. A stem-leaf diagram displays all the original data values.
3. To be useful, at least 5 stems are needed. Depending upon the data, adjustments in the choice of stems may be necessary.
4. As an additional step, you can arrange the leaves so that they are ordered.

Note that the data set given in the text at the opening of Section 16-2 (page 532), though reordered, differs from the data set of this Model Problem in only 2 grades. The set in the text has 2 grades of 100 that have been replaced by 2 grades of 99 in the Model Problem.

Elicit that a way to amend the stem-leaf diagram we have already drawn to accommodate the change in 2 scores from 99 to 100 is as shown.

4	5
5	00
6	526
7	74732805825
8	52369031
9	38505
10	00

Also, let students compare the histogram that emerges from the stem-leaf diagram above with the histogram shown in the text for this same set of data (see the opening of Section 16-4, page 545). Note how the choice of intervals (for example, 40–49 rather than 41–50) affects the two histograms.

If you wish to have your students draw additional stem-leaf diagrams, you can assign the data given in Exercises 1–4 of Section 16-2 (pages 535–537).

16-5 THE MEAN, THE MEDIAN, AND THE MODE

Because of broad popular use of the term "average" and confusion about its meaning, more precise terms are used in the study of statistics. Three measures of central tendency are introduced: the mean, the median, and the mode. As students learn the procedures to determine each of these measures for a given set of data, they should discuss when one measure of central tendency may prove to be more representative than another for the data presented.

Discuss the expression "statistics lie." Can people use statistics to back up a claim or to support one argument over another, thereby actually engaging in deceit? How are the different measures of central tendency involved? Cite an example: Suppose someone claimed that the average yearly income of families on his block was over $40,000. If the yearly incomes of all the neighbors on the block were recorded, when would one measure of central tendency be more accurate than another for determining the average income? If all but one of the incomes recorded were between $25,000 and $35,000, how would one income of $200,000 affect the average?

The sets of data in the text are deliberately kept small in order to provide simple exercises. Students should understand that for such sets of data, the mode would not be considered a significant measure of central tendency.

Computer Activities (16-5) The following program performs the computation for finding the mean.

```
100    REM   THIS PROGRAM WILL PERFORM THE
110    REM   COMPUTATION TO FIND THE MEAN.
120    PRINT "I WILL HELP YOU DO THE ARITHMETIC"
130    PRINT "NEEDED TO FIND THE MEAN."
140    PRINT
150    LET S = 0
160    PRINT "HOW MANY NUMBERS DO YOU HAVE IN YOUR"
170    PRINT "SET OF DATA? ENTER THIS NUMBER."
180    INPUT A
190    PRINT
200    PRINT "EACH TIME I WRITE A QUESTION MARK,"
210    PRINT "TYPE IN ONE OF THE NUMBERS IN YOUR DATA."
220    PRINT "THEN PRESS THE RETURN. I WILL FIND THE"
230    PRINT "MEAN AFTER YOU ENTER ALL ";A;" SCORES."
240    FOR I = 1 TO A
250    INPUT D
260    LET S = S + D
270    NEXT I
280    PRINT
290    PRINT "THE SUM OF THE ";A;" NUMBERS IS ";S;"."
300    PRINT
310    PRINT "THE MEAN = ";S;" / ";A;" = ";S / A;"."
320    PRINT
330    PRINT "DO YOU HAVE ANOTHER SET OF DATA FOR"
340    PRINT "WHICH YOU WANT TO FIND THE MEAN?"
350    INPUT R$
360    IF R$ = "Y" OR R$ = "YES" THEN 140
370    END
```

The following program will find the median of a set of numbers. The necessary steps are listed on the screen as the computation is performed.

```
100    REM   THIS PROGRAM WILL FIND THE
110    REM   MEDIAN OF A SET OF NO MORE
120    REM   THAN ONE HUNDRED NUMBERS.
130    DIM A(100)
140    PRINT "TO USE THIS PROGRAM TO FIND THE MEDIAN,"
150    PRINT "THERE CAN BE NO MORE THAN 100 NUMBERS"
160    PRINT "IN YOUR SET OF DATA."
170    PRINT
180    PRINT "HOW MANY NUMBERS ARE IN YOUR SET"
190    PRINT "OF DATA? ENTER THIS NUMBER AND THEN"
200    PRINT "PRESS 'RETURN'."
```

```
210     PRINT
220     INPUT K
230     IF K > 100 THEN 150
240     PRINT "EACH TIME I WRITE A QUESTION MARK,"
250     PRINT "ENTER ONE OF THE NUMBERS FROM THE"
260     PRINT "SET OF DATA AND THEN PRESS 'RETURN'."
270     PRINT
280     FOR N = 1 TO K
290     INPUT A(N)
300     NEXT N
310     PRINT "NOW I MUST FIRST PUT THE NUMBERS"
320     PRINT "IN ORDER. WAIT A MOMENT."
330     PRINT
340     PRINT
350     FOR J = 1 TO K - 1
360     FOR I = 1 TO K - 1
370     IF A(I) <= A(I + 1) THEN 410
380     LET T = A(I)
390     LET A(I) = A(I + 1)
400     LET A(I + 1) = T
410     NEXT I
420     NEXT J
430     PRINT "HERE IS THE SET OF DATA IN ORDER."
440     FOR N = 1 TO K
450     PRINT A(N)
460     NEXT N
470     PRINT "NOW I WILL CHOOSE THE MIDDLE NUMBER."
480     IF K / 2 =  INT (K / 2) THEN 550
490     LET M =  INT (K / 2) + 1
500     PRINT "SINCE THERE IS AN ODD NUMBER OF SCORES"
510     PRINT "IN YOUR SET OF DATA, THE MEDIAN IS THE"
520     PRINT "NUMBER THAT IS ";M;" FROM EITHER END."
530     PRINT "THE MEDIAN IS ";A(M);"."
540     GOTO 620
550     LET M = K / 2
560     PRINT "SINCE THERE IS AN EVEN NUMBER OF"
570     PRINT "SCORES IN YOUR SET OF DATA, THE MEDIAN"
580     PRINT "IS THE AVERAGE OF THE TWO MIDDLE"
590     PRINT "NUMBERS, ";A(M);" AND ";A(M + 1)
600     PRINT "THE MEDIAN IS "(A(M) + A(M + 1)) / 2
610     PRINT
620     PRINT "DO YOU HAVE ANOTHER SET OF DATA"
630     PRINT "FOR WHICH YOU WANT TO FIND THE"
640     PRINT "MEDIAN? (Y OR N)"
650     INPUT R$
660     IF R$ = "Y" OR R$ = "YES" THEN 180
670     END
```

16-6 MEASURES OF CENTRAL TENDENCY AND GROUPED DATA

In this section, measures of central tendency are determined for data grouped in intervals of length one and in intervals other than length one. It is important to realize that the mode or the number appearing most often may, at times, not lie in the modal interval.

It is possible that, for a set of data with an even number of scores, the average for the two middle scores could be between two intervals. In all exercises of this section, the data is deliberately given so that the median will always be found within a specific interval. When working with grouped data with intervals of length greater than one, only the interval containing the median is required. In more advanced courses in statistics, the median can be approximated as a specific value within an interval.

16-7 CUMULATIVE FREQUENCY HISTOGRAMS AND PERCENTILES

Students take many different standardized tests in school, such as achievement tests, IQ tests, and the SATs. The results of these tests indicate something about student performance. Students should know how to interpret these results. What does it mean if a student's score lies at the lower quartile or at the 85th percentile? Answers to these questions can be found by studying a cumulative frequency histogram that includes a scale of percents.

As a project, list the grades you recorded on the last exam for the entire class. Have the students determine the three measures of central tendency and construct a table of the grouped data, a frequency histogram, and a cumulative frequency histogram for this data. Without identifying the grades of specific students, have the class find quartile and percentile values.

You may wish to introduce another graphing technique that is useful in exploring and summarizing a group of data. The graph called a **whisker-box plot** provides a visual summary of five important values associated with a data set: the three quartile values, and the two extreme values.

Model Problem

Construct a whisker-box plot for the following data set, which consists of weights (in kilograms) of a group of 30 athletes.

50, 50, 70, 76, 57, 81, 76, 54, 58, 64,
51, 57, 76, 62, 84, 67, 72, 80, 92, 65,
60, 51, 53, 51, 57, 61, 57, 53, 82, 71.

Procedure:

1. Calculate the three quartile values.
   a. Arrange the scores in order.
   Since we will be counting positions, a columnar arrangement is convenient. The scores are shown in order from smallest to largest.

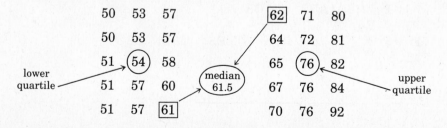

b. Find the value of the median.

Since the number of scores (30) is even, there are two middle scores (in the 15th and 16th positions). Take the average of the two middle scores.

$$\text{median value} = \frac{61 + 62}{2} = 61.5$$

c. Find the value of the lower quartile.

To find the position of the lower quartile, take half of the median position. When the median position is not an integer, first round up to the next integer.

In this example, the median is between the 15th and 16th positions. Thus, use the 16th position in the calculation.

$$\text{lower quartile position} = \frac{\text{16th position}}{2} = \text{8th position}$$

$$\text{lower quartile value} = 54$$

d. Find the value of the upper quartile.

To find the position of the upper quartile, use the position count of the lower quartile, but count now from the other direction.

Thus, beginning with the largest score, the upper quartile is 8 scores back.

$$\text{upper quartile value} = 76$$

2. Note the extreme values.

$$\text{lowest value} = 50$$
$$\text{highest value} = 92$$

3. Construct the whisker-box plot.

a. Above a number scale, plot the values of the three quartiles and of the two extremes.

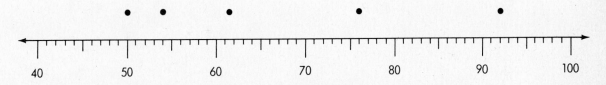

b. Draw a *box* between the lower and upper quartiles.

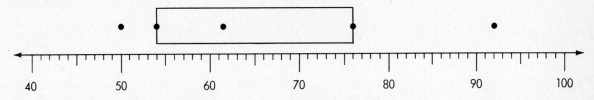

c. Mark the median with a line segment across the box.

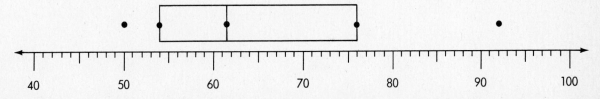

d. Draw the *whiskers* by connecting the lower extreme to the lower quartile, and the upper extreme to the upper quartile.

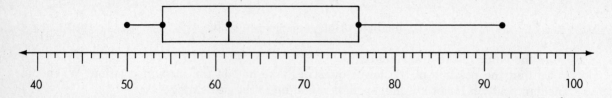

Observations from the graph:

1. Since the median divides the box into obviously unequal parts, the box shows a lack of symmetry in the data.
2. The long right-hand whisker shows that there is at least one value that is substantially larger than the others.
3. The short left-hand whisker shows that the set does not contain any unusually small values.

   If you wish to have your students draw additional whisker-box plots, you can assign the data given in Exercises 1–4 of Section 16-2 (pages 535–537).
   Note that this type of graph can also be drawn using a vertical scale.

SAT PREPARATION EXERCISES (Chapter 16)

In 1–16, select the letter of the correct answer.

1. Fifty chickens can lay 1,000 eggs in 30 days. At the same rate, how long would it take 25 chickens to lay 500 eggs?
(A) 15 days   (B) 20 days
(C) 30 days   (D) 60 days

2. If the mean of x and y is z, and the mean of p and q is r, what is the mean of $x, y, p,$ and q?
(A) $2(z + r)$ (B) $z + r$
(C) $\dfrac{z + r}{2}$ (D) $\dfrac{z + r}{4}$

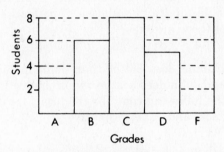

Figure for #3 and 4

3. The partially completed graph above is a frequency distribution for the grades in a math class of 25 students. Only passing grades have been represented. How many students received F?
(A) 4   (B) 3   (C) 2   (D) 1

4. If a student is selected at random from those with a passing grade, what is the probability that the student received a B or better?
(A) $\dfrac{6}{25}$ (B) $\dfrac{6}{22}$ (C) $\dfrac{9}{25}$ (D) $\dfrac{9}{22}$

5. Select the set of scores for which the following is true:
mode < mean, and mean = median
(A) 80, 80, 80, 82, 83
(B) 80, 80, 82, 82, 82
(C) 80, 80, 82, 83, 85
(D) 80, 82, 82, 82, 84

CUMULATIVE FREQUENCY HISTOGRAM

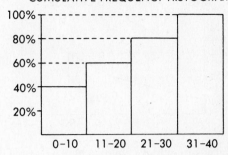

Figure for #6 and 7

6. For the cumulative frequency histogram shown above, which interval contains the median?
(A) 0-10 (B) 11-20 (C) 21-30 (D) 31-40

7. If values in the interval 0-10 are assigned the grade of A, values in 11-20 are assigned B, 21-30 assigned C, and 31-40 assigned D, what grade is the mode?
(A) A   (B) B   (C) C   (D) D

8. The average of 80, 83, 89, and x is the same as the average of 80, 83, and 86. Then the average of 82 and x is
(A) 80   (B) 81   (C) 82   (D) 83

9. The average of 3 positive numbers $x, y,$ and z is 15. If $y = 10$, then $x + z$ equals
(A) 5   (B) 15   (C) 35   (D) 45

10. A list of numbers 2, 4, 8, . . . is formed by doubling each of the preceding numbers. What is the remainder when the 15th number is divided by 6?
(A) 0   (B) 2   (C) 4   (D) 6

11. In a list of 7 different test scores, arranged in ascending order, two scores have been erased: 75, 80, _____, 82, _____, 89, 90. Which of the following could *not* be the mean?
(A) 82   (B) $82\frac{6}{7}$ (C) 83   (D) $83\frac{4}{7}$

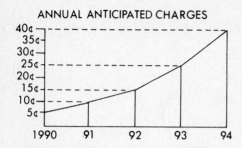

ANNUAL ANTICIPATED CHARGES

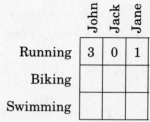

Figure for #14 and 15

12. Between which years will charges increase by the greatest percent?
    (A) 1990-91   (B) 1991-92
    (C) 1992-93   (D) 1993-94

14. Three athletes compete in a 3-part contest of running, biking, and swimming. Winning each contest earns 3 points, and second place earns one point. The scores shown above are after the running contest. Which of the following is an impossible total accumulation of points for any of these athletes?
    (A) 1   (B) 4   (C) 5   (D) 8

Grade	A	B	C	D	F
Students	4		10	8	4

13. The chart above shows how some students in a class performed on a test. If 90% of the class passed (got a D or better), then how many more students got a B than got an A?
    (A) 8   (B) 10   (C) 12   (D) 14

15. If Jane does better than John in biking, and John does best in swimming, which of the following could be the totals for John, Jack, and Jane, respectively?
    (A) 4, 5, 3   (B) 4, 3, 5
    (C) 6, 2, 4   (D) 7, 2, 3

16.   *p:* The average of x, y, and 8 is 5.
       q: The sum of x and y is 8.
    Which of the following is true for all values of x and y?
    (A) $p \rightarrow q$ (B) $p \rightarrow \sim q$
    (C) $\sim p \rightarrow q$ (D) $\sim p \rightarrow \sim q$

SUGGESTED TEST ITEMS (Chapter 16)

1. The weights, in grams, of 10 apples are 123, 134, 127, 130, 127, 129, 127, 128, 137, and 128. Find:
   a. the mean   **b.** the median   **c.** the mode

2. The mean of 5 consecutive odd integers is 55. What are the integers?

3. Amanda's scores on 4 spelling tests were 85, 93, 88, and 81. What was her score on a fifth test if the mean of the 5 scores is 86?

4. A butcher divided 30 pounds of ground meat into packages with a mean weight of 1.2 pounds. How many packages of meat were there?

5. What is the mode for the following set of numbers?
$$2, 5, 4, 5, 3, 6, 5, 2, 3, 6, 7, 5, 3, 5, 7, 6, 5$$

6. What is the value of x if the mean and mode of the following set of numbers are equal?
$$12, 15, 13, 15, 17, 15, x$$

7. Express, in terms of a, the mean of $3a - 1$, $5a + 2$, and $a - 7$.

8. The students in Mrs. Collins's class were absent the following numbers of days during a one-month period:
   0, 2, 1, 4, 1, 6, 1, 0, 1, 5, 0, 5, 0, 4, 5, 4, 1, 0, 2, 1, 1, 0, 0, 1
   a. Organize the data into a table showing frequency and cumulative frequency. Use intervals of 1 day, starting with 0.
   b. Draw a frequency histogram.
   c. Draw a cumulative frequency histogram.
   d. Find the median number of days absent.
   e. Find the number of days that is the lower quartile.
   f. Find the mean number of days absent.
   g. Find the number of days that is the upper quartile.
   h. What is the probability that a student chosen at random from this class was absent for 5 days?
   i. What is the probability that a student chosen at random from this class was absent for 3 days?
   j. What is the probability that a student chosen at random from this class was absent less than 10 days?

BONUS: Construct a set of data consisting of 8 integers with the following characteristics.
The mean, median, and mode are all the same number.
The number 85 occurs 3 times.
No other number occurs more than once.
The smallest number is 78.
The lower quartile is 83.
The upper quartile is 87.

CHAPTER 17

The Coordinate Plane

Aims

- To show how algebraic relations between two variables can be described by points and lines in the coordinate plane.

- To graph polygons and to find simple areas.

- To graph a linear equation by using either solutions of the equation or the slope-intercept method.

- To represent direct variation graphically.

- To write an equation of a line from given information.

- To graph linear inequalities by using shaded areas.

- To apply coordinates to simple transformations.

- To graph equations involving absolute values.

17-1 ORDERED NUMBER PAIRS AND POINTS IN A PLANE

The one-dimensional number line on which a number can be graphed is combined with a second number line to determine the coordinate plane used to graph number pairs. Although any two intersecting lines could be used, the lines or axes are drawn perpendicular to each other for greater simplicity in determining distance.

The graphs of points on the axes pose special problems for most students. Be alert to the fact that a few students may be plotting all coordinate points incorrectly by reversing the order.

Now, with respect to the coordinate plane, students should recognize other important meanings for familiar expressions. For example, $x > 0$ means the abscissa is positive, $y < 0$ means the ordinate is negative.

17-2 GRAPHING POLYGONS AND FINDING AREAS

A polygon can be graphed in the coordinate plane by graphing its vertices and joining them in order. This section gives students practice in finding points that are graphs of ordered pairs while reviewing some of the properties of polygons studied in Chapter 11.

By counting boxes or performing subtractions, students can find horizontal and vertical distances and, thus, determine simple areas.

17-3 FINDING SOLUTION SETS OF OPEN SENTENCES IN TWO VARIABLES

Students were introduced to solution sets of open sentences containing one variable in Chapter 3. Now, open sentences in two variables are examined. Each solution can be written as an ordered pair. The solution set may contain a finite or an infinite number of ordered pairs, depending upon such conditions as the replacement set for a variable. Set notation is convenient when the solution set is infinite.

When finding solutions of an open sentence in two variables, it is recommended that the sentence be transformed into an equivalent one that has y alone as one member (that is, solve the sentence for y). This approach makes it easier to use substitution for each element of the replacement set. Students need to be reminded that multiplication or division of both members of an inequality by a negative number reverses the inequality. Encourage students to check some ordered pairs of the solution set in the original equation or inequality.

Computer Activity (17-3) The following program will give the student practice in finding pairs of values that lie on the line determined by an equation in two variables. The equations are generated with random constants and coefficients.

Note: On some computers, RND (1) may have to be changed to RND (0).

```
100   REM   THIS PROGRAM WILL GENERATE A
110   REM   LINEAR EQUATION IN X AND Y.
120   REM   THE USER IS ASKED TO FIND THE
130   REM   COORDINATES OF POINTS ON THE
140   REM   LINE.
150   PRINT "THIS PROGRAM WILL ASK YOU TO FIND THE"
160   PRINT "COORDINATES OF THREE POINTS ON A LINE"
170   PRINT "WHOSE EQUATION IS GIVEN."
180   LET K = 0
190   PRINT
200   PRINT "WHICH FORM OF THE EQUATION DO YOU"
210   PRINT "PREFER?"
220   PRINT "    FORM 1: Y = AX + B"
230   PRINT "    FORM 2: AX + BY = C"
240   PRINT "ENTER 1 OR 2."
250   INPUT D
260   PRINT
270   LET A =  INT ( RND (1) * 7) - 3
280   IF A = 0 THEN 270
290   LET B =  INT ( RND (1) * 3) - 2
300   IF B = 0 THEN 290
310   LET C =  INT ( RND (1) * 20) - 10
320   LET W = 0
330   IF D = 2 THEN  GOSUB 680
340   IF D = 1 THEN  GOSUB 730
350   PRINT "ENTER THE COORDINATES IN THE FORM X,Y."
360   INPUT X,Y
370   IF D = 2 AND  ABS (A * X + B * Y - C) > .0001 THEN 470
380   IF D = 1 AND  ABS (Y - A * X - C) > .0001 THEN 470
390   PRINT
400   PRINT "THAT IS A CORRECT PAIR."
```

```
410    LET K = K + 1
420    IF K = 3 THEN 620
430    PRINT
440    PRINT "FIND ANOTHER PAIR IN THE FORM X,Y."
450    GOTO 360
460    PRINT
470    PRINT "WHEN X = ";X;" AND Y = ";Y
480    PRINT "THE GIVEN EQUATION IS FALSE."
490    LET W = W + 1
500    IF W = 3 THEN 540
510    PRINT
520    PRINT "TRY AGAIN."
530    GOTO 330
540    IF D = 2 THEN 590
550    PRINT " ONE PAIR OF VALUES IS 0,";C
560    PRINT " ANOTHER PAIR OF VALUES IS 1,";A + C
570    PRINT " A THIRD PAIR OF VALUES IS 2,";2 * A + C
580    GOTO 620
590    PRINT " ONE PAIR OF VALUES IS 0,";C / B
600    PRINT " ANOTHER PAIR OF VALUES IS 1,";(C - A) / B
610    PRINT " A THIRD PAIR OF VALUES IS 2,";(C - 2 * A) / B
620    PRINT
630    PRINT "DO YOU WANT TO TRY ANOTHER EQUATION?"
640    PRINT "(Y OR N)"
650    INPUT R$
660    IF R$ = "Y" OR R$ = "YES" THEN 180
670    GOTO 790
680    PRINT A;"X ";
690    IF B > 0 THEN  PRINT " + "
700    PRINT B;"Y = ";C
710    PRINT
720    RETURN
730    PRINT "Y = ";A;"X ";
740    IF C > 0 THEN  PRINT " + ";
750    IF C = 0 THEN 780
760    PRINT C
770    PRINT
780    RETURN
790    END
```

17-4 GRAPHING A LINEAR EQUATION IN TWO VARIABLES BY MEANS OF ITS SOLUTIONS

In this section, students are introduced to the graphs of first-degree equations in two variables that can be written in the form $Ax + By + C = 0$. Although two points determine a line, stress that we plot three or more points to be sure the graph is correct.

Again, it is recommended that an equivalent equation with y alone on one side be used to construct the table of values. Remind students that when the domain is the set of signed numbers, any signed number may be used as a value for x. However, it is convenient to choose values of x so that both numbers in the resulting solution will be integral. For example, when finding solutions of the equation $y = \frac{3}{4}x - 2$, choose multiples of 4 for x in order that the corresponding values of y will be integral.

Computer Activities (17-4) Programs can be written to produce a table of values for a specific equation.

```
10   REM   THIS PROGRAM PRODUCES
20   REM   TWENTY ORDERED PAIRS
30   REM   THAT SATISFY THE
40   REM   EQUATION Y = 3X / 4 - 2.
50   PRINT "X","Y"
60   FOR X = 1 TO 20
70   PRINT X,3 / 4 * X - 2
80   NEXT X
90   END
```

By plotting only coordinates in which x and y are both integers, we can quickly determine the graph of the equation. The program can be altered on line 70 to include other linear equations.

To yield a table of values in which x and y are only integers, a STEP may be attached to a FOR-NEXT loop.

```
10   PRINT "X","Y"
20   FOR X = 0 TO 24 STEP 4
30   PRINT X,3 / 4 * X - 2
40   NEXT X
50   END
```

17-5 GRAPHING LINES PARALLEL TO THE X-AXIS OR Y-AXIS

In earlier chapters, an equation such as $x = 2$ was graphed as a point on a number line. If we wish to graph such an equation in the coordinate plane, any point whose abscissa is 2 satisfies the equation, since no restriction has been placed on y, and y can have any value. Thus, the graph of $x = 2$ is an infinite set of points, a vertical line 2 units to the right of the y-axis.

Since every point that lies on the x-axis has an ordinate of 0, the equation of the x-axis is $y = 0$. Similarly, since the abscissa of each point is 0 on the y-axis, the equation of the y-axis is $x = 0$.

Elicit that an equation of the line that passes through $(3, 5)$ and $(-2, 5)$, for example, is $y = 5$, and that such a line, one in which the ordinate of every point is the same, is parallel to the x-axis.

You might ask some of the exercises in another form, and even extend them. For example, another way to ask Exercise 15a is: Write an equation of the line that is parallel to the x-axis and that passes through the point $(0, 1)$.

Extend this from a point that is on an axis to a point that is in the plane: Write an equation of the line that is parallel to the x-axis and that passes through the point $(2, 1)$. Note with the class that the same equation, $y = 1$, is an answer for the original question and the two related questions.

17-6 THE SLOPE OF A LINE

Students should recognize the various symbols that represent the slope of a line, such as m, $\frac{\Delta y}{\Delta x}$, and $\frac{y_2 - y_1}{x_2 - x_1}$. They should be able to use the given definition of slope, the ratio of the vertical change to the horizontal change, to compute slopes, and they should be able to identify lines that have positive slopes, negative slopes, zero slope, and no slope.

Remind students, especially when they are working with negative values in computing slopes, that the subtractions to obtain Δy and Δx must be performed in the same order. Either of the two given points may be selected as the first point, and the other as the second point, and that order must be maintained for

161

both Δy and Δx. Thus, the slope between $(-1, 4)$ and $(7, -3)$, for example, can be computed in either of the following ways:

$$\frac{4 - (-3)}{-1 - 7} = \frac{4 + 3}{-8} = \frac{7}{-8}$$

$$\frac{-3 - 4}{7 - (-1)} = \frac{-7}{7 + 1} = \frac{-7}{8}$$

Point out that $\frac{7}{-8}$ and $\frac{-7}{8}$ are each equivalent to $-\frac{7}{8}$.

The equivalence of fractions is particularly important for students to recognize when they are trying to graph a line by the point-slope method. Model Problem 2 shows that starting at the point $(2, -1)$, we draw the line whose slope is $\frac{3}{2}$ by moving 3 units upward and 2 units to the right to get to another point on the line, $+\frac{3}{2} = \frac{+3}{+2}$. Since $\frac{-3}{-2}$ is equivalent to $+\frac{3}{2}$, we could also get from one point to another on this line by moving 3 units downward and 2 units to the left.

Other exercises for students to consider are:

1. Do the points $A(2, 4)$, $B(3, 6)$, and $C(4, 8)$ lie on the same line? (Are the three points *collinear*?)
   Answer: The points do lie on the same line (are collinear) since the slope of $\overleftrightarrow{AB} = \frac{2}{1}$, and the slope of $\overleftrightarrow{BC} = \frac{2}{1}$, and both $\overleftrightarrow{AB}$ and $\overleftrightarrow{BC}$ pass through point B.

2. Write an equation of a line with zero slope.
   Answer: Any line of the form $y = b$.

3. Explain why the line $x = 3$ has no defined slope.
   Answer: Choose two points on the line such as $(3, 1)$ and $(3, 5)$, and show that the slope here involves the undefined operation of division by zero: $\frac{5 - 1}{3 - 3} = \frac{4}{0}$, undefined.

Computer Activity (17-6) The following program allows the student to enter the coordinates of two points. Before giving the value of the slope, it asks the student to find the slope of the line determined by those points.

```
100   REM     THIS PROGRAM WILL DETERMINE
110   REM     THE SLOPE OF A LINE FROM THE
120   REM     COORDINATES OF TWO POINTS ON
130   REM     THE LINE.
140   PRINT "FROM THE COORDINATES OF TWO POINTS,"
150   PRINT "THE SLOPE OF THE LINE THROUGH THESE TWO"
160   PRINT "POINTS CAN BE DETERMINED."
170   PRINT "ENTER THE COORDINATES OF EACH POINT"
180   PRINT "IN THE FORM X,Y."
190   PRINT
200   PRINT "FOR THE FIRST POINT, ENTER COORDINATES"
210   INPUT X1,Y1
220   PRINT
230   PRINT "FOR THE SECOND POINT, ENTER COORDINATES"
240   INPUT X2,Y2
250   PRINT "ON A PIECE OF PAPER, FIND THE SLOPE FOR"
260   PRINT "THESE COORDINATES, REDUCED TO LOWEST"
270   PRINT "TERMS. WHEN YOU ARE READY TO COMPARE"
280   PRINT "YOUR ANSWER WITH THE SOLUTION, TYPE C."
290   INPUT R$
300   LET D = X2 - X1
310   IF D = 0 THEN 500
320   LET N = Y2 - Y1
```

```
330  IF  INT (N / D) = N / D THEN 520
340  IF D < N THEN 380
350  LET B =  ABS (D)
360  LET A =  ABS (N)
370  GOTO 400
380  LET B =  ABS (N)
390  LET A =  ABS (D)
400  LET R = B - INT (B / A) * A
410  IF R = 0 THEN 450
420  LET B = A
430  LET A = R
440  GOTO 400
450  IF N * D < 0 THEN 480
460  PRINT "THE SLOPE IS "; ABS (N) / A;"/"; ABS (D) / A
470  GOTO 530
480  PRINT "THE SLOPE IS - "; ABS (N) / A;"/"; ABS (D) / A
490  GOTO 530
500  PRINT "THE LINE HAS NO SLOPE."
510  GOTO 530
520  PRINT "THE SLOPE IS ";N / D
530  PRINT
540  PRINT "DO YOU WANT TO TRY ANOTHER? (Y OR N)"
550  INPUT R$
560  IF R$ = "Y" OR R$ = "YES" THEN 190
570  END
```

17-7 GRAPHING DIRECT VARIATION

The graph of two variables that vary directly is a straight line through the origin. Simple, familiar examples of direct variation are used in this section to show how slope and the constant of variation are related. (The topic of direct variation was first considered in Section 12-5.)

The equations $\frac{y}{x} = 3$ and $y = 3x$ are not always equivalent. Although all of the solutions of $\frac{y}{x} = 3$ are solutions of $y = 3x$, (0, 0) is a solution of $y = 3x$ but is not a solution of $\frac{y}{x} = 3$. Discuss with students when (0, 0) is or is not a solution for a problem. For example, when the number of cups of lemonade (y) that can be made from x cups of frozen concentrate can be expressed as $y = 3x$, the set of non-negative numbers is a reasonable domain and range. One possible solution is that 0 cups of lemonade can be made from 0 cups of concen-

trate. However, when $y = 3x$ describes the relationship between the perimeter of an equilateral triangle (y) and the measure of one of its sides (x), the set of positive numbers is a reasonable domain and range. The solution set does not include (0, 0).

The text stresses that it is important to be aware of the unit being used in a relationship. Note that, since a ratio compares two quantities that are measured in the *same unit,* the resulting ratio is independent of the unit used (lemonade problem: ratio is 3). However, since a rate compares two quantities of *different types,* the rate changes with the unit used (cereal-box problem: rate can be expressed as $\frac{1}{6}$ carton/second or as 10 cartons/minute). Elicit how "cancellation" can be used to convert 10 cartons per minute to $\frac{1}{6}$ carton per second.

$$10 \, \frac{\text{cartons}}{\text{minute}} \cdot \frac{1 \, \text{minute}}{60 \, \text{seconds}} = \frac{10}{60} \, \frac{\text{cartons}}{\text{seconds}} = \frac{1}{6} \, \frac{\text{carton}}{\text{second}}$$

163

17-8 THE SLOPE AND Y-INTERCEPT OF A LINE

If y is isolated as one member in a linear equation, students should be able to identify the slope and y-intercept of the graph merely by looking at the equation. Stress the general form $y = mx + b$.

Given the equation $2y = 4x - 6$, it is not uncommon for students to state that the slope is 4 and the y-intercept is 6. The equation must be solved for y in terms of x so that it is in slope-intercept form before we can read the slope and y-intercept directly from the equation.

After some practice with nonzero slopes, ask for the general form of a linear equation whose slope is zero. Show that $y = mx + b$, or $y = 0 \cdot x + b$, becomes $y = b$ for these equations. Can a line with no slope, such as the graph of $x = 5$, be represented by an equation of the form $y = mx + b$? Note that this slope-intercept form cannot be used when the slope m is undefined.

The statement that two lines are parallel if and only if their slopes are equal is examined and accepted at this point without proof.

17-9 GRAPHING A LINEAR EQUATION IN TWO VARIABLES BY THE SLOPE-INTERCEPT METHOD

The use of the slope-intercept method of graphing an equation reinforces the meaning of the terms slope and y-intercept.

Remind students that when the slope is an integer, it can be written as a ratio with a denominator of 1. For example, a slope of 3 can be written as the ratio $\frac{3}{1}$ as well as equal ratios $\frac{6}{2}$, $\frac{9}{3}$, etc. Mention again that a negative ratio can be considered to be the ratio of a positive number to a negative one, or the ratio of a negative number to a positive one. For example, $-\frac{2}{3}$ can be thought of as $\frac{-2}{3}$ or as $\frac{2}{-3}$. Have students use both forms in order to convince themselves that either form will give points on the same line.

Ask students what advantages they see in graphing linear equations by this method, as opposed to listing a table of values. Are there any disadvantages? Can all lines be graphed using the slope-intercept method? For example, can we use the slope-intercept method to graph the line whose equation is $y = 8$? (Yes, $m = 0$ and $b = 8$.) Or $x = 2$? (No, there is neither a slope nor a y-intercept.)

17-10 WRITING AN EQUATION FOR A LINE

The slope and the y-intercept can be used to write an equation for a line. In Section 17-8, these two values were given. In this section, either the slope and some point on the line other than the y-intercept or two points on the line are given.

Students are required to write an equation of a line parallel to a given line and passing through a particular point. Slopes of perpendicular lines are not considered at this level.

17-11 GRAPHING A LINEAR INEQUALITY IN TWO VARIABLES

The graph of any equation in the form $y = mx + b$ divides the coordinate plane into three sets of points: the set of points on the line, the set of points in the half-plane above the line, and the set of points in the half-plane below the line. This means that a half-plane that is the graph of $y > mx + b$ must lie above the line $y = mx + b$ for given values of m and b.

What about the graph of $x > -2$? Since the plane divider, the graph of $x = -2$, is a vertical line, the solution set is the half-plane to the right. The half-plane to the left represents the graph of $x < -2$.

Stress that a test point should be selected to check if the correct half-plane has been chosen. Make sure the test point is not on the line. It is convenient to choose $(0, 0)$ as the test point because it simplifies the computation. Before students shade in the appropriate half-plane, have them check to see if the plane divider belongs to the graph of the open sentence (solid line) or does not belong to the graph (dashed line).

17-12 COORDINATES AND TRANSFORMATIONS

To reinforce the intuitive notion of reflection introduced in Chapter 11, this section provides practice with reflections over the x-axis and the y-axis, and with translation. This section may be considered optional.

17-13 GRAPHS INVOLVING ABSOLUTE VALUE

This section presents some absolute-value equations for which the graphs consist of rays or segments of lines. This material may be considered optional.

SAT PREPARATION EXERCISES (Chapter 17)

In 1–17, select the letter of the correct answer.

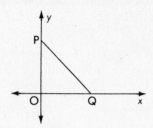

1. The area of the triangle is 8, and the coordinates of P are (0, 4). What are the coordinates of Q?
   (A) (4, 0)　　　　　(B) (2, 0)
   (C) (1, 0)　　　　　(D) $\left(\frac{1}{2}, 0\right)$

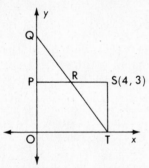

2. The area of rectangle $OPST$ equals the area of triangle TQO. Then the coordinates of R are
   (A) (3, 3)　　　　　(B) (4, 2)
   (C) (2, 3)　　　　　(D) (2, 4)

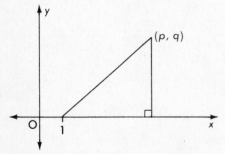

3. What is the area of the triangle?
   (A) $\dfrac{q(p-1)}{2}$　　　(B) $\dfrac{p(q+1)}{2}$
   (C) $\dfrac{p(q-1)}{2}$　　　(D) $\dfrac{q(p+1)}{2}$

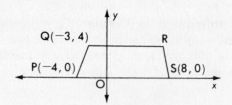

4. If $PQRS$ is an isosceles trapezoid, then the coordinates of R are
   (A) (3, 4)　　　　　(B) (4, 4)
   (C) (7, 4)　　　　　(D) (8, 4)

5. If (0, 1) and (3, 7) are both points on the graph of line m, which of the following points also lies on the graph of line m?
   (A) (3, 8)　　　　　(B) (2, 6)
   (C) (1, 3)　　　　　(D) (2, 4)

6. Line k passes through the point (3, 7). If line k has no slope, then k must pass through which of the following points?
   (A) (0, 7)　　　　　(B) (3, 0)
   (C) (0, 0)　　　　　(D) (−3, −7)

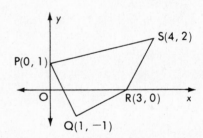

7. Which segment above has the greatest slope?
   (A) $\overline{PQ}$　(B) $\overline{QR}$　(C) $\overline{RS}$　(D) $\overline{PS}$

8. What kind of triangle is formed by the intersection of the lines $x = 1$, $y = -2$, and $x + y = 5$?
   (A) scalene
   (B) isosceles
   (C) equilateral
   (D) acute

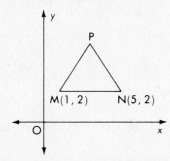

9. Isosceles triangle *MNP* has an area of 6, and *P* lies on the perpendicular bisector of $\overline{MN}$. What are the coordinates of *P*?
(A) (3, 5)   (B) (5, 4)
(C) (4, 3)   (D) (4, 5)

10. A pencil lies on graph paper with the eraser at $(-5, 10)$ and the point at $(7, -2)$. If the pencil is moved without changing its direction until the point is at the origin, then the eraser is in which quadrant?
(A) I   (B) II   (C) III   (D) IV

11. Which is an equation of the line that passes through $(1, p)$ and the origin?
(A) $y = px$ (B) $y = x + p$
(C) $x = py$ (D) $y = x - p$

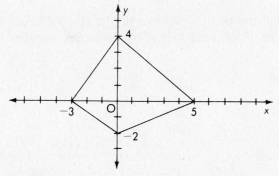

12. What is the area of the quadrilateral above?
(A) 14   (B) 20   (C) 24   (D) 48

13. Let $(a, b) \oplus (c, d) = \left(\dfrac{a + c}{2}, \dfrac{b + d}{2}\right)$. For example, $(1, 1) \oplus (3, 5) = (2, 3)$. Which choice is equivalent to $(1, 1) \oplus (5, 9)$?
(A) $(1, 1) \oplus (9, 5)$ (B) $(2, 3) \oplus (4, 5)$
(C) $(4, 6) \oplus (2, 4)$ (D) $(1, 0) \oplus (5, 8)$

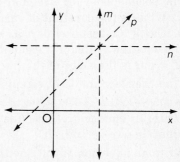

14. If the equation of *m* is $x = 3$, and the equation of *n* is $y = 4$, then the equation of line *p* could *not* be
(A) $x - y = -1$ (B) $2y = x + 5$
(C) $y = \dfrac{2}{3}x + 2$ (D) $x = y - 2$

15. If $(2, 3)$ is a point on the graph of $3x + ky = -9$, then which of the following points is also on the line?
(A) $(0, -3)$ (B) $(-3, 1)$
(C) $(4, 6)$ (D) $(7, 6)$

16. Triangle *ABC* is isosceles, with *A* at $(1, 1)$ and *B* at $(5, 1)$. Which of the following could *not* be point *C*?
(A) $(3, 3)$ (B) $(3, -2)$
(C) $(1, 5)$ (D) $(5, -5)$

17. *ABCD* is a square with vertex *A* at $(2, 3)$.
  p: The area of *ABCD* is 25.
  q: Point *C* is $(7, 8)$.
Which of the following statements must be true?
(A) $p \wedge q$ (B) $p \rightarrow q$
(C) $q \rightarrow p$ (D) $p \leftrightarrow q$

SUGGESTED TEST ITEMS (Chapter 17)

1. Find the value of k such that $(-1, k)$ is a point on the graph of $2x - y = 3$.
2. In what quadrant is the point $(4, -1)$?
3. Draw the graph of each of the following:
    a. $y = -2x + 4$ **b.** $x - 2y = 6$ **c.** $x = 3$ **d.** $y = -4$
4. Write an equation of the line whose slope is 3 and whose y-intercept is -1.
5. The perimeter (y) of a regular pentagon varies directly as the length of one side (x).
    a. What is the constant of variation if $y = 10$ when $x = 2$?
    b. Using the result of part **a**, write an equation for y in terms of x.
    c. Draw the graph of the equation written in part **b**.
    d. What is the slope of the line drawn in part **c**?
6. Find the slope and y-intercept of each of the following:
    a. $y = 2x + 1$ **b.** $x + y = 7$ **c.** $x - 2y = 6$ **d.** $y = 3$
7. Write an equation of the line through the point $(0, 2)$ that is parallel to the line whose equation is $y = 3x - 1$.
8. Write an equation of the line through $(-2, 3)$ and $(-2, 0)$.
9. The sum of the ordinate and twice the abscissa of a point is greater than or equal to 2.
    a. Write the sentence as an inequality.
    b. Graph the inequality written in part **a**.
10. What is the slope of the line through the points $(2, 2)$ and $(4, -4)$?
11. **a.** Graph the points $A(-1, 0)$, $B(5, 0)$, and $C(2, 4)$ and draw $\triangle ABC$.
    b. If $\overline{CD}$ is the altitude to $\overline{AB}$, what are the coordinates of D?
    c. Find AB.
    d. Find CD.
    e. Find the area of $\triangle ABC$.
    f. What is an equation of the line of symmetry of $\triangle ABC$?
12. Sketch the graph of $|y| = |x + 2|$.

BONUS: One vertex of a rectangle is at $(1, 2)$ and the point of intersection of the diagonals is at $(5, 4)$. Find the coordinates of the other vertices of the rectangle if two sides are parallel to the x-axis.

CHAPTER 18

Systems of Linear Open Sentences in Two Variables

Aims

- To solve linear systems in two variables, both graphically and algebraically.
- To graph the solution sets of systems of inequalities.
- To solve problems by using a pair of simultaneous equations in two variables.

Students are presented first with a graphic approach to a solution. As the need for a more exact method of solution becomes apparent, the algebraic methods of addition and substitution are examined. Verbal problems, in which two variables can be identified, are solved using systems of equations.

18-1 GRAPHIC SOLUTION OF A SYSTEM OF LINEAR EQUATIONS IN TWO VARIABLES

Students should understand that the solution set of a system of linear equations may have one ordered pair (consistent equations, represented by two lines that intersect), no ordered pairs (inconsistent equations, represented by two lines that are parallel), or an infinite number of ordered pairs (dependent equations, represented by two lines that coincide).

You may wish to encourage students to re-write each equation in the form $y = mx + b$. In this way, the type of solution set that will occur should become apparent before the lines are graphed:

(1) If the system is a pair of consistent equations, the slopes are unequal.
(2) If the system is a pair of inconsistent equations, the slopes are equal and the y-intercepts are unequal.
(3) If the system is a pair of dependent equations, the slopes are equal, and the y-intercepts are equal.

Only those equations that are consistent will then need to be graphed in the plane to determine the point of intersection.

You may want to teach Section 18-5 next, in order to complete the work with graphic solutions before considering the algebraic solution.

18-2 ALGEBRAIC SOLUTION OF A SYSTEM OF SIMULTANEOUS LINEAR EQUATIONS BY USING ADDITION

The example in which the solution set of a system of equations is an ordered pair whose coordinates are not both integers makes it clear that at times the solution is difficult to read from a graph. The algebraic method of this section uses addition to solve the system of equations after the equations have been written as equivalent ones with additive inverses as the coefficients of one variable.

Mention that this is just one procedure for solving a system of equations. In the next section, the substitution method is discussed.

Regardless of the method, the basis of solution is to treat the two equations in two variables simultaneously so that one equation in one variable emerges.

Computer Activity (18-2) This program will allow students to compare their solution of a pair of simultaneous linear equations with that of the computer.

```
100   REM   THIS PROGRAM WILL GIVE THE
110   REM   COMMON SOLUTION OF TWO LINEAR
120   REM   EQUATIONS.
130   PRINT "TO USE THIS PROGRAM TO FIND THE COMMON"
140   PRINT "SOLUTION OF TWO LINEAR EQUATIONS, THE"
150   PRINT "EQUATIONS MUST BE IN THE FORM"
160   PRINT "AX + BY = C."
170   PRINT
180   PRINT "ENTER THE COEFFICIENT OF X, THE"
190   PRINT "COEFFICIENT OF Y, AND THE CONSTANT FROM"
200   PRINT "THE FIRST EQUATION, IN THE FORM A,B,C."
210   INPUT A1,B1,C1
220   PRINT "ENTER THE COEFFICIENT OF X, THE"
230   PRINT "COEFFICIENT OF Y, AND THE CONSTANT FROM"
240   PRINT "THE SECOND EQUATION, IN THE FORM A,B,C."
250   INPUT A2,B2,C2
260   PRINT
270   PRINT "ON PAPER, FIND THE COMMON SOLUTION."
280   PRINT "COMPARE YOUR SOLUTION WITH THE ONE THAT"
290   PRINT "THE COMPUTER WILL GIVE."
300   PRINT "PRESS 'C' WHEN READY TO CONTINUE."
310   INPUT R$
320   PRINT
330   IF A1 * B2 - B1 * A2 = 0 THEN 380
340   PRINT "X = ";(C1 * B2 - B1 * C2) / (A1 * B2 - B1 * A2)
350   PRINT "Y = ";(A1 * C2 - C1 * A2) / (A1 * B2 - B1 * A2)
360   PRINT
370   GOTO 410
380   PRINT "THIS PAIR OF EQUATIONS DOES NOT HAVE"
390   PRINT "A UNIQUE SOLUTION."
400   PRINT
410   PRINT "DO YOU WANT TO DO ANOTHER? (Y OR N)"
420   INPUT R$
430   IF R$ = "Y" OR R$ = "YES" THEN 170
440   END
```

18-3 ALGEBRAIC SOLUTION OF A SYSTEM OF SIMULTANEOUS LINEAR EQUATIONS BY USING SUBSTITUTION

In this section, students learn to solve a system of equations by using the substitution method to eliminate one of the variables. This method is easily applied when a coefficient of one of the variables is 1 or -1. The substitution method appears in a variety of problems studied in Courses II and III, particularly in systems involving equations beyond the first degree.

After students have practiced using the substitution method, they have the opportunity, in Exercises 19–33, to decide which of the two algebraic methods to apply. When going over the homework in class, you may wish to have two different solutions shown for one system.

As enrichment, you may wish to demonstrate how to solve a system of three linear equations in three variables. Here are a model problem and some exercises.

Solve the system of equations and check.

$$3x + y + 2z = 6$$
$$x + y + 4z = 3$$
$$2x + 3y + 2z = 2$$

How To Proceed

(1) Eliminate one variable using any combination of the given equations. Thus, to eliminate z from equations [A] and [B]: in equation [A] multiply by 2; in equation [B] multiply by -1; add to obtain equation [D].

(2) Eliminate the same variable using a different combination of the given equations. Thus, to eliminate z from equations [A] and [C]: in equation [C], multiply by -1; add to obtain Equation [E].

(3) Solve the resulting equations [D] and [E] in two variables, x and y, to find the values of those variables.

(4) Substitute the values of the variables found in step (3) in any convenient equation involving the third variable. Thus, in equation [A], replace x by 2 and y by -1 to find the value of z.

Solution

[A] $3x + y + 2z = 6$
[B] $x + y + 4z = 3$
[C] $2x + 3y + 2z = 2$

In [A], M_2: $6x + 2y + 4z = 12$
In [B], M_{-1}: $-x - y - 4z = -3$
[D] $5x + y \qquad = 9$

[A] $3x + y + 2z = 6$
In [C], M_{-1} $-2x - 3y - 2z = -2$
[E] $x - 2y \qquad = 4$

In [D], M_2: $10x + 2y = 18$
[E] $x - 2y = 4$
$11x \qquad = 22$
$x = 2$

In [D], let $x = 2$.
$5(2) + y = 9$
$10 + y = 9$
$y = -1$

[A] $3x + y + 2z = 6$
$3(2) - 1 + 2z = 6$
$2z = 1$
$z = \frac{1}{2}$

Check: Substitute 2 for x, -1 for y, and $\frac{1}{2}$ for z in all the given equations to verify that the resulting sentences are true.

Answer: Since $x = 2$, $y = -1$, and $z = \frac{1}{2}$, the solution is $\left(2, -1, \frac{1}{2}\right)$, or the solution set is $\{(2, -1, \frac{1}{2})\}$.

Note. A variable may be eliminated by using a combination of all three equations. Thus, z may be eliminated by using the combination $[A] + [C] - [B]$, or x may be eliminated by using the combination $[B] + [C] - [A]$. However, in order to obtain a system of two equations in two variables, the same variable must be eliminated from each combination of equations.

Exercises

In 1–9, solve each system of equations and check.

1. $x + 3y + 2z = 13$
$x - 2y + 3z = 6$
$2x + 2y - z = 3$

2. $a + 3b + 2c = 6$
$3a - 6b - 2c = 9$
$2a - 3b - 4c = 9$

3. $r + 3s + t = 3$
$r + 6s - t = 2$
$4r + 9s - 2t = 1$

4. $3x - 2y - 3z = -1$
$6x + y + 2z = 7$
$9x + 3y + 4z = 9$

5. $x - 2y + 20z = 1$
$3x + y - 4z = 2$
$2x + y - 8z = 3$

6. $x + 2y - z = 5$
$2x + z = -1$
$3x - 4y = 2z + 7$

7. $2x + y + 3z = -2$
$5x = 5 - 2y$
$2y + 3z = -13$

8. $3x + 2y = 5$
$4x = 3z + 7$
$6y - 6z = -5$

9. $3a + 2c = 2$
$4b + c = 6$
$2a + 3b = 10$

Answers

1. $x = 1, y = 2, z = 3$

2. $a = 4\frac{1}{2}, b = 1, c = -\frac{3}{4}$

3. $r = -\frac{1}{2}, s = \frac{2}{3}, t = 1\frac{1}{2}$

4. $x = \frac{2}{3}, y = -3, z = 3$

5. $x = 2, y = -7, z = -\frac{3}{4}$

6. $x = 1, y = \frac{1}{2}, z = -3$

7. $x = 3, y = -5, z = -1$

8. $x = 2, y = -\frac{1}{2}, z = \frac{1}{3}$

9. $a = 2, b = 2, c = -2$

18-4 SOLVING VERBAL PROBLEMS BY USING TWO VARIABLES

At times, it is easier to solve a verbal problem by using two variables rather than one variable. Once a verbal problem is translated into a system of linear equations, the methods used to solve linear systems are applied.

Number problems, geometry problems, and business problems are stressed in this section. Other verbal problems concerning motion, investment, coins, mixture, and the like may be considered.

Some of the problems presented in Chapter 2 to be solved by a trial-and-error strategy can be easily solved by an algebraic strategy using a system of linear equations. You may want to have students compare the two strategies.

18-5 GRAPHING SOLUTION SETS OF SYSTEMS OF INEQUALITIES

In Section 17-11, students learned how to graph a linear inequality in two variables. This concept is now extended to graph the solution set of a system of inequalities.

It is helpful to graph a system of inequalities by using either chalk of different colors or shading in different directions to distinguish the regions. Students should be careful when determining boundaries to use a dashed line when the boundary is not included. The pair of coordinates at the intersection of two boundary lines is a pair of the solution set only when both boundaries are solid lines, that is, included in the solution of the inequalities. Test points should always be points in the interior of the region and not on a boundary line.

If time permits, you may wish to introduce some basic ideas of linear programming as an application of graphing. This area of mathematics is used to solve problems in science and industry.

In 1–10, select the letter of the correct answer.

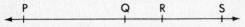

1. If Q is the midpoint of $\overline{PS}$, $PQ = x$, and $QR = y$, then RS equals
   (A) $x - y$ (B) $x + y$
   (C) $2x - y$ (D) $2x + y$

2. If $x + y = 3 + k$ and $2x + 2y = 10$, then k is
   (A) 7   (B) 6   (C) 4   (D) 2

3. If $2x + 3y = k$ and $4x = 7y$, then y equals
   (A) $\frac{k}{10}$ (B) $k - 6\frac{1}{2}$ (C) $\frac{2k}{10}$ (D) $\frac{2k}{13}$

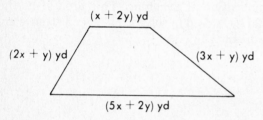

4. The quadrilateral above is to be enclosed in fencing that can be purchased in rolls of $(2x + y)$ yards each. How many rolls should be purchased to build the fence?
   (A) 6   (B) 5   (C) 4   (D) 3

5. If $x + y = 3$ and $x^2 - y^2 = 6$, then the reciprocal of $\dfrac{1}{x - y}$ equals
   (A) $\frac{1}{6}$ (B) $\frac{1}{3}$ (C) $\frac{1}{2}$ (D) 2

6. Which coordinates name a member of the solution set of the system shown below?
   $$x > 3$$
   $$x + y < 2$$
   (A) $(4, -1)$ (B) $(4, -3)$
   (C) $(3, -3)$ (D) $(5, 1)$

7. If $2x + 5y = 5$ and $x - 2y = 7$, then the average of x and y is
   (A) 12   (B) 6   (C) 4   (D) 2

8. If $2x + 3y = 7$ and $x + 5y = -9$, then $2(3x + 8y)$ equals
   (A) 2   (B) -2 (C) 4   (D) -4

9. If $2x + 3y = 3$ and $x + 2y = 1$, then $x + y$ is what percent of $3x + 5y$?
   (A) 25   (B) $33\frac{1}{3}$ (C) 50   (D) 75

10. If $3x + 2y = 7$ and $kx - y = 5$, then x equals
    (A) $\dfrac{12}{3 + 2k}$ (B) $\dfrac{17}{3 + 2k}$
    (C) $\dfrac{12}{3 + k}$ (D) $\dfrac{17}{3 + k}$

Questions 11–17 each consist of two quantities, one in Column A and one in Column B. You are to compare the two quantities and choose:
   A if the quantity in Column A is greater;
   B if the quantity in Column B is greater;
   C if the two quantities are equal;
   D if the relationship cannot be determined from the information given.

Notes

1. In certain questions, information concerning one or both of the quantities to be compared is centered above the two columns.
2. In a given question, a symbol that appears in both columns represents the same thing in Column A as it does in Column B.
3. Letters such as x, n, and k stand for real numbers.

Column A	*Column B*
$2x + y = -3$	
11. $\lvert x \rvert$ when $y = 3$	$\lvert y \rvert$ when $x = 0$
The graph of $2x - 3y = 12$	
12. The measure of the acute angle the above line makes with the x-axis	The measure of the acute angle the above line makes with the y-axis

SAT PREPARATION EXERCISES (Chapter 18 Cont.)

$$x + y = 5$$
$$x - y = 2$$

13. $x^2 + x - y - y^2$ 10

$$2x + 3y + 2k = 30$$
$$x + y + k = 10$$

16. y $10 + k$

$$2x + y = 4$$
$$3x + 2y = 6$$

14. $x + y$ $x - y$

$$2x + y = 6$$
$$x + y = 2$$

17. $x + (6 - 2x)$ $2(2 - y) + y$

$$3x + 2y = 7$$
$$-x - 4y = 2$$

15. $x - y$ 4

SUGGESTED TEST ITEMS (Chapter 18)

1. Solve graphically and check:

$$3x - y = 5$$
$$x - y = 1$$

2. **a.** Graph the following system of inequalities:

$$y \geq 2x - 2$$
$$x + 2y < 4$$

   b. Select, from the solution set drawn in part **a**, the pair of integers having the largest sum.

3. Solve algebraically and check:

   a. $2x - 5y = 16$ **b.** $4x + 3y = 0$
       $7x + 4y = 13$ $y = 2x + 20$

4. **a.** Solve algebraically and check:

$$2x + y = 8$$
$$y = 2x - 2$$

   b. Solve graphically the same system of equations.

5. Write one value of a for which the equations of the following system are inconsistent.

$$2x + y = a$$
$$4x = 7 - 2y$$

6. Write the value of m for which the equations of the following system are dependent.

$$y = mx + 3$$
$$x + 2y = 6$$

7. Last year, Albert planted a rectangular garden with a perimeter of 34 feet. This year, he made his garden half as long and twice as wide. The perimeter of the new garden is 26 feet. Find the dimensions of each garden.

8. At the first meeting of the Chess Club, there were 12 students present. After efforts were made to increase interest in the club, twice as many girls and three times as many boys attended the second meeting as attended the first. If there were 29 students at the second meeting, how many boys and how many girls attended each meeting?

BONUS: Of the spectators at a basketball game, all but 36 were students, all but 70 were parents, and all but 82 were faculty. How many spectators were there at the game? How many of the spectators were parents, how many were faculty, and how many were students?

CHAPTER 19

The Real Numbers

Aims

- To define the set of real numbers.

- To introduce irrational numbers and rational approximations.

- To demonstrate the fundamental operations with square-root radicals.

- To use the irrational number π in computations associated with the circle.

19-1 THE SET OF RATIONAL NUMBERS

In previous chapters, the text has referred to natural numbers, whole numbers, and integers. Nonnegative fractions were said to belong to the set of numbers of arithmetic. Now, the set of rational numbers is introduced, and all previously mentioned sets of numbers can be considered as subsets of this set.

Thus, the set of rational numbers has all the properties of the set of integers, one of its subsets. In addition, the existence of a multiplicative inverse for every nonzero rational number means that the set of rational numbers is closed under division by a nonzero element of the set. Also, the set of rational num-

bers, unlike some of its subsets, is everywhere dense.

After students have had some experience expressing repeating decimals as fractions, you may wish to explore some patterns. For example, when summarizing one-digit repetends, we see:

$$.\overline{1} = \frac{1}{9}$$

$$.\overline{2} = \frac{2}{9}$$

$$.\overline{3} = \frac{3}{9}$$

.

.

.

$$.\overline{a} = \frac{a}{9}$$

Patterns also emerge for two-digit and three-digit repetends:

$$.\overline{ab} = \frac{ab}{99}$$

$$.\overline{abc} = \frac{abc}{999}$$

This pattern extends for n-digit repetends.

Interested students can continue to discover patterns by allowing the repetition to begin after the first decimal place. This is what happens as a one-digit repetend begins its repetition in successive decimal places:

$$.0\overline{a} = \frac{a}{90}$$

$$.00\overline{a} = \frac{a}{900}$$

$$.000\overline{a} = \frac{a}{9,000}$$

$$\vdots$$

This is what happens as a two-digit repetend begins its repetition in successive decimal places:

$$.0\overline{ab} = \frac{ab}{990}$$

$$.00\overline{ab} = \frac{ab}{9,900}$$

$$.000\overline{ab} = \frac{ab}{99,000}$$

$$\vdots$$

This patterning is true for n-digit repetends as they begin their repetitions in successive decimal places.

Computer Activity (19-1) This program can be used to find the decimal representation of a rational number. If the rational number is a repeating decimal, the computer will display a rounded value that is only an approximation. The pattern that repeats, however, may sometimes be evident in the value given by the computer.

```
100  REM    THIS PROGRAM WILL GIVE A
110  REM    DECIMAL APPROXIMATION OF A
120  REM    RATIONAL NUMBER.
130  PRINT
140  PRINT "ENTER THE NUMERATOR OF THE FRACTION."
150  INPUT A
160  PRINT "ENTER THE DENOMINATOR OF THE FRACTION."
170  INPUT B
180  PRINT
190  PRINT "A DECIMAL APPROXIMATION FOR ";A;" / ";B
200  PRINT "IS ";A / B
210  PRINT
220  PRINT "DO YOU WANT TO DO ANOTHER? (Y OR N)"
230  INPUT R$
240  IF R$ = "Y" OR R$ = "YES" THEN 130
250  END
```

19-2 THE SET OF IRRATIONAL NUMBERS

Any number that has an infinite, nonrepeating decimal expansion is called an irrational number. Some examples in which the digits form a nonrepeating decimal can be given, such as .1234567891011 . . . or 122333444455555666666 . . . . However, students should realize that numbers such as π, $\sqrt{2}$, $\sqrt{3}$, etc. are the more frequently encountered irrational numbers. Such numbers satisfy a mathematical description. For example, $\sqrt{2}$ is that number whose square is 2.

You may wish to present the usual indirect proof that $\sqrt{2}$ is irrational, but students will more fully appreciate this proof in Course III, where number systems are reconsidered.

Since π is an irrational number, why is 3.14 sometimes used to represent π? Students should be aware that a rational approximation of an irrational number is often useful.

However, they must recognize the distinction between the irrational number and its rational approximation.

19-3 THE SET OF REAL NUMBERS

The set of irrational numbers together with the set of rational numbers completes the real number line. The number line enables us to order the irrational numbers in the same way that rational numbers are ordered on the number line.

The decimal expansion of real numbers can also be used to order them. Students should expand the bar notation before making comparisons. For example, to compare .382 and $.\overline{38}$, write $.\overline{38}$ as .383838 . . . . Since the first two digits are the same in each number, the digits in the third decimal place tell us that $.382 < .\overline{38}$.

The eleven properties of real numbers under the operations of addition and multiplication are listed and symbolized. Students will study these properties again in Course II as they continue the study of algebraic computation.

Not all properties that are true for the operation of addition are true for subtraction. For example, subtraction is not commutative $(a - b \neq b - a)$ and subtraction is not associative $((a - b) - c \neq a - (b - c))$. However, since subtraction can be rewritten as addition, the commutative and associative properties can be used as shown:

$$a - b = a + (-b) = (-b) + a$$
$$(a - b) - c = (a + (-b)) + (-c)$$
$$= a + ((-b) + (-c))$$

Similarly, not all properties that are true for multiplication are also true for division. For example, division is not commutative $(a \div b \neq b \div a)$ and division is not associative $((a \div b) \div c \neq a \div (b \div c))$. However, since division can be rewritten as multiplication, the commutative and associative properties can be used as shown:

$$a \div b = a \cdot \left(\frac{1}{b}\right) = \left(\frac{1}{b}\right) \cdot a$$
$$(a \div b) \div c = \left(a \cdot \left(\frac{1}{b}\right)\right) \cdot \left(\frac{1}{c}\right) = a \cdot \left(\left(\frac{1}{b}\right) \cdot \left(\frac{1}{c}\right)\right)$$

The operations of subtraction and division do not have identities. It is true that, for all a, $a - 0 = a$; however, $0 - a \neq a$. Therefore, 0 cannot be an identity for subtraction. Similarly, it is true that, for all a, $a \div 1 = a$; however, $1 \div a \neq a$. Therefore, 1 cannot be an identity for division.

19-4 FINDING A RATIONAL ROOT OF A NUMBER

It is important that students understand the symbolism associated with square roots.

1. The principal or positive square root is expressed by using no sign or by using $+$. $(\sqrt{36} = +\sqrt{36} = 6)$

2. The negative square root is expressed by using $-$. $(-\sqrt{36} = -6)$

3. Both square roots are expressed by using both signs, $\pm$. $(\pm\sqrt{36} = \pm 6)$

The roots of an equation of the form $x^2 = a$, where a is positive, are both square roots of a, that is, $\pm\sqrt{a}$. Therefore, the solution set of $x^2 = 36$ is $\{-6, 6\}$ or $\{\pm 6\}$.

Discuss the square root of a negative number. Students should understand that the square root of a negative number does not exist in the set of real numbers.

Students are introduced briefly to other roots of a number in the general form $\sqrt[n]{b}$, where n is the index of the radical and b is the radicand. Be sure that students understand that when no index is written, it is understood to be 2. Compare even and odd roots of negative numbers.

$\sqrt{-4}$ does not exist in the set of real numbers since the product of two equal factors cannot be -4.

$\sqrt[3]{-8} = -2$ since $-2(-2)(-2) = -8$

$\sqrt[4]{-16}$ does not exist in the set of real numbers since the product of four equal factors cannot be -16.

$\sqrt[5]{-32} = -2$ since $-2(-2)(-2)(-2)(-2) = -32$

It is useful for students to memorize the list of perfect squares from $1^2 = 1$ to $25^2 = 625$.

Point out that in Exercise 54, to evaluate $\sqrt{(-9)^2}$, we must carry out the squaring process first to obtain a number that is defined for the set of real numbers, that is, the square root of a positive number. Thus, $\sqrt{(-9)^2} = \sqrt{81} = 9$. Notice that we cannot apply the definition of inverse operations here because the operation of square root is not defined for a negative number in the set of real numbers.

To evaluate $\sqrt{(9)^2}$, we can apply the definition of inverse operations, thus obtaining 9. Of course, we can also square first.

19-5 SQUARE ROOTS THAT ARE IRRATIONAL NUMBERS

In this section, students are introduced to irrational numbers, such as $\sqrt{5}$, that can never be expressed as a terminating or repeating decimal.

Students must realize that rational approximations for irrational numbers are not exact values. Thus, $\sqrt{2} \neq 1.4$ and $\sqrt{2} \neq 1.414$. Rather, we state $\sqrt{2} \approx 1.414$ ($\sqrt{2}$ is *approximately* equal to 1.414). As an additional example, cite the output from a computer or a calculator, where the number is restricted to 8 or 9 digits.

19-6 USING A TABLE TO FIND SQUARES AND SQUARE ROOTS

Remind students that the table of square roots on page 706 lists the square roots of numbers correct to the nearest thousandth. Since many calculators have a square-root key, demonstrate how to find $\sqrt{2}$ on a calculator and note the display. Suppose the calculator displays 1.414213562 as the square root of 2. In what cases would the value 1.414213562 be used for calculation rather than the value 1.414 that is listed in the table? A discussion about precision and realistic application of radical numbers is suitable at this point.

Point out that in Exercises 22–25, to evaluate $\sqrt{a^2 + b^2}$, the order of operations is important. Let students convince themselves that $\sqrt{a^2 + b^2} \neq a + b$.

Computer Activity (19-6) This program could replace the table as a means of finding the square root of a number.

```
100   REM    THIS PROGRAM USES A FUNCTION
110   REM    THAT IS PART OF THE ROM OF THE
120   REM    COMPUTER TO FIND THE SQUARE
130   REM    ROOT OF A POSITIVE NUMBER.
140   PRINT
150   PRINT "ENTER A POSITIVE NUMBER."
160   INPUT A
170   IF A <= 0 THEN 140
180   PRINT "THE SQUARE ROOT OF ";A;" IS "; SQR (A)
190   PRINT
200   PRINT "DO YOU WANT TO DO ANOTHER?(Y OR N)"
210   INPUT R$
220   IF R$ = "Y" OR R$ = "YES" THEN 140
230   END
```

19-7 USING DIVISION TO FIND APPROXIMATE SQUARE ROOTS

Students should learn one method for finding a square root: either the "divide and average" procedure presented in this section or, for more able students, the square-root algorithm, which is not shown in this text.

Although the use of calculators and computers makes these techniques obsolete, students should make use of these procedures in order to understand the principles behind the computation. The repetitive nature of the divide and average method makes it easy to program on a calculator or computer.

Computer Activity (19-7) This program finds the square root of a number by using the divide and average method.

```
100    REM    THIS PROGRAM USES THE DIVIDE
110    REM    AND AVERAGE METHOD OF FINDING
120    REM    THE SQUARE ROOT OF A POSITIVE
130    REM    NUMBER TO FOUR DECIMAL PLACES.
140    PRINT
150    PRINT "ENTER A POSITIVE NUMBER."
160    INPUT A
170    IF A <= 0 THEN 140
180    LET X1 = A / 2
190    LET X2 = A / X1
200    IF  ABS (X2 - X1) < .00001 THEN 230
210    LET X1 = (X2 + X1) / 2
220    GOTO 190
230    LET R =   INT (X2 * 10000 + .5) / 10000
240    PRINT "THE SQUARE ROOT OF ";A;" IS ";R
250    PRINT
260    PRINT "DO YOU WANT TO DO ANOTHER? (Y OR N)"
270    INPUT R$
280    IF R$ = "Y" OR R$ = "YES" THEN 140
290    END
```

19-8 FINDING THE PRINCIPAL SQUARE ROOT OF A MONOMIAL

Students often write $\sqrt{a^9}$ as a^3. Show that if this calculation is true, then $a^3 \cdot a^3 = a^9$ must also be true. But, since we add exponents when powers of like bases are multiplied, $a^3 \cdot a^3 = a^6$, not a^9. Similarly, ask why the square root of any monomial in the form $\sqrt{a^n}$, where n is a positive even integer, is computed as $\left| a^{\frac{n}{2}} \right|$. In the exercises on page 657, all the radicands are perfect squares.

19-9 SIMPLIFYING A SQUARE-ROOT RADICAL

Often, when simplifying a radical, students do not find the largest perfect square factor. Therefore, the radical is not expressed in sim- plest form. If this is the case, remind students to make sure that the remaining radicand has no perfect square factor other than 1. The process may have to be repeated, especially when the largest perfect square factor is not easily recognizable (example: $\sqrt{180}$). Note that this process is similar to reducing fractions to lowest terms.

We now have a method of simplifying a square-root radical in the form $\sqrt{a^n}$, where n is a positive odd integer (example: $\sqrt{a^5} = \sqrt{a^4}\sqrt{a} = a^2\sqrt{a}$).

Remind students with numerical examples that the square root of the sum or difference of nonnegative numbers is not equal to the respective sum or difference of the square roots of the numbers.

The text also shows how to approximate square roots of large numbers.

19-10 ADDING AND SUBTRACTING RADICALS

Compare the addition and subtraction of radicals to the same operation involving fractions or monomials.

Like Fractions
$$\frac{8}{9} + \frac{7}{9} = (8 + 7)\frac{1}{9} = \frac{15}{9}$$

Like Monomials
$$8x + 7x = (8 + 7)x = 15x$$

Like Radicals
$$8\sqrt{2} + 7\sqrt{2} = (8 + 7)\sqrt{2} = 15\sqrt{2}$$

Unlike fractions can always be changed to like fractions and combined.

$$\frac{1}{10} + \frac{1}{3} = \frac{3}{30} + \frac{10}{30} = \frac{13}{30}$$

Unlike monomials cannot be changed to like monomials unless some special relationship among the variables is present. For example, if we know that $y = 5x$, then $2x + 3y$ can be expressed as a monomial, $17x$. Otherwise, the binomial $2x + 3y$ is in simplest form.

Unlike radicals may or may not be able to be combined.

$$2\sqrt{2} + 3\sqrt{3} \text{ is in simplest form.}$$
$$\sqrt{50} + \sqrt{8} = 5\sqrt{2} + 2\sqrt{2} = 7\sqrt{2}$$

19-11 MULTIPLYING SQUARE-ROOT RADICALS

Just as $(5x)(3y) = (5 \cdot 3)(xy) = 15xy$, so also $(5\sqrt{2})(3\sqrt{3}) = (5 \cdot 3)(\sqrt{2 \cdot 3}) = 15\sqrt{6}$. Students should recognize that like and unlike square-root radicals can be multiplied.

Ask what happens when any square-root radical is multiplied by itself. For example:

Multiply: 1. $\sqrt{7} \cdot \sqrt{7} = \sqrt{49} = 7$
2. $\sqrt{24} \cdot \sqrt{24} = \sqrt{576} = 24$

As students realize that $(\sqrt{a})^2 = a$ when $a \geq 0$, they will discover that it is not necessary to multiply the radicands to find the product.

19-12 DIVIDING SQUARE-ROOT RADICALS

Be sure students apply the following property of square-root radicals correctly:

$$\sqrt{\frac{a}{b}} = \frac{\sqrt{a}}{\sqrt{b}} \quad \text{and} \quad \frac{\sqrt{a}}{\sqrt{b}} = \sqrt{\frac{a}{b}}$$

Some students will try to divide and simplify in cases when the property does not apply. For example: $\frac{\sqrt{12}}{2} \neq \sqrt{6}$. If this error occurs, ask students to check by multiplying. Does $2\sqrt{6} = \sqrt{12}$? Since $\sqrt{24} = \sqrt{4} \cdot \sqrt{6} = 2\sqrt{6}$, and $\sqrt{24} \neq \sqrt{12}$, we know that $2\sqrt{6} \neq \sqrt{12}$. How can we simplify $\frac{\sqrt{12}}{2}$? The correct procedure, namely $\frac{\sqrt{12}}{2} = \frac{\sqrt{4} \cdot \sqrt{3}}{2} = \frac{2\sqrt{3}}{2} = \sqrt{3}$, can lead into a discussion of the cancellation laws.

The process of rationalizing the denominator is formalized in Course III.

19-13 THE GEOMETRY OF THE CIRCLE

In this section, students are shown the relationships that exist among radii, diameters, and chords of a circle. Ask why a radius is not a chord. How may the fact that a diameter is the longest chord of a circle relate to a popular expression such as "viewpoints that are *diametrically* opposed"?

Note that π (the ratio of the circumference to the length of the diameter, or $\frac{C}{d} = \pi$) is defined prior to the circumference of the circle ($C = \pi d$ or $C = 2\pi r$).

Answers should be left in terms of π unless rational approximations are specifically called for in a problem. If a specific approximate value for π is not stated, the students may choose among $\frac{22}{7}$, 3.14, or 3.1416.

19-14 AREA AND VOLUME RELATED TO THE CIRCLE

Emphasize that it is the circle and all points in the interior of the circle that comprise the area of a circle. The area of a circle, πr^2, is a measure of square units.

The volumes of solid figures related to the circle are discussed. The formulas for the volume of a right circular cylinder, a cone, and a sphere all include π.

Problems concerning related changes are provided in the exercises.

Computer Activity (19-14) The following program finds rational approximations of the area and circumference of circles. Note that the RND (1) function may have to be adjusted to the specific computer being used.

```
100    REM   THIS PROGRAM PROVIDES
110    REM   PRACTICE IN FINDING RATIONAL
120    REM   APPROXIMATIONS OF AREA
130    REM   AND CIRCUMFERENCE OF CIRCLES.
140    PRINT "DO YOU WISH TO FIND THE AREA (A) OR"
150    PRINT "THE CIRCUMFERENCE (C) OF A CIRCLE?"
160    PRINT "TYPE A OR C"
170    INPUT R$
180    IF R$ = "A" OR R$ = "AREA" THEN 210
190    IF R$ = "C" OR R$ = "CIRCUMFERENCE" THEN 210
200    GOTO 160
210    LET N =  INT ( RND (1) * 100) + 1
220    LET P =  INT ( RND (1) * 2)
230    IF P = 0 THEN 340
240    PRINT "THE RADIUS OF THE CIRCLE = ";N
250    IF R$ = "A" OR R$ = "AREA" THEN K = 3.14 * N * N
260    IF R$ = "C" OR R$ = "CIRCUMFERENCE" THEN K = 6.28 * N
270    PRINT "LET PI =3.14"
280    PRINT "ON A SEPARATE PIECE OF PAPER, FIND ";R$
290    PRINT "TO CHECK YOUR ANSWER, TYPE S."
300    INPUT S$
310    PRINT
320    PRINT R$;"=";K
330    GOTO 380
340    PRINT "THE DIAMETER OF THE CIRCLE = ";N
350    IF R$ = "A" OR R$ = "AREA" THEN K = 3.14 * N * N / 4
360    IF R$ = "C" OR R$ = "CIRCUMFERENCE" THEN K = 3.14 * N
370    GOTO 270
380    PRINT
390    PRINT "DO YOU WISH TO TRY ANOTHER?(Y OR N)"
400    INPUT B$
410    IF B$ = "Y" OR B$ = "YES" THEN 140
420    END
```

SAT PREPARATION EXERCISES (Chapter 19)

Questions 1–12 each consist of two quantities, one in Column A and one in Column B. You are to compare the two quantities and choose:

A if the quantity in Column A is greater;
B if the quantity in Column B is greater;
C if the two quantities are equal;
D if the relationship cannot be determined from the information given.

Notes

1. In certain questions, information concerning one or both of the quantities to be compared is centered above the two columns.
2. In a given question, a symbol that appears in both columns represents the same thing in Column A as it does in Column B.
3. Letters such as x, n, and k stand for real numbers.

Column A	Column B
1. $\dfrac{1}{4} + \dfrac{1}{9}$	$\sqrt{\dfrac{1}{4}} + \sqrt{\dfrac{1}{9}}$
2. 2	$\sqrt[3]{9}$
3. $\dfrac{1}{5}$	$\sqrt{\dfrac{1}{24}}$
4. $2\sqrt{3}$	$(\sqrt{3})^2$
5. $\sqrt{\dfrac{16}{25}}$	$\left(\dfrac{16}{25}\right)^2$

6. The area of a square whose side measures $\dfrac{3}{2}\sqrt{2}$ | The area of a square whose side measures $\dfrac{1}{2}\sqrt{18}$

7. $\dfrac{\sqrt{3} + \sqrt{3}}{\sqrt{3}}$	$\dfrac{\sqrt{5} + \sqrt{5}}{\sqrt{5}}$

$$x = \sqrt{5}, \, y = \sqrt{3}$$

8. 3	$(x + y)(x - y)$

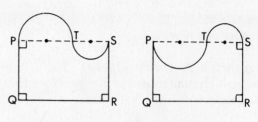

$$PQ = 5, PT = 5, TS = 3$$

9. The perimeter of the solid-bordered figure above | The perimeter of the solid-bordered figure above

10. The diameter of a circle with a circumference of 8π | The diameter of a circle with an area of 17π

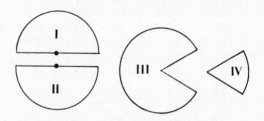

Two circles of equal area are cut to form figures I, II, III, and IV.

11. The sum of the perimeters of figures I and II | The sum of the perimeters of figures III and IV

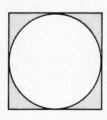 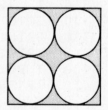

The squares have equal areas.

12. The area shaded above | The area shaded above

In 13–22, select the letter of the correct answer.

13. The area of a rectangle is 64 and the base is $4\sqrt{2}$. The perimeter must be

(A) $32\sqrt{2}$ (B) $24\sqrt{2}$

(C) $16\sqrt{2}$ (D) $12\sqrt{2}$

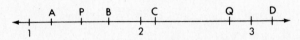

14. If P is located at $\sqrt{2}$ and Q is located at $\sqrt{8}$, then which of the following points is located closest to the average of $\sqrt{2}$ and $\sqrt{8}$?

(A) A (B) B (C) C (D) D

15. $\dfrac{\sqrt{x}}{\sqrt{y}} = k$, where k is a whole number. Which number pair below does *not* satisfy the preceding condition?

(A) $(100, 25)$ (B) $(36, 9)$

(C) $(12, 9)$ (D) $(54, 6)$

16. If $\sqrt{36x^6} = 48$, then $\sqrt{36x^2}$ equals

(A) 6   (B) 12   (C) 16   (D) 24

17. If $x + \sqrt{2} = \sqrt{4}$ and $y + \sqrt{8} = \sqrt{16}$, then the ratio of x to y equals

(A) $\dfrac{\sqrt{2}}{\sqrt{16}}$ (B) $\dfrac{1}{4}$ (C) $\dfrac{1}{\sqrt{2}}$ (D) $\dfrac{1}{2}$

18. If $\sqrt{8}x - \sqrt{3}y = 1$, which of the following does *not* lie on the graph of the line?

(A) $(\sqrt{2}, \sqrt{3})$ (B) $(-\sqrt{8}, -\sqrt{27})$

(C) $(-1, \sqrt{3})$ (D) $(4\sqrt{2}, 5\sqrt{3})$

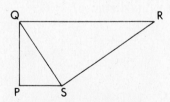

$$\triangle QPS \sim \triangle RSQ$$

19. If $QS = 6$, $SR = 6\sqrt{2}$, and $QR = 12$, then QP equals

(A) 6   (B) 3   (C) $3\sqrt{2}$ (D) $\sqrt{2}$

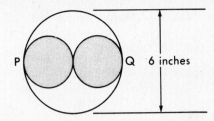

20. The two shaded circles touch each other at the center of the large circle, and touch the large circle at P and Q. What is the ratio of the shaded area to the unshaded area?

(A) $\dfrac{1}{1}$ (B) $\dfrac{1}{2}$ (C) $\dfrac{1}{3}$ (D) $\dfrac{1}{4}$

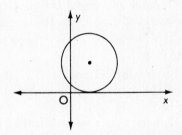

21. If the circumference of the circle above is 16π, then the coordinates of the center could be

(A) $(16, 8)$ (B) $(8, 16)$

(C) $(4, 8)$ (D) $(8, 4)$

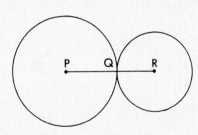

22. Circles P and R intersect in point Q and no other point. If $PR = x$ and the circumference of circle P is 6π, then the circumference of circle R is

(A) $(x - 3)\pi$ (B) $2(x - 3)\pi$

(C) $(x - 6)\pi$ (D) $2(x - 6)\pi$

SUGGESTED TEST ITEMS (Chapter 19)

1. Tell whether the number is rational or irrational.
   a. 7   **b.** $\sqrt{7}$ **c.** π **d.** $\sqrt{169}$ **e.** $.73$ **f.** $.\overline{73}$ **g.** $2 + \sqrt{2}$
   h. $.202002000200002\ldots$

2. Simplify each of the following.
   a. $\sqrt{3} + \sqrt{27}$ **b.** $\sqrt{98} - \sqrt{32}$ **c.** $3\sqrt{2}\,(4\sqrt{3})$
   d. $5\sqrt{5}\,(3\sqrt{5})$ **e.** $\sqrt{\dfrac{64}{4}}$ **f.** $\sqrt{\dfrac{125}{5}}$ **g.** $\dfrac{\sqrt{72}}{3}$

3. Simplify each of the following. Assume that all variables represent positive numbers.
   a. $\sqrt{121\,a^4}$ **b.** $\sqrt{.36x^2}$ **c.** $\left(\sqrt{3y^3}\right)^2$ **d.** $\sqrt{a}\,(3\sqrt{a})$

4. Find the approximate value of $\sqrt{20}$ to the nearest tenth.

5. Solve and check:
   a. $x^2 = 1.44$ **b.** $5x^2 = 245$

6. The radius of a circle is 12 cm. Express the circumference:
   a. in terms of π **b.** to the nearest tenth

7. The diameter of a circle is 6 m. Express the area:
   a. in terms of π **b.** to the nearest tenth

8. Express in terms of π the volume of a right circular cylinder if the radius is 5 and the height is 4.

9. A right circular cylinder and a cone have congruent bases and equal heights. What is the ratio of the volume of the cylinder to the volume of the cone?

In 10–13, select the expression that best completes the statement.

10. A set of numbers that is not closed under addition and multiplication is the set of
    (1) integers   (2) rationals   (3) irrationals   (4) reals

11. A numerical expression that is an irrational number is
    (1) $(\sqrt{2})^2$ (2) $(2 + \sqrt{2})(2 - \sqrt{2})$ (3) $(2 + \sqrt{2})^2$ (4) $\sqrt{2}(\sqrt{8})$

12. The largest number in $\{.\overline{3},\ .31,\ .\overline{31},\ .3\overline{1}\}$ is
    (1) $.\overline{3}$ (2) $.31$ (3) $.\overline{31}$ (4) $.3\overline{1}$

13. If the diameter of a circle is multiplied by 4, then the area is multiplied by
    (1) 2   (2) 4   (3) 8   (4) 16

BONUS: A bicycle wheel with a 26-inch diameter revolves 10 times. How many times must a bicycle wheel with a diameter of 20 inches turn to cover the same distance?

CHAPTER **20**

Quadratic Equations

Aims

- To solve quadratic equations of the form $ax^2 + bx + c = 0$ $(a \neq 0)$ by factoring, and to solve incomplete quadratic equations of the form $ax^2 + c = 0$ $(a \neq 0)$.

- To use the quadratic formula.

- To introduce verbal problems involving quadratic relationships, including the Pythagorean Theorem.

- To graph quadratic equations of the form $y = ax^2 + bx + c$ $(a \neq 0)$.

20-1 THE STANDARD FORM OF A QUADRATIC EQUATION

In Chapter 17, a linear equation is described as a first-degree equation in two variables written in the form $ax + by + c = 0$, where a, b, and c, are signed numbers, with a and b not both zero. In this section, a quadratic equation is described as a second-degree equation in one variable that can be written in the standard form $ax^2 + bx + c = 0$, where a, b, and c are real numbers and $a \neq 0$. Ask why $a \neq 0$. (If $a = 0$, then the equation is no longer of degree two.)

Procedures for solving equations containing fractional coefficients should be reviewed first before transforming an equation such as $\frac{x^2}{2} + 3 = \frac{x}{4}$ into the standard form.

20-2 USING FACTORING TO SOLVE A QUADRATIC EQUATION

The procedure for solving a quadratic equation by factoring rests on the multiplication property of 0 that allows us to apply the principle $ab = 0$ if and only if $a = 0$ or $b = 0$. Once students have been introduced to this application, they sometimes incorrectly try to apply the principle in solving an equation such as $x^2 - 5x = 6$ by factoring to get $x(x - 5) = 6$, and then setting each factor equal to 6. Emphasize that in order to apply the principle, one member of the equation must be 0.

Remind students that, in general, the check for a quadratic equation consists of two parts, a check for each root. When both roots are the same number, that value should be written only once in the solution set. This is true when the left member of $ax^2 + bx + c = 0$ represents a perfect square trinomial. For example, the solution set of $x^2 - 2x + 1 = 0$ is $\{1\}$ since $x^2 - 2x + 1 = (x - 1)^2$.

After students become accustomed to solving quadratic equations by factoring, they sometimes try to carry out this procedure even when there is no equation. For example, later, when an occasion arises simply to factor a trinomial such as $x^2 - 5x + 6$, some students will incorrectly write: $x = 2$ or $x = 3$. (This is similar to situations that occur when students confuse operations with fractions and the procedure to solve an equation containing frac-

187

tions—see Section 14-7 of this manual). When this type of error occurs, ask students to remember that there is a difference between having an equation to solve and having an expression on which to perform operations.

Computer Activity (20-2)   The following program can be used by the students to check their answers to Exercises 1–48 on pages 684 and 685 or other exercises of their own choosing.

```
100   REM     THIS PROGRAM WILL SOLVE A
110   REM     QUADRATIC EQUATION THAT HAS
120   REM     RATIONAL ROOTS.
130   PRINT "IN ORDER TO USE THIS PROGRAM TO FIND"
140   PRINT "THE RATIONAL ROOTS OF A QUADRATIC"
150   PRINT "EQUATION, THE EQUATION MUST BE IN THE"
160   PRINT "FORM AX ^ 2 + BX + C = 0, THAT IS,"
170   PRINT "IN STANDARD FORM."
180   PRINT
190   PRINT "ENTER THE VALUES OF A, B, AND C."
200   INPUT A,B,C
210   LET D = B * B - 4 * A * C
220   IF D < 0 THEN 440
230   LET S =  SQR (D)
240   IF  ABS ( INT (S) - S) > .00001 THEN 470
250   LET N1 =  - 1 * B + S
260   LET N2 =  - 1 * B - S
270   LET D1 = 2 * A
280   IF  ABS ( INT (N1 / D1) - N1 / D1) < .00001 THEN 400
290   LET N = N1
300   GOSUB 530
310   PRINT "ONE ROOT IS ";
320   PRINT  INT (N1 / A + .5);" / "; INT (D1 / A + .5)
330   IF  ABS ( INT (N2 / D1) - N2 / D1) < .00001 THEN 420
340   LET N = N2
350   GOSUB 530
360   PRINT "THE OTHER ROOT IS ";
370   PRINT  INT (N2 / A + .5) /  INT (D1 / A + .5)
380   GOTO 450
390   PRINT
400   PRINT "ONE ROOT IS ";N1 / D1
410   GOTO 330
420   PRINT "THE OTHER ROOT IS ";N2 / D1
430   GOTO 450
440   PRINT "THIS EQUATION HAS NO REAL ROOTS."
450   PRINT
460   GOTO 480
470   PRINT "THIS EQUATION HAS IRRATIONAL ROOTS."
480   PRINT
490   PRINT "DO YOU WANT TO TRY ANOTHER? (Y OR N)"
500   INPUT R$
510   IF R$ = "Y" OR R$ = "YES" THEN 190
520   GOTO 650
530   IF N < D1 THEN 570
540   LET B =  ABS (N)
```

```
550    LET A =  ABS (D1)
560    GOTO 590
570    LET B =  ABS (D1)
580    LET A =  ABS (N)
590    LET R = B -  INT (B / A) * A
600    IF  ABS (R) < .1 THEN 640
610    LET B = A
620    LET A = R
630    GOTO 590
640    RETURN
650    END
```

20-3 SOLVING INCOMPLETE QUADRATIC EQUATIONS

An incomplete quadratic equation (pure quadratic equation) can be written in the form $ax^2 + c = 0$, where $a \neq 0$. Since the first-degree term is not present, this quadratic equation always has an equivalent equation of the form $x^2 = n$ where $n = \frac{-c}{a}$. At this level, n is restricted to a nonnegative real number. Since every positive real number has two real square roots, then $x = \sqrt{n}$ or $x = -\sqrt{n}$. The solution set may contain roots that are rational numbers or irrational numbers.

Ask students to solve $x^2 + 36 = 0$. Why can't we solve this equation at this time? (There is no real number whose square is negative.) Can the solution set of an incomplete quadratic equation have one root that is rational while the other root is irrational? (No; $\sqrt{n}$ and $-\sqrt{n}$ are either both rational, when n is a perfect square, or both irrational, when n is not a perfect square.)

20-4 THE QUADRATIC FORMULA

This section may be considered to be optional. The quadratic formula is studied in Course II. However, teachers may wish to introduce it here if students ask about the solution of an equation in which the polynomial in standard form is not factorable. Students should understand that only equations with rational roots can be solved by factoring in the set of integers but the quadratic formula can be used to solve any quadratic equation.

You may wish to show students the derivation of the quadratic formula. In the two approaches that follow, the second avoids fractions until the last step.

Approach 1

Given the general quadratic equation: $\qquad ax^2 + bx + c = 0\ (a \neq 0)$

1. Divide by a to obtain a leading coefficient of 1.
$$x^2 + \frac{bx}{a} + \frac{c}{a} = 0$$

2. Transform the equation, keeping only variable terms on the left.
$$x^2 + \frac{bx}{a} = -\frac{c}{a}$$

3. Form a perfect square trinomial on the left by adding $\left(\frac{b}{2a}\right)^2$ or $\frac{b^2}{4a^2}$; add the same value on the right.
$$x^2 + \frac{bx}{a} + \left(\frac{b}{2a}\right)^2 = \left(\frac{b}{2a}\right)^2 - \frac{c}{a}$$
$$x^2 + \frac{bx}{a} + \frac{b^2}{4a^2} = \frac{b^2}{4a^2} - \frac{c}{a}$$

4. Factor the left member; simplify the right.
$$\left(x + \frac{b}{2a}\right)^2 = \frac{b^2}{4a^2} - \frac{4ac}{4a^2}$$
$$\left(x + \frac{b}{2a}\right)^2 = \frac{b^2 - 4ac}{4a^2}$$

189

5. Take the square root of both members.

$$\left(x + \frac{b}{2a}\right) = \pm\sqrt{\frac{b^2 - 4ac}{4a^2}}$$

$$x + \frac{b}{2a} = \frac{\pm\sqrt{b^2 - 4ac}}{2a}$$

6. Add $\frac{-b}{2a}$ to both members.

$$x = \frac{-b}{2a} \pm \frac{\sqrt{b^2 - 4ac}}{2a}$$

7. Combine terms on the right.

$$x = \frac{-b \pm \sqrt{b^2 - 4ac}}{2a}$$

Approach 2

Given the general quadratic equation:

$$ax^2 + bx + c = 0 \ (a \neq 0)$$

1. Multiply by $4a$.

$$4a^2x^2 + 4abx + 4ac = 0$$

2. Transform the equation.

$$4a^2x^2 + 4abx = -4ac$$

3. Form a perfect square. Since $(2ax + b)^2 = 4a^2x^2 + 4abx + b^2$, add b^2 to both members.

$$4a^2x^2 + 4abx + b^2 = b^2 - 4ac$$

4. Factor the left member.

$$(2ax + b)^2 = b^2 - 4ac$$

5. Take the square root of both members.

$$2ax + b = \pm\sqrt{b^2 - 4ac}$$

6. Add $-b$ to both members.

$$2ax = -b \pm \sqrt{b^2 - 4ac}$$

7. Divide both members by $2a$.

$$x = \frac{-b \pm \sqrt{b^2 - 4ac}}{2a}$$

20-5 USING THE THEOREM OF PYTHAGORAS

On page 692, the text shows a numerical geometric interpretation of the algebraic relation $c^2 = a^2 + b^2$ where c represents the measure of the hypotenuse of a right triangle, and a and b represent the measures of the legs.

Similar triangles are used to demonstrate the truth of the Pythagorean Theorem. Although many students may find this demonstration difficult, it provides a review of many of the ideas developed earlier in the course.

Another demonstration of the Theorem of Pythagoras that you may wish to present to the class uses the areas of two congruent squares, as shown at the right.

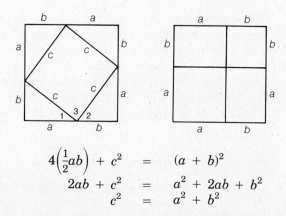

$$4\left(\frac{1}{2}ab\right) + c^2 = (a + b)^2$$
$$2ab + c^2 = a^2 + 2ab + b^2$$
$$c^2 = a^2 + b^2$$

In presenting this demonstration, ask the students how we know that the quadrilateral with four sides of length c inscribed in the figure at the left is a square. (The sum of the measures of $\angle 1$, $\angle 2$, and $\angle 3$ is 180° and the sum of the measures of $\angle 1$ and $\angle 2$ is 90°. Therefore, $\angle 3$ is a right angle.)

Computer Activity (20-5)   The following program can be used to find the measure of the third side of a right triangle when the measures of any two sides are entered. In some cases, results will be rational approximations.

```
100    REM     THIS PROGRAM WILL USE THE
110    REM     PYTHAGOREAN THEOREM TO FIND
120    REM     THE MEASURE OF THE LEG OR OF
130    REM     THE HYPOTENUSE OF A RIGHT TRIANGLE.
140    PRINT
150    PRINT "CHOICE 1:"
160    PRINT "FIND THE MEASURE OF THE HYPOTENUSE"
170    PRINT "OF A RIGHT TRIANGLE WHEN THE"
180    PRINT "MEASURES OF THE LEGS ARE GIVEN."
190    PRINT
200    PRINT "CHOICE 2:"
210    PRINT "FIND THE MEASURE OF ONE LEG OF A"
220    PRINT "RIGHT TRIANGLE WHEN THE MEASURES OF"
230    PRINT "THE HYPOTENUSE AND THE OTHER LEG"
240    PRINT "ARE GIVEN."
250    PRINT
260    PRINT "ENTER YOUR CHOICE: 1 OR 2"
270    INPUT S
280    PRINT
290    IF S = 2 THEN 360
300    PRINT "ENTER THE MEASURES OF THE LEGS OF THE"
310    PRINT "RIGHT TRIANGLE, SEPARATED BY A COMMA."
320    INPUT A,B
330    LET C =  SQR (A ^ 2 + B ^ 2)
340    PRINT "THE MEASURE OF THE HYPOTENUSE IS ";C
350    GOTO 510
360    PRINT "ENTER THE MEASURE OF THE HYPOTENUSE OF"
370    PRINT "THE RIGHT TRIANGLE."
380    INPUT C
390    PRINT
400    PRINT "ENTER THE MEASURE OF THE LEG OF THE"
410    PRINT "RIGHT TRIANGLE."
420    INPUT A
430    IF A < C THEN 480
440    PRINT "THE MEASURE OF THE HYPOTENUSE MUST BE"
450    PRINT "GREATER THAN THE MEASURE OF THE LEG."
460    PRINT "TRY AGAIN."
470    GOTO 360
480    LET B =  SQR (C ^ 2 - A ^ 2)
490    PRINT
500    PRINT "THE MEASURE OF THE OTHER LEG IS ";B
510    PRINT
520    PRINT "DO YOU WANT TO DO ANOTHER?(Y OR N)"
530    INPUT R$
540    IF R$ = "Y" OR R$ = "YES" THEN 140
550    END
```

20-6 USING QUADRATIC EQUATIONS TO SOLVE PROBLEMS

Frequently, verbal problems involving geometric figures or number relationships can be solved by an algebraic strategy that uses a quadratic equation. This important section gives students problem-solving experience as well as practice in finding the roots of quadratic equations. Make sure that students understand that, often, one of the roots of the equation written to solve the problem is not an answer to the problem.

20-7 GRAPHING $y = ax^2 + bx + c$

This section may be considered to be optional. However, it is good for students to see the difference between the graph of a first-degree equation (a straight line) and the graph of a second-degree equation (a curve, in this case, a parabola). Present in class at least one equation where the coefficient of x^2 is negative. Be sure that students understand that in order to evaluate $-x^2$ for some value of x, we must first square the value of x and then take the opposite of that square. Since the square of any real number is nonnegative, its opposite is always nonpositive. That is, the value of $-x^2$ is always negative or zero.

Since graphs of second-degree equations are studied in detail in Course II, it is not necessary to expect competence at this level.

SAT PREPARATION EXERCISES (Chapter 20)

In 1-16, select the letter of the correct answer.

1. What percent of the perimeter of the square is the perimeter of the equilateral triangle?

    (A) 75% (B) 50% (C) $33\frac{1}{3}$% (D) 25%

2. What is the distance from point $(1, -1)$ to point $(6, 11)$?
    (A) 13 (B) 12 (C) 11 (D) 10

3. Each segment in the figure above has a length of 1 cm and each angle measures 90°. How many segments of length $\sqrt{2}$ cm can be drawn, lying in the interior, with both endpoints on the border of the figure?
    (A) 2 (B) 4 (C) 8 (D) 10

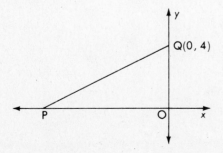

4. If the slope of $\overline{PQ} = \frac{1}{2}$, then $PQ =$

    (A) 8 (B) $4\sqrt{5}$ (C) $3\sqrt{10}$ (D) 9

5. The square of a number increased by 2 more than the number is 60. An equation that could be used to find the number x is
    (A) $x^2 + 2x = 60$
    (B) $(x + 2)^2 + x = 60$
    (C) $x^2 + x + 2 = 60$
    (D) $x^2 + (x + 2)^2 = 60$

6. If $\frac{x^2}{6} = \frac{3}{2}$, what is the sum of the two roots of the equation?
    (A) 0 (B) 3 (C) 6 (D) 9

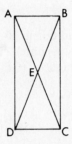

7. $ABCD$ is a rectangle. Diagonals $\overline{AC}$ and $\overline{BD}$ intersect at E. If $AD = 12$ and $DC = 5$, then ED is
    (A) 5 (B) 6.5 (C) 8.5 (D) 13

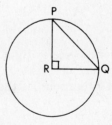

8. If $PQ = 8\sqrt{2}$, what is the area of circle R?
    (A) 16π (B) 32π (C) 64π (D) 128π

9. If the area of $\triangle JKL$ is 2 and KL is 2.5, then JK is
    (A) 1.25 (B) 0.8 (C) 1.6 (D) 0.625

SAT PREPARATION EXERCISES (Chapter 20 Cont.)

In 10 and 11, refer to the following figure in which $\angle PQR$ is a right angle.

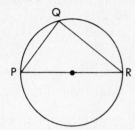

10. If $PQ = 6$ and $QR = 8$, what is the area of the circle?
    (A) 25π (B) 36π (C) 64π (D) 100π

11. If PR is 17 and QR is 15, then PQ is what percent of the perimeter of the triangle?
    (A) 50% (B) 40% (C) 30% (D) 20%

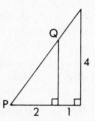

12. The length of $\overline{PQ}$ is

    (A) 5 (B) $\frac{5}{2}$ (C) $\frac{5}{3}$ (D) $\frac{10}{3}$

13. Six congruent isosceles right triangles are arranged in four different ways, shown below. Which formation has the least perimeter?

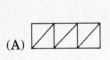

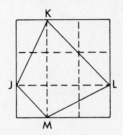

14. The square above is divided by the dashed lines into 9 one-foot squares. What is the perimeter, in feet, of the quadrilateral $JKLM$ inscribed in the square?
    (A) $8\sqrt{2}$ (B) $4\sqrt{5} + 3\sqrt{2}$
    (C) $2\sqrt{2} + 2\sqrt{5}$ (D) $3\sqrt{2} + 2\sqrt{5}$

15. Let $a \mathbf{T} b = \sqrt{a^2 + b^2}$ for all real numbers a and b. Which of the following is *not* equal to $4 \mathbf{T} 5$?
    (A) $(4 \mathbf{T} 4) \mathbf{T} 3$ (B) $2\sqrt{10} \mathbf{T} 1$
    (C) $(6 \mathbf{T} 2) \mathbf{T} 1$ (D) $(3 \mathbf{T} 3) \mathbf{T} 5$

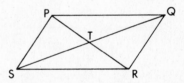

16. In parallelogram $PQRS$, $m\angle SPR = 90$, $PS = 4$, and $ST = 5$. Then, $PQ =$
    (A) $2\sqrt{13}$ (B) 6 (C) 8 (D) $3\sqrt{5}$

SUGGESTED TEST ITEMS (Chapter 20)

In 1–6, solve and check.

1. $x^2 - 7x + 12 = 0$

2. $x^2 - 5x = 6$

3. $a^2 - 25 = 0$

4. $y^2 - 5y = 0$

5. $b(2b + 1) = 36$

6. $\dfrac{x + 1}{16} = \dfrac{2}{x - 3}$

7. The sum of the squares of two consecutive integers is 145. Find the integers. (There are two solutions.)

8. Find the length of the hypotenuse of a right triangle if the lengths of the legs are 24 inches and 7 inches.

9. Find the length of the longer leg of a right triangle if the length of the hypotenuse is 41 cm and the length of the shorter leg is 9 cm.

10. The dimensions of a rectangle are 5 inches by 4 inches. Find the length of a diagonal:
a. in radical form　**b.** to the nearest tenth

11. The base of a triangle is 4 cm longer than the altitude. The area of the triangle is 30 cm^2. Find the length of the base and of the altitude.

12. A baseball diamond is a square that measures 90 feet between bases. At a point 20 feet from third base on the line between second and third base, the third baseman catches the ball and throws it to first base. How far did he throw the ball?

13. Use the quadratic formula to find the roots of $x^2 - 4x + 1 = 0$.

14. Sketch the graph of $y = x^2 - 2x - 1$ from $x = -2$ to $x = 4$.

BONUS: Vertex O of rectangle $OBCD$ is at the center of circle O and vertex C is on the circle. Point B is on radius $\overline{OA}$, $BD = 13$, and $BA = 7$. Find the area of the rectangle and of the circle.

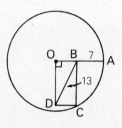

BONUS: Solve graphically and check:

$$y = x^2 - 4x + 1$$
$$y = 2x - 4$$

ANSWERS FOR SAT PREPARATION EXERCISES

Chapter 1

1. B	2. A	3. A	4. B	5. D
6. B	7. A	8. A	9. B	10. C
11. B	12. C	13. B	14. D	15. A
16. C	17. B			

Chapter 2

1. B	2. B	3. B	4. A	5. C
6. E	7. C	8. B	9. B	10. A
11. D	12. B	13. B	14. C	15. B
16. C	17. E	18. B	19. B	20. B

Chapter 3

1. A	2. C	3. C	4. B	5. B
6. C	7. A	8. A	9. D	10. C
11. B	12. B	13. C	14. A	15. D
16. C	17. C	18. D	19. B	20. D

Chapter 4

1. B	2. C	3. B	4. A	5. A
6. D	7. C	8. D	9. A	10. D
11. C	12. C	13. C	14. A	15. B

Chapter 5

1. A	2. C	3. D	4. C	5. C
6. C	7. D	8. A	9. A	10. D
11. C	12. C	13. D		

Chapter 6

1. A	2. B	3. C	4. D	5. C
6. B	7. B	8. D	9. A	10. C
11. B	12. D	13. B		

Chapter 7

1. C	2. A	3. B	4. A	5. C
6. D	7. A	8. B	9. A	10. C
11. B	12. A	13. C	14. D	15. C
16. D	17. D	18. C	19. D	20. A
21. C	22. A	23. D	24. C	

Chapter 8

1. A	2. D	3. C	4. D	5. C
6. B	7. C	8. C	9. A	10. D
11. C	12. C	13. B	14. C	15. B
16. A	17. D	18. B	19. D	

Chapter 9

1. C	2. A	3. B	4. C	5. B
6. D	7. B	8. A	9. A	10. C
11. D	12. B	13. B	14. A	15. D
16. D	17. D			

Chapter 10

1. A	2. C	3. A	4. A	5. C
6. C	7. A	8. C	9. A	10. D
11. B	12. D	13. A	14. D	15. D
16. A	17. A			

Chapter 11

1. C	2. C	3. A	4. B	5. B
6. B	7. A	8. C	9. A	10. C
11. D	12. B	13. B	14. D	15. C
16. D	17. B			

Chapter 12

1. A	2. D	3. B	4. B	5. B
6. A	7. A	8. A	9. C	10. B
11. A	12. C	13. B	14. D	15. D
16. A	17. D	18. B	19. C	20. A
21. B	22. B	23. B	24. B	25. A
26. A				

Chapter 13

1. C	2. D	3. C	4. A	5. B
6. C	7. A	8. C	9. A	10. B
11. A	12. C	13. C	14. A	15. D
16. B	17. D	18. C	19. C	

Chapter 14

1. B	2. A	3. A	4. C	5. A
6. B	7. B	8. C	9. D	10. C
11. D	12. C	13. D	14. B	

Chapter 15

1. B	2. C	3. A	4. D	5. C
6. A	7. B	8. C	9. D	10. D
11. D	12. A	13. B	14. C	15. C
16. B	17. C	18. A	19. D	20. D

Chapter 16

1. C	2. C	3. B	4. D	5. C
6. B	7. A	8. B	9. C	10. B
11. A	12. A	13. B	14. D	15. C
16. B				

Chapter 17

1. A	2. C	3. A	4. C	5. C
6. B	7. C	8. B	9. A	10. B
11. A	12. C	13. C	14. D	15. D
16. D	17. C			

Chapter 18

1. A	2. D	3. D	4. A	5. D
6. B	7. D	8. D	9. C	10. B
11. C	12. B	13. A	14. C	15. A
16. D	17. B			

Chapter 19

1. B	2. B	3. B	4. A	5. A
6. C	7. C	8. A	9. C	10. B
11. C	12. C	13. B	14. C	15. C
16. B	17. D	18. C	19. C	20. A
21. C	22. B			

Chapter 20

1. A	2. A	3. D	4. B	5. C
6. A	7. B	8. C	9. C	10. A
11. D	12. D	13. B	14. D	15. D
16. A				

ANSWERS FOR SUGGESTED TEST ITEMS

Chapter 1

1. (4) 2. (2) 3. 16
4. a. $\frac{1}{2}$ avg $\frac{1}{6}$ b. .5 c. 2% d. 8%
5. a. 6 b. 4 c. 1 d. .36
6. a. true, distributive property
   b. true, commutative property of addition
   c. true, addition property of 0
   d. true, associative property of multiplication
   e. false
7. a. > b. < c. >
8. a. 5.5 b. 9 c. 3
9. a. $\overrightarrow{BA}, \overrightarrow{BD}, \overrightarrow{BC}$ b. $\angle ABC$ c. 108
10. a. {1, 2, 3, . . ., 10, 12} b. {3, 6, 9}
    c. {11, 12, 13, . . ., 20} d. U e. $\varnothing$

Bonus I: The commission
Bonus II: $(3 + 3 \div 3 - 3) \times 3 = 3$

Chapter 2

1. Sylvia, $15; Sara, $9
2. 10 kisses, or 5 kisses and 2 peppermints, or 4 peppermints
3. Monday, 3; Tuesday, 6; Wednesday, 12; Thursday, 24; Friday, 48
4. Ann is Mrs. Carroll's daughter, and she works for Mrs. Adams; Beth is Mrs. Burke's daughter, and she works for Mrs. Carroll; Chris is Mrs. Adams' daughter, and she works for Mrs. Burke.
5. 29 6. 227 7. 59 oz. 8. 10
9. The cashier made a mistake.

Chapter 3

1. a. $n + 12$ b. $n - 7$ c. $2n + 4$
   d. $n - 6$ e. $\frac{n + 4}{3}$
2. a. $x + 5$ b. $10c$ c. $60h + m$ d. $25q + 10d$
   e. $35 + .15 (m - 100)$
3. 1, 17, a, b, $17a$, $17b$, ab, $17ab$
4. base is x, exponent is 7
5. a. $3a^2$ b. $5x^3y^5$ c. $(5a)^3$
6. a. 1 b. 1 c. 64 d. 4 e. 3 f. 37
   g. 16 h. 0
7. 59 8. $c = 4n + p$ 9. 77 cm^2 10. {4, 5}

Chapter 4

1. a. conditional b. identity c. identity
   d. conditional
2. a. 5 b. 6 c. 5.0 d. 14 e. 4 f. 36 g. 7
   h. 1 i. 54 j. $\frac{1}{3}$
3. 4
4. a. $3n - 5 = 28$ b. 11
5. a. $\frac{1}{2}n + 7 = 19$ b. 24
6. a. $3n - 7 = 23$ b. 10
7. a. $2n + 6 = 18$ b. 6
8. $3n + 8 = 35$; $n = 9$

Bonus I: 8 dimes, or 2 quarters and 3 dimes
Bonus II: 23; 9 cm

Chapter 5

1. a. yes b. no c. no d. yes e. no f. no
2. a. true b. false c. true d. open
   e. true f. open
3. a. $\sim r$ b. true
4. a. $\sim p \wedge q$ b. false
5. a. $\sim q \vee r$ b. false
6. a. $\sim p \rightarrow \sim q$ b. true
7. a. $q \rightarrow \sim p$ b. false
8. a. I do not study French. b. true
9. a. I study French and do not study biology.
   b. false
10. a. If biology is a science, then I do not study biology. b. false
11. a. I study biology or biology is not a science.
    b. true
12. a. {1,2,3,4} b. {5,6,7,8,9,10} c. {7,8,9,10}
    d. $\varnothing$ e. {7,8,9,10}
13. a. Today is Monday.
    b. Tomorrow is not Wednesday.
14. a. It does not rain. b. I will walk home.
15. is false 16. is true
17. is true 18. is true
19. is false 20. may be true or false

Bonus: Ben, Andy, Donna, Carlos, and Elsie

Chapter 6

1. *a.* $\sim p \to \sim q$ *b.* true
2. *a.* $\sim(p \wedge q) \to r$ *b.* true
3. *a.* $(r \vee \sim r) \to p$ *b.* true
4. *a.* $p \leftrightarrow r$ *b.* false
5. *a.* If today is not Wednesday, then tomorrow is not Thursday.
   b. If tomorrow is Thursday, then today is Wednesday.
   c. If tomorrow is not Thursday, then today is not Wednesday.
6. *a.* If a carrot is not a vegetable, then vegetables grow on trees.
   b. If vegetables do not grow on trees, then a carrot is a vegetable.
   c. If vegetables grow on trees, then a carrot is not a vegetable.

7. *a.* (1)

p	q	$\sim q$	$p \to \sim q$
T	T	F	F
T	F	T	T
F	T	F	T
F	F	T	T

(2)

p	q	$\sim p$	$\sim q$	$\sim p \vee \sim q$
T	T	F	F	F
T	F	F	T	T
F	T	T	F	T
F	F	T	T	T

(3)

p	q	$\sim q$	$p \wedge \sim q$
T	T	F	F
T	F	T	T
F	T	F	F
F	F	T	F

b. (1) and (2)

8. *a.*

p	q	$\sim p$	$\sim q$	$p \wedge q$	$\sim(p \wedge q)$	$\sim p \vee \sim q$	$\sim(p \wedge q) \leftrightarrow (\sim p \vee \sim q)$
T	T	F	F	T	F	F	T
T	F	F	T	F	T	T	T
F	T	T	F	F	T	T	T
F	F	T	T	F	T	T	T

b. yes; it is true for all possible truth values of p and q.

9. true   10. false   11. cannot be determined   12. true

Bonus: 5; yes

Chapter 7

1. 4
2. 7
3. 6
4. -6
5. 4
6. 30
7. -22
8. -13
9. 0
10. -14.1
11. -4
12. 0
13. -3
14. 17
15. 4
16. 3
17. 6
18. 12
19. $-15\frac{1}{4}$
20. -5.7
21. 15
22. 56
23. -49
24. -42
25. 0
26. -1.6
27. -5
28. 9
29. 4
30. -17
31. 60
32. 0
33. 12
34. 42
35. -18
36. 14
37. 4
38-41 graphs
42. $x = 2$
43. $x = 1$
44. $x = -6$
45. $x = -2$
46. $x = 18$
47. $x = -4$

Bonus: One possibility for each is provided below.

$1 = 7 + 2(-3)$	$16 = 2(11) + 2(-3)$
$2 = 11 + 3(-3)$	$17 = 11 + 2(3)$
$3 = 3$	$18 = 11 + 7$
$4 = 7 + 1(-3)$	$19 = 2(11) + 1(-3)$
$5 = 11 + 2(-3)$	$20 = 11 + 3(3)$
$6 = 2(3)$	$21 = 3(7)$
$7 = 7$	$22 = 2(11)$
$8 = 11 + 1(-3)$	$23 = 11 + 4(3)$
$9 = 3(3)$	$24 = 8(3)$
$10 = 3 + 7$	$25 = 2(11) + 3$
$11 = 11$	$26 = 3(11) + 1(-7)$
$12 = 4(3)$	$27 = 9(3)$
$13 = 7 + 2(3)$	$28 = 4(7)$
$14 = 11 + 3$	$29 = 2(11) + 7$
$15 = 5(3)$	$30 = 10(3)$

Chapter 8

1. $-3a^3$	**2.** $-ab$	**3.** $-30a^2b^2$
4. $-27x^3$	**5.** $-6x^4$	**6.** $-4a^3b^3$
7. $10y$	**8.** $8cd$	**9.** $48r^3s^4$
10. $7a$	**11.** $-4x^3$	**12.** 5
13. $3x^3$	**14.** *a.* $3xy$ *b.* $22xy$	
15. (4)	**16.** (3)	**17.** (1)
18. (4)	**19.** (1)	**20.** 3.2×10^3
21. 9.3×10^7	**22.** 5.4×10^{-2}	**23.** 2×10^{-6}
24. 80,000	**25.** 1,700,000,000	**26.** .073
27. .0000005		

Bonus: Pour from a full 5-k container into the 2-k container twice to fill the 4-k sack. Use what remains for the 1-k sack.

Pour from a full 5-k container into the 2-k container to fill the 2-k sack. Use what remains for the 3-k sack.

Use the 5-k container to fill the 5-k sack.

Chapter 9

1. *a.* $x^3 - 3x^2 + 12x - 2$; 3rd
  b. $y^4 + 5y - 7$; 4th

2. $-7a + 6b$	**3.** $3x + 8$
4. $3c^3 - c^2d + cd^2$	**5.** $2ab + 21a$
6. $-4m$	**7.** $-3x + 22$
8. $2x^2 + 7x - 4$	**9.** $4a^2 - 20a + 25$
10. $14y - x$	**11.** $9r^2 - 25$
12. $11x^2 + x + 3$	

13. *a.* $8x - 6$ *b.* $3x^2 + 5x - 28$ *c.* 2, or any value less than or equal to $\frac{7}{3}$

14. $4a^2 - 12a + 9$ **15.** $4x - 17$

Bonus: 17 and 18.

No. Of 2 consecutive counting numbers, one must be odd and one must be even. An odd number squared is odd and an even number squared is even; thus, the difference between the squares cannot be an even number.

Chapter 10

1. $a = 4$	**2.** $x = 9$	**3.** $y = 5$	**4.** $d = 1$
5. $b = 128$	**6.** $c = 67$	**7.** $x = \frac{1}{2}$	**8.** $x = -4$
9. $r = 6$	**10.** $x = -\frac{1}{2}$	**11.** $s = 0$	**12.** $y = -6$

13. $h = \dfrac{3V}{A}$ **14.** *a.* $C = \frac{5}{9}(F - 32)$ *b.* $C = -10$

15. 7	**16–20.** graphs	**21.** (2)
22. (1)	**23.** $4\frac{1}{2}$	

Bonus: 72

200

Chapter 11

1. *a.* $\overrightarrow{EB}$ *b.* ∠CEA, ∠CEB, ∠DEA, ∠DEB
  c. ∠CBE, ∠CAE, ∠BCE, ∠ACE
  d. ∠CBH, ∠CAG, ∠FCB, ∠FCA *e.* $\overline{EA}$
  f. ∠CAE *g.* B *h.* $\overleftrightarrow{CD}$ *i.* (3)

2. *a.* 95 *b.* 85 *c.* 85 *d.* 95

3. m∠A = 76, m∠B = 56, m∠C = 48

4. *a.* 118 *b.* 118 *c.* 62 *d.* 62

5. 76   **6.** 80, 100   **7.** 20

8. rectangle: 2 lines through the center, 1 vertical, 1 horizontal
  trapezoid: 1 vertical line through the midpoints of the bases
  hexagon: 6 lines; 3 through opposite vertices, 3 through the midpoints of opposite sides

9. H, point and line; E, line; A, line; R, neither; T, line; S, point.

Bonus: Draw the image of the campfire, using the river as a line of reflection. The shortest distance between the hiker and the image is a straight line. The point of intersection of this line with the river determines the shortest path.

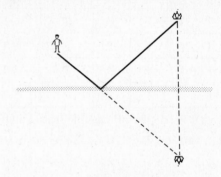

Chapter 12

1. 1:3	**2.** 6:1	**3.** 4:5	**4.** 1 to 400
5. 1.2 boxes per second		**6.** 384 miles	
7. $x = 8$	**8.** $a = 6$	**9.** $y = 18$	**10.** $x = 9$
11. 3	**12.** 40, 40, 100	**13.** 25%	**14.** 21
15. 25	**16.** 14	**17.** 32 cm, 40 cm, 56 cm	

Bonus I: 20; 5

Bonus II:

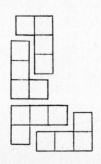

Chapter 13

1. $3^2 \cdot 5 \cdot 11$ 2. $1,2,3,5,6,9,10,15,18,30,45,90$
3. $6ab$
4. $25a^2b^4$
5. $4x^2 - 4x + 1$
6. $2x^2 + 3x - 9$
7. $y^2 - 49$
8. $6a(2a - b)$
9. $(a - 2)(a - 3)$
10. $(s - 5)(s + 5)$
11. $2r^2(4r - 1)$
12. $(x + 10)(x - 2)$
13. $(y + 3)^2$
14. $(2x + 3)(x - 2)$
15. $(4b + 3)(b + 3)$
16. $4(c^2 + 4)$
17. $(3b + 4)(3b - 4)$
18. $5(y - 2)(y + 2)$
19. $5(x - 1)^2$
20. $6x^2 + x - 1$
21. $2s - 3$

Bonus I: Let $2n - 1 =$ the smaller odd integer
and $2n + 1 =$ the larger odd integer.
Product $= (2n - 1)(2n + 1) = 4n^2 - 1$
Square of their average $= (2n)^2 = 4n^2$

Also true for even integers.

Let $2n =$ the smaller even integer
and $2n + 2 =$ the larger even integer.
Product $= 2n(2n + 2) = 4n^2 + 4n$
Square of their average $= (2n + 1)^2$
$\qquad\qquad\qquad\qquad = 4n^2 + 4n + 1$

Bonus II: $x^2 - 1 = (x - 1)(x + 1)$

Chapter 14

1. -4
2. $\dfrac{x}{3y}$
3. $\dfrac{a + b}{2}$
4. $\dfrac{3c - 1}{3c^2}$
5. $\dfrac{2x + 1}{10x}$
6. $\dfrac{2x}{5}$
7. $\dfrac{y - 2}{y}$
8. $9x$
9. $\dfrac{3}{5}$
10. $\dfrac{15x^2 + 1}{5x}$
11. $\dfrac{11x - 16}{15}$
12. $\dfrac{4}{9}$
13. $-\dfrac{3a + 21}{10a}$
14. $\dfrac{2}{7}$
15. $\dfrac{23b}{10}$
16. $x = 4$
17. $a = 5$
18. $y = 54$
19. $x = 19$
20. $b = 4$
21. $d = 25$
22. 18
23. 10

Bonus: $\dfrac{31}{60}$; 60

Chapter 15

1. a. 24 b. $5,040$ c. 120 d. 60 e. 9 2. 70%
3. a. $\dfrac{12}{20} \cdot \dfrac{11}{19} = \dfrac{132}{380}$ or $\dfrac{33}{95}$ b. $\dfrac{8}{20} \cdot \dfrac{7}{19} = \dfrac{56}{380}$ or $\dfrac{14}{95}$
   c. $\dfrac{12}{20} \cdot \dfrac{8}{19} + \dfrac{8}{20} \cdot \dfrac{12}{19} = \dfrac{192}{380}$ or $\dfrac{48}{95}$
4. $6!$ or 720 5. $12P3$ or $1,320$ 6. 60

7. $\dfrac{4}{52} \cdot \dfrac{3}{51} = \dfrac{12}{2,652}$ or $\dfrac{1}{221}$
8. $8!$ or $40,320$ 9. $.9$ 10. $\dfrac{4}{36}$ or $\dfrac{1}{9}$

11. a.
HHHH	HTHH	THHH	TTHH
HHHT	HTHT	THHT	TTHT
HHTH	HTTH	THTH	TTTH
HHTT	HTTT	THTT	TTTT

   b. 16 c. $\dfrac{6}{16}$ or $\dfrac{3}{8}$ d. $\dfrac{15}{16}$
12. Let $x =$ the number of red marbles
$\dfrac{x - 10}{4x - 10} = \dfrac{1}{6}$
25 red, 75 green
13. a.
A,B	B,A	C,A	D,A	E,A	F,A
A,C	B,C	C,B	D,B	E,B	F,B
A,D	B,D	C,D	D,C	E,C	F,C
A,E	B,E	C,E	D,E	E,D	F,D
A,F	B,F	C,F	D,F	E,F	F,E

   b. $\dfrac{2}{30}$ or $\dfrac{1}{15}$ c. $\dfrac{16}{30}$ or $\dfrac{8}{15}$ d. $\dfrac{20}{30}$ or $\dfrac{2}{3}$
14. a. $5!$ or 120 b. $2 \cdot 4 \cdot 3 \cdot 2 \cdot 1 = 48$
   c. $\dfrac{48}{120}$ or $\dfrac{2}{5}$

Bonus: 10 possible 15's: Total number
in sample space:

6	6	3
6	5	4
6	4	5
6	3	6
5	6	4
5	5	5
5	4	6
4	6	5
4	5	6
3	6	6

$6 \cdot 6 \cdot 6 = 216$

$$P(E) = \frac{n(E)}{n(S)} = \frac{10}{216} = \frac{5}{108}$$

Chapter 16

1. a. 129 b. 128 c. 127 2. $51,53,55,57,59$
3. 83 4. 25 5. 5 6. 18 7. $3a - 2$

8. a.

Interval	Frequency	Cumulative Frequency
0	7	7
1	8	15
2	2	17
3	0	17
4	3	20
5	3	23
6	1	24

b, c. graphs d. 1 e. 0 f. $1\frac{7}{8}$ g. 4
h. $\frac{3}{24}$ or $\frac{1}{8}$ i. 0 j. 1

Bonus: $78,83,85,85,85,87,88,89$

Chapter 17

1. $k = -5$ 2. IV 3. graphs
4. $y = 3x - 1$
5. *a.* 5 *b.* $y = 5x$ *c.* graph *d.* 5
6. *a.* $m = 2; b = 1$ *b.* $m = -1; b = 7$
   c. $m = \frac{1}{2}; b = -3$ *d.* $m = 0, b = 3$
7. $y = 3x + 2$ 8. $x = -2$
9. *a.* $y + 2x \geq 2$ *b.* graph
10. -3
11. *a.* graph *b.* (2,0) *c.* 6 *d.* 4
    e. 12 *f.* $x = 2$
12. The graph is the union of the lines $y = x + 2$
    and $y = -x - 2$

Bonus: (1,6), (9,6), (9,2)

Chapter 18

1. (2,1) 2. *a.* graph *b.* (1,1)
3. *a.* $(3, -2)$ *b.* $(-6,8)$
4. *a.* $(\frac{5}{2},3)$ *b.* graph 5. 3, or any $a \neq \frac{7}{2}$
6. $m = -\frac{1}{2}$
7. last year, 14 ft. by 3 ft.; this year, 7 ft. by 6 ft.
8. first, 7 girls and 5 boys;
   second, 14 girls and 15 boys

Bonus: $p + f = 36$
       $s + f = 70$
       $s + p = 82$
94 spectators; 24 parents, 12 faculty, 58 students

Chapter 19

1. *a.* rational *b.* irrational *c.* irrational
   d. rational *e.* rational *f.* rational
   g. irrational *h.* irrational
2. *a.* $4\sqrt{3}$ *b.* $3\sqrt{2}$ *c.* $12\sqrt{6}$ *d.* 75 *e.* 4 *f.* 5
   g. $2\sqrt{2}$
3. *a.* $11a^2$ *b.* $.6x$ *c.* $3y^3$ *d.* $3a$ 4. 4.5
5. *a.* $x = \pm 1.2$ *b.* $x = \pm 7$
6. *a.* 24π *b.* 75.4
7. *a.* 9π *b.* 28.3 8. 100π 9. 3:1
10. (3) 11. (3) 12. (1) 13. (4)

Bonus: 13

Chapter 20

1. $x = 3$ or $x = 4$ 2. $x = -1$ or $x = 6$
3. $a = 5$ or $a = -5$ 4. $y = 0$ or $y = 5$
5. $b = -\frac{9}{2}$ or $b = 4$ 6. $x = -5$ or $x = 7$
7. -9 and -8; 8 and 9 8. 25 9. 40
10. *a.* $\sqrt{41}$ *b.* 6.4 11. $b = 10, h = 6$
12. $10\sqrt{130}$ ft. or 114.0 ft.
13. $2 \pm \sqrt{3}$ 14. graph

Bonus I: rectangle, $6\sqrt{133}$; circle, 169π
Bonus II: graph; $(1, -2)$, (5,6)

ANSWERS FOR TEXTBOOK EXERCISES

Chapter 1. Numbers, Sets, and Operations

1-1 The Basic Operations: *pages 5–6*

1. 12
2. none
3. 32
4. none
5. 40
6. 0
7. 400
8. 1
9. 6
10. 6
11. 0
12. none
13. 175
14. 74
15. 1,026
16. 54
17. 16
18. 9
19. 24
20. 5
21. 3
22. 12
23. 88
24. 32
25. 29
26. 9
27. 3 − 12
28. 10 × 0
29. 14 ÷ 14
30. 75 × 80
31. 522 ÷ 29
32. 1
33. 0
34. 76
35. 1,000
36. 1,910
37. 0
38. no answer; every counting number is a whole number.
39. no answer; every whole number has a successor which is larger; there is no largest whole number.
40. 0
41. 9
42. 1. e 2. b 3. c 4. g 5. i 6. a 7. f 8. h 9. d

49. $\frac{19}{4}$ or $4\frac{3}{4}$
50. 4.75
51. $\frac{9}{10}$ or .9
52. $\frac{4}{9}$
53. .35 or $\frac{7}{20}$
54. 2.05 or $\frac{41}{20}$ or $2\frac{1}{20}$
55. 3
56. 5
57. 1
58. 5.5 or $5\frac{1}{2}$
59. 82.5 or $82\frac{1}{2}$
60. 3.5
61. $\frac{5}{8}$
62. $\frac{4}{6}$ or $\frac{2}{3}$
63. $\frac{5}{8}$
64. .35
65. 1.35
66. 1.32
67. .05
68. $\frac{3}{4}$%
69. .1
70. 2%
71. .09
72. $1\frac{1}{4}$%
73. 8
74. 11
75. 8
76. 1.2
77. .2
78. .8
79. .4 or .40
80. $\frac{2}{5}$
81. $\frac{1}{5}$
82. $\frac{8}{5}$
83. $\frac{8}{5}$ or 1.6
84. $\frac{5}{8}$
85. Mary Rose; the operation max
86. 2.75 miles; either addition and division, or avg
87. *a.* 2 *b.* 4 *c.* 1
   d. the smallest whole number greater than or equal to $\frac{b}{24}$
88. *a.* 2 *b.* 2 *c.* none
   d. the largest whole number less than or equal to $\frac{c}{19}$

1-2 The Numbers of Arithmetic: *pages 10–12*

Note: In exercises 1 to 5, many other answers are possible.

1. $\frac{4}{1}, \frac{8}{2}, \frac{12}{3}, \ldots$
2. $\frac{0}{1}, \frac{0}{2}, \frac{0}{3}, \ldots$
3. $\frac{1}{2}, \frac{2}{4}, \frac{3}{6}, \ldots$
4. $\frac{2}{6}, \frac{3}{9}, \frac{4}{12}, \ldots$
5. $\frac{5}{4}, \frac{10}{8}, \frac{15}{12}, \ldots$
6. *a.* 1 *b.* 0, 1, $\frac{0}{1}$ *c.* 0, 1, $\frac{0}{1}$ *d.* $\frac{1}{1}$
7. $\frac{10}{5}$ or 2
8. 2.00 or 2
9. $\frac{8}{8}$ or 1
10. $\frac{13}{4}$ or $3\frac{1}{4}$
11. $\frac{7}{7}$ or 1
12. 2.40 or 2.4
13. $\frac{5}{8}$
14. $\frac{27}{6}$ or $\frac{9}{2}$ or $4\frac{1}{2}$
15. 4
16. $\frac{21}{14}$ or $\frac{3}{2}$ or $1\frac{1}{2}$
17. 1
18. 1.6
19. 6.15
20. 5
21. 1.57
22. 48
23. $\frac{11}{10}$ or $1\frac{1}{10}$
24. $\frac{17}{10}$ or $1\frac{7}{10}$
25. $\frac{73}{18}$ or $4\frac{1}{18}$
26. $\frac{13}{8}$ or $1\frac{5}{8}$
27. $\frac{47}{15}$ or $3\frac{2}{15}$
28. $\frac{41}{6}$ or $6\frac{5}{6}$
29. $\frac{33}{10}$ or $3\frac{3}{10}$
30. $\frac{19}{8}$ or $2\frac{3}{8}$
31. $\frac{3}{2}$ or $1\frac{1}{2}$
32. $\frac{4}{5}$
33. 6
34. 16
35. $\frac{2}{3}$
36. $\frac{5}{2}$ or $2\frac{1}{2}$
37. $\frac{1}{3}$
38. 3
39. 4.07
40. 1.99
41. 1.81
42. 2.89
43. .40 or .4
44. .3000 or .3
45. .025
46. .02
47. $1\frac{4}{5}$ or $\frac{9}{5}$
48. 1.8

1-3 Bases, Exponents, and Powers: *page 14*

1. 81
2. 1,000
3. 125
4. 225
5. 100,000
6. 1,024
7. $\frac{1}{9}$
8. $\frac{1}{4}$
9. $\frac{1}{1,000}$
10. $\frac{9}{16}$
11. $\frac{1}{10,000}$
12. $\frac{8}{9}$
13. .64
14. .125
15. .09
16. .0016
17. .00001
18. .0625
19. 1.331
20. 9.61
21. 6.25
22. 6.25 or $6\frac{1}{4}$
23. 9.61 or $9\frac{61}{100}$
24. $\frac{64}{27}$ or $2\frac{10}{27}$
25. *a.* 25, 125, 625   *b.* $(5)^4$
26. *a.* .25, .36, .49   *b.* $(.7)^2$
27. *a.* 1.21, 1.331, 1.4641   *b.* $(1.1)^4$
28. *a.* 1, 1.44, 1.96   *b.* $(1.4)^2$
29. *a.* $\frac{1}{25}, \frac{1}{36}, \frac{1}{49}$ *b.* $(\frac{1}{5})^2$
30. *a.* .001, .04, .3   *b.* $(.3)^1$
31. *a.* .125, .16, .0016   *b.* $(.4)^2$
32. *a.* 3.375, 1.96, 2.0736   *b.* $(1.5)^3$

1-4 Order of Operations:
pages 17–18

1. *a.* the sum of 6 and 1 is to be added to 20; 27
   b. add 6 to 20, then add 1 to that result; 27
2. *a.* the sum of 4 and 3 is to be subtracted from 18; 11
   b. subtract 4 from 18, then add 3 to that result; 17
3. *a.* the difference of 3 and $\frac{1}{2}$ is to be subtracted from 12; $9\frac{1}{2}$
   b. subtract 3 from 12, then subtract $\frac{1}{2}$ from that result; $8\frac{1}{2}$
4. *a.* 15 is to be multiplied by the sum of 2 and 1; 45
   b. multiply 15 by 2, then add 1 to result; 31
5. *a.* the sum of 12 and 8 is to be divided by 4; 5
   b. the quotient of 8 and 4 is to be added to 12; 14
6. *a.* 48 is to be divided by the difference of 8 and 4; 12
   b. 4 is to be subtracted from the quotient of 48 and 8; 2
7. *a.* the square of 5 is to be added to 7; 32
   b. the sum of 7 and 5 is to be squared; 144
8. *a.* the square of 3 is to be multiplied by 4; 36
   b. the product of 4 and 3 is to be squared; 144
9. $(10 + 8) - 5$ 10. $(25 - 15) + 7$
11. $8 \times (6 - 2)$ 12. $(10 \times 5) - 12$
13. $(12 - 2) \times (3 + 4)$ 14. $(16 \times 3) - (20 \div 5)$
15. 14   16. 29   17. 32
18. 41   19. 16   20. 26
21. 18   22. 100   23. 3
24. 16   25. 8   26. 2,700
27. 81   28. 4   29. 169
30. 337   31. 144   32. 388
33. 106   34. 18   35. 24
36. 15   37. 3   38. 34
39. 49   40. 50   41. 2
42. 4   43. 8   44. 2
45. 12   46. 23   47. 43
48. 18   49. 8   50. 60
51. 3,525   52. 100   53. 12
54. 25   55. 8   56. 190
57. 8   58. 108   59. 65
60. *a.* $2(8) + 3(8)$ *b.* 40¢
61. *a.* $30(\frac{3}{4}) + 55(\frac{3}{2})$ *b.* 105 mi
62. *a.* $2(.38) + 3(.69)$ *b.* $2.83
63. *a.* $5(.29) + 3(.75) + 1.75$ *b.* $5.45
64. One answer is shown. Others are possible.
    a. $3 + 2 - 1 = 4$
    b. $1 \times 3 + 1 = 4$
    c. $(1 + 2) \div 3 + 4 = 5$
    d. $(4 + 3 - 2) \times 1 = 5$
    e. $(6 \times 6 - 6) \div 6 = 5$
    f. $6 + 6 \times (6 - 6) = 6$

1-5 Properties of Operations:
pages 23–25

1. 0   2. 1
3. *a.* 9 *b.* 0 *c.* 9 *d.* 0 *e.* $\frac{2}{3}$ *f.* $\frac{2}{3}$
4. 8   5. 5   6. 15
7. 6   8. $\frac{1}{3}$ 9. 4
10. 5   11. 7   12. 50
13. 1   14. 8   15. 6
16. 6   17. $\frac{1}{2}$ 18. 0
19. 1   20. 9   21. yes
22. no; $10(\frac{1}{2} + \frac{1}{5}) = 10 \times \frac{1}{2} + 10 \times \frac{1}{5}$
23. no; $(7 + 9)5 = 7 \times 5 + 9 \times 5$
24. yes
25. no; $2(y + 6) = 2y + 2 \times 6$
26. yes   27. yes
28. no; $4b(c - 2) = 4bc - 4b \times 2$
29. yes   30. yes
31. true; yes   32. false; no   33. false; no
34. true; yes   35. true; yes   36. false; no
37. true; yes   38. false; no   39. false; no
40. true; yes   41. false; no   42. false; no
43. *a.* 0 *b.* 0   44. 1   45. 0
46. $9 \times 7 + 9 \times 3$ 47. $12(\frac{1}{2} + \frac{1}{3})$
48. $4p + 4q$ 49. $2(x - y)$
50. $(8 + 13)t = 21t$ 51. $15m - 7m$
52. (3)   53. (4)
54. *a.* 7 *b.* 9 *c.* different *d.* no
55. *a.* $3 \times (2 + 1) \div 3 = 3$
    b. $4 \times 3 \div (2 + 2) = 3$
    c. $(8 + 8 \div 8 - 8) \times 8 = 8$
    d. $3 \div 3 + 3 \times (3 - 3) = 1$
    e. $3 \div (3 + 3) \times (3 - 3) = 0$
    f. $0 \times (12 \times 3 - 16 \div 8) = 0$

1-6 Comparing Numbers:
pages 27–28

1. true   2. false   3. false
4. true   5. true   6. $25 > 20$
7. $12 + 3 < 20$ 8. $6 - 3 < 5 + 4$
9. $80 \div 4 > 6 + 3$ 10. $9 + 4 < 10 \times 5$
11. $8 + 7 > 20 \div 5$
12. the sum of 9 and 8 is greater than 16
13. the difference of 12 and 2 is less than or equal to the product of 4 and 7
14. the sum of 5 and 24 is not less than the quotient of 90 and 3
15. false   16. false   17. true
18. true   19. true   20. true
21. true   22. false   23. false
24. any number except 6
25. any number greater than 10
26. any number greater than 6
27. any number except 2
28. any number greater than or equal to 1
29. any number less than or equal to 3.3
30. 7   31. 9   32. 0
33. $8 < 14,\ 8 \neq 14,\ 8 \not> 14$
34. $9 > 3,\ 9 \neq 3,\ 9 \not< 3$

35. $15 \not< 15$, $15 = 15$, $15 \not> 15$
36. $.11 < .6$, $.11 \neq .6$, $.11 \not> .6$
37. $.3 > .21$, $.3 \neq .21$, $.3 \not< .21$
38. $.8 > .80$, $.8 = .80$, $.8 \not< .80$
39. $.8 > .08$, $.8 \neq .08$, $.8 \not< .08$
40. $\frac{2}{3} < \frac{3}{4}$, $\frac{2}{3} \neq \frac{3}{4}$, $\frac{2}{3} \not> \frac{3}{4}$
41. $\frac{1}{5} > \frac{1}{8}$, $\frac{1}{5} \neq \frac{1}{8}$, $\frac{1}{5} \not< \frac{1}{8}$
42. *a.* the bookstore ($6.75 vs. $7.50)
    b. the catalog ($15.20 vs. $16.20)
    c. both are the same ($10.80).
43. *a.* the local shop ($3 vs. $3.30)
    b. mail ($4.38 vs. $4.80)
44. *a.* Both are the same ($7.50).
    b. $1.50 per page ($9 vs. $7.50 per hour)

1-7 Number Lines: *pages 30–32*

1. T $\frac{1}{2}$
    E $1\frac{1}{2}$
    A 2
    R $2\frac{1}{2}$
    S 3
2. B $\frac{2}{3}$
    E $1\frac{1}{3}$
    A 2
    T $2\frac{2}{3}$
    S 3
3. R $\frac{1}{4}$
    E $\frac{3}{4}$
    A $1\frac{1}{4}$ or $1\frac{1}{2}$
    D 2
    Y 3
4. Graphs
5. *a.* E *b.* I *c.* H *d.* K *e.* C *f.* F *g.* L
6. *a.* left *b.* $12 < 18$
7. *a.* right *b.* $29 > 23$
8. *a.* right *b.* $\frac{9}{2} > \frac{4}{2}$
9. *a.* right *b.* $\frac{1}{4} > \frac{1}{8}$
10. *a.* left *b.* $3\frac{2}{3} < 5\frac{1}{3}$
11. *a.* right *b.* $3.9 > 1.3$
12. *a.* left *b.* $3.1 < 9.3$
13. *a.* right *b.* $.5 > .05$
14. *a.* left *b.* $11 < 110$
15. *a.* left *b.* $.47 < 4.7$
16. *a.* left *b.* $6.4 < 6.45$
17. *a.* right *b.* $.95 > .905$
18. 4, 16
19. $\frac{1}{4}, \frac{1}{2}$
20. 2.5, 3.2
21. $2\frac{3}{5}, 2.8$
22. 2.3, 9
23. 6, 9, 11
24. $\frac{1}{4}, \frac{2}{3}, \frac{7}{8}$
25. 2.6, 3.2, 4.3
26. $3\frac{1}{4}, 3\frac{1}{3}, 3.75$
27. *a.* $9 < 13 < 17$ *b.* $17 > 13 > 9$
28. *a.* $4\frac{1}{2} < 5\frac{1}{3} < 6\frac{1}{4}$ *b.* $6\frac{1}{4} > 5\frac{1}{3} > 4\frac{1}{2}$
29. *a.* $4.7 < 5.3 < 6.6$ *b.* $6.6 > 5.3 > 4.7$
30. *a.* $4.5 < 4\frac{7}{8} < 5\frac{1}{4}$ *b.* $5\frac{1}{4} > 4\frac{7}{8} > 4.5$
31. *a.* $0 < .1 < .12$ *b.* $.12 > .1 > 0$
32. *a.* $.05 < .5 < .55$ *b.* $.55 > .5 > .05$
33. *a.* $\frac{1}{5} < \frac{1}{4} < \frac{1}{3}$ *b.* $\frac{1}{3} > \frac{1}{4} > \frac{1}{5}$
34. *a.* $.13 < .3 < \frac{1}{3}$ *b.* $\frac{1}{3} > .3 > .13$
35. *a.* $.9 < .909 < .91$ *b.* $.91 > .909 > .9$

1-8 Operations in Geometry: *pages 37–39*

1. *a.* 4 *b.* 6 *c.* 2 *d.* 2 *e.* 9 *f.* 2
2. *a.* M *b.* E *c.* I *d.* E *e.* L *f.* M
3. $\overline{PE}, \overline{MW}, \overline{IO}, \overline{SR}$ **4.** 2
5. 18   **6.** 23
7. *a.* 3 *b.* 3 *c.* 6 *d.* 15 *e.* 15 *f.* 6
8. *a.* 1.5 *b.* 1.5 *c.* 3 *d.* 7.5 *e.* 7.5 *f.* 3
9. 4   **10.** 5   **11.** 16.5

12. 28.5   **13.** 10.4   **14.** 5.4
15. $\frac{3}{6}$ or $\frac{1}{2}$ **16.** $\frac{25}{8}$ or $3\frac{1}{8}$ **17.** 16
18. 20   **19.** 10   **20.** $19\frac{2}{3}$
21. 13 or 11   **22.** 15 or 9   **23.** 22 or 2
24. 24 or 0   **25.** $12\frac{1}{2}$ or $11\frac{1}{2}$ **26.** 13.5 or 10.5
27. 12.8 or 11.2 **28.** $12\frac{2}{3}$ or $11\frac{1}{3}$
29. *a.* $\overrightarrow{BA}, \overrightarrow{BD}, \overrightarrow{BC}$ *b.* $\angle ABC, \angle DBC, \angle ABD$
    c. $\angle ABC$ *d.* $180°$
30. *a.* $20°$ *b.* $90°$ *c.* $70°$ *d.* $95°$ *e.* $180°$ *f.* $160°$
31. $\angle ABQ, \angle QBC$

1-9 Sets: *pages 42–44*

1. Tuesday, Thursday   **2.** 4, 6, 8, 10
3. 1, 4, 9, 16, 25, 36, 49, 64, 81
4. {2, 4, 6, 8, . . .}
5. {11, 12, 13, 14, . . . , 999}
6. finite non-empty set
7. finite non-empty set   **8.** empty set
9. infinite set   **10.** finite non-empty set
11. finite non-empty set **12.** infinite set
13. finite non-empty set **14.** infinite set
15. empty set   **16.** infinite set
17. the set of months whose names begin with J
18. the set of even counting numbers
19. the set of counting numbers less than 1,000 that are evenly divisible by 3
20. $A = B$ **21.** $C \neq D$ **22.** $K \neq L$
23. *a.* one-to-one correspondence *b.* equivalent
24. *a.* not a one-to-one correspondence
    b. not equivalent
25. *a.* one-to-one correspondence *b.* equivalent
26. *a.* no
    b. one of the elements of set B cannot be matched with an element of set A.
27. true; each element in the first set is in the second set.
28. false; $9 \notin \{6, 7, 8\}$
29. true; the empty set $\varnothing$ is a subset of every set.
30. true; each element in the first set is in the second set.
31. true; each element in the first set is in the second set (every set is a subset of itself).
32. true; every square is a rectangle.
33. true; every element in the first set is in the second set.
34. true; 4 is a counting number.
35. false; 4 is not an odd number.
36. true; 5 is not an even number.
37. false; 5 is less than 10.
38. {13}, {14}, {15}
39. {13, 14}, {14, 15}, {13, 15}
40. {13, 14, 15} **41.** { } or $\varnothing$ **42.** {5}, $\varnothing$
43. {3, 7}, {3}, {7}, $\varnothing$
44. {m, l, g}, {m, l}, {m, g}, {l, g}, {m}, {l}, {g}, $\varnothing$
45. {0}, $\varnothing$
46. {true, false}, {true}, {false}, $\varnothing$
47. {1, 2, 3, 4}, {1, 2, 3}, {1, 2, 4}, {1, 3, 4}, {2, 3, 4}, {1, 2}, {1, 3}, {1, 4}, {2, 3}, {2, 4}, {3, 4}, {1}, {2}, {3}, {4}, $\varnothing$
48. {0, 1, 2, 3, 4, 5}   **49.** {2, 4, 6, 8}
50. {5, 6, 7, 8, 9, 10, 11}

1-10 Operations With Sets: *page 46*

1. {3} 2. {1, 3}
3. {1, 2, 3, 4, 5, 6}
4. {1, 2, 3, 4, 6} 5. {3, 4, 6} 6. { } or ∅
7. {1, 3, 4, 5, 6} 8. {3, 4, 5, 6}
9. {1, 2, 3, 4, 5, 6}
10. {2, 3, 4} 11. {1, 3, 4} 12. {1, 3, 4, 5}
13. {1, 2, 5} 14. {5} 15. {1, 3, 4, 5}
16. {3, 4} 17. {1, 2, 3, 4} 18. *B*
19. *B* 20. *D* 21. *A*
22. ∅ 23. *C* 24. *C*
25. *A* 26. *C* 27. *D*
28. *D* 29. *B* 30. *U*
31. *U* 32. *B* 33. *U*
34. *a.* 5 *b.* 3 *c.* 2 *d.* 0

1-11 Review Exercises: *pages 47–48*

1. 9.14 2. 7.86 3. 5.44
4. 30 5. $\frac{5}{6}$ 6. $3\frac{1}{18}$
7. 24 8. 4 9. 19

10. 1.6 11. 18 12. .3
13. $\frac{2}{5}$ 14. $1\frac{1}{3}$ 15. 8
16. 68 17. 10 18. .0256
19. 100 20. 56 21. false
22. true 23. false
24. .14 < 1.4 < 14
25. $\frac{1}{7} < \frac{1}{5} < \frac{1}{3}$ 26. .012 < .102 < .2
27. *a.* 2 *b.* commutative property of addition
28. *a.* 2 *b.* associative property of addition
29. *a.* 1 *b.* multiplication property of one
30. *a.* 0 *b.* multiplication property of zero
31. *a.* 5 *b.* distributive property
32. *a.* 5 *b.* commutative property of multiplication
33. *a.* 3 *b.* 9 *c.* 18 *d.* 6
34. *a.* T *b.* R
35. *a.* 90° *b.* 180° *c.* ∠ACB *d.* 90°
36. 12 or 22 37. {2, 4} 38. {1, 2, 4, 5, 6}
39. {3, 6} 40. {6} 41. ∅
42. {1, 3, 5, 7, 9, 11}
43. g 44. h 45. a
46. e 47. b 48. d
49. f 50. c

Chapter 2. Problem Solving

In this chapter, hints suggest how to apply appropriate strategies. In every case, other approaches are possible and students should be encouraged to propose alternative solutions.

2-1 Guessing and Checking: *pages 51–52*

1. 36 and 24   30 and 30 no
   34 and 26 no
   36 and 24 √

2. Cynthia, 9; Sylvia, 4   6 and 7 no
   5 and 8 no
   4 and 9 √

3. 4 nickels, 20 dimes

   12 nickels + 12 dimes = $1.80 } need more dimes
   6 nickels + 18 dimes = $2.10 }
   4 nickels + 20 dimes = $2.20 √

4. 2 with 3 legs, 16 with 4 legs

Number of Stools		Total Number of Legs
With 3 Legs	With 4 Legs	
8	10	24 + 40 = 64 }need more
4	14	12 + 56 = 68 }4-legged
2	16	6 + 64 = 70 √ }stools

5. 20 gardenia, 30 rose

Number of Corsages		Total Number of Flowers
Gardenia	Rose	
30	20	60 + 60 = 120 }need more }rose }corsages
20	30	40 + 90 = 130 √

6. 25 and 52   43   52
             −34   −25
              9 no 27 √

7. 25   25   15
       − 5   + 5
        20   20 √

8. Shelly, $35; John, $25

Shelly	John	
25	15	25 − 5 = 15 + 5, but 25 + 5 ≠ 2(15 − 5)
30	20	30 − 5 = 20 + 5, but 30 + 5 ≠ 2(20 − 5)
35	25	35 − 5 = 25 + 5, and 35 + 5 = 2(25 − 5) √

2-2 Using a Simpler Related Problem: *pages 53–54*

1. 10 dimes, 40 quarters
   1 dime + 4 quarters = $1.10
   Use 10 times as many, for $11.
2. $6,000   Trip   1
            Repairs   3
            Savings 2(3) 6   10,000 ÷ 10 = 1,000
            Total   10   Use 6 × 1,000

3. 3, 6, 12, 24, and 3 sold
Try small numbers: $1 + 2 + 4 + 8 = 15$
$48 \div 15 = 3$, remainder 3
$\hookrightarrow$ Use 3 as a multiplier:
$1 \times 3, 2 \times 3, 4 \times 3, 8 \times 3$

4. 495 $1 + 2 + 3 + \ldots + 9 = 45$
$$\frac{50(9) = 450}{495}$$

5. 10 cookies, 5 cookies and 3 brownies,
or 6 brownies
Consider 30¢ for cookies @ 3¢ and brownies @ 5¢.
$10(3) = 30$ or $5(3) + 3(5) = 30$ or $6(5) = 30$

6. 10 donuts, 6 donuts and 5 pastries,
or 2 donuts and 10 pastries
Consider 50¢ for donuts @ 5¢ and pastries @ 4¢.
$10(5) = 50$, or $6(5) + 5(4) = 50$,
or $2(5) + 10(4) = 50$

7. 5,285

Number of Families	1 Child	2 Children	0 Children		Total Number of Children
13	$7 \times 1 +$	$3 \times 2 +$	3×0	$=$	13
21	$13 \times 1 +$	$4 \times 2 +$	4×0	$=$	21
30	$20 \times 1 +$	$5 \times 2 +$	5×0	$=$	30

The number of children is the same as the number of families.

2-3 Working Backward: *pages 55–56*

1. 8th $1 + 6 + 5 - 4$
2. 40 $5 + 5 + 10 + 20$
3. 8 $2 + 1 + 1 = 4$ $4 = \frac{1}{2} \times ?$
4. \$175 $40 = \frac{1}{3} \times \underset{120}{?}$ $120 = \frac{4}{5} \times \underset{150}{?}$
$150 + 25 = 175$
5. 18 $3 = \frac{1}{3} \times \underset{9}{?}$ $9 = \frac{1}{2} \times \underset{18}{?}$
6. 6 $19 - (5 + 2) = 12$ $12 \div 2 = 6$
7. 40 $28 + 32 = 60$ had no cat
$100 - 60 = 40$
8. 178 $10 + 12 = 22$ do not study biology
$200 - 22 = 178$

2-4 Discovering Patterns: *page 58*

1. 5,050 $1 + 2 + 3 + \ldots + 100$ $\dfrac{100(101)}{2}$
$100 + 99 + 98 + \ldots + 1$

2. 2,550 $2 + 4 + 6 + \ldots + 100$ $\dfrac{50(102)}{2}$
$100 + 98 + 96 + \ldots + 2$

3. 100 $1 + 3 + 5 + \ldots + 19$ $\dfrac{10(20)}{2}$
$19 + 17 + 15 + \ldots + 1$

4. 90 $1 + 2 + 3 + \ldots + 12$ $\dfrac{12(13)}{2}$
$12 + 11 + 10 + \ldots + 1$
78 on the hour + 12 half-hour strikes

5. 57   1   3   7   13   21   31   43
    +2 +4 +6   +8   +10   +12   +14

6. 1,458   2   6   18   54   162   486
    ×3   ×3   ×3   ×3   ×3   ×3

7. 255   1   3   7   15   31   63   127
    +2   +4   +8   +16   +32   +64   +128

8. 84 $\begin{array}{c} 4(3) = 12 \\ \underline{\times 2} \\ 24 \end{array}$ $\begin{array}{c} 8(2) = 16 \\ \underline{\times 2} \\ 32 \end{array}$ $\begin{array}{c} 1(5) = 5 \\ \underline{\times 2} \\ 10 \end{array}$ $\begin{array}{c} 6(7) = 42 \\ \underline{\times 2} \\ 84 \end{array}$

9. 36 $\begin{array}{c} 2(3) = 6 \\ \hookrightarrow \underline{\times 2} \\ 12 \end{array}$ $\begin{array}{c} 3(5) = 15 \\ \hookrightarrow \underline{\times 3} \\ 45 \end{array}$ $\begin{array}{c} 4(5) = 20 \\ \hookrightarrow \underline{\times 4} \\ 80 \end{array}$ $\begin{array}{c} 3(4) = 12 \\ \hookrightarrow \underline{\times 3} \\ 36 \end{array}$

2-5 Drawing Pictures and Diagrams: *pages 60–61*

1. 8
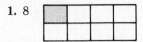

2. 6
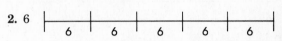

3. 13
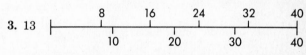

The 8-foot and 10-foot intervals first meet at 40 feet. One post less in 40 feet results in 3 less in 120 feet.
In 120 feet, use 12 posts 10 feet apart, plus one at the start.

4. 21
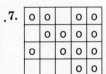
  $\dfrac{60}{3} + 1$

5. 6 dogs, 4 pens | I | I | I | I | II |
| II | II | II |

6. 15 dolls, 7 shelves | II | II | II | II | II | II | II | I |
| III | III | III | III | III | III |

In 7 and 8, many arrangements are possible. Interchanging rows or columns gives other arrangements.

7. | o | o | | o | o |
|---|---|---|---|---|
| | o | o | o | o |
| o | | o | o | o |
| | | | o | o |

8.
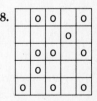

2-6 Making Lists and Charts: *page 63*

1.

Color	White	Blue	Assorted
Label	Assorted	White	Blue

2.

	Mark	Jay	Fred
Sister	Joan	Marion	Sally
Date	Marion	Sally	Joan

3.

Carnations	30	21	12	3
Roses		0	2	4	6

4. 9 ways

Ones	20	15	10	10	5	5	0	0	0
Fives	0	1	2	0	1	3	4	2	0
Tens	0	0	0	1	1	0	0	1	2

5.

Ones	8	7	7	7	6	6	6	5	5	4	4	3
Fives	0	1	0	0	2	0	1	3	2	4	3	5
Tens	0	0	1	0	0	2	1	0	1	0	1	0
Twenties	0	0	0	1	0	0	0	0	0	0	0	0

↑ ↑   ↑ ↑ ↑ ↑ ↑ ↑ ↑ ↑

6. Use the results of Exercise 5, as shown by the arrows.

7. 19   Consider multiples of 5, plus 4.
14 no   19 √

8. 59   Consider odd multiples of 5, plus 4.
19 no   29 no   39 no   49 no   59 √

2-7 Choosing and Combining Strategies: *pages 66–67*

1. 41 red, 40 black   Draw a 3 × 3 diagram.

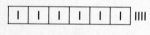

There is one more red square than black. (using a simpler problem, drawing a diagram)

2. 1 kilogram

Bucket	**Kitten**	**Rabbit**	
2	1	3	1 + 3 ≠ 6
1	2	4	2 + 4 = 6 √

(guessing; making a chart)

3. 10 people, 6 benches

(guessing; drawing a diagram)

4. 35 adults, 64 children

Adults	**Children**	**Total for Tickets**
39	60	156 + 150 = 306 no
35	64	140 + 160 = 300 √

(guessing; making a chart)

5. $ 8,000 $\frac{1}{2}$(car + 10,000) = car + 1,000
Try car values.
4,000: $\frac{1}{2}$(14,000) ≠ 5,000
6,000: $\frac{1}{2}$(16,000) ≠ 7,000
8,000: $\frac{1}{2}$(18,000) = 9,000 √
(guessing and checking)

6. 48 $\frac{1}{3} + \frac{1}{2} + \frac{1}{8} = \frac{23}{24}$ $2 = \frac{1}{24} \times ?$
(working backward)

7. Sample solutions are shown. Many are possible.
(drawing a diagram)

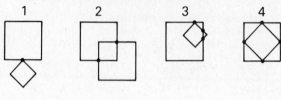

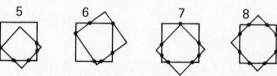

8. *a.* See chart.

Number of Weekdays in the Month	20	21	22	23
Rosa's Monthly Earnings	$640	$672	$704	$736
Who Earns More?	Tony	Tony	Rosa	Rosa

b. Rosa

Yearly Earnings	
Tony	$680 × 12 = $8,160
Rosa	Estimate 260 weekdays × 32 = $8,320

(making charts)

9. 16 gumdrops, 4 chocolate drops

Gumdrops	**Chocolate Drops**	**Total Cost**
12	8	3¢ + 32¢ ≠ 20¢
16	4	4¢ + 16¢ = 20¢ √

(guessing; making a chart)

10. 35   Five of each type of triangle shown
(drawing dragrams)

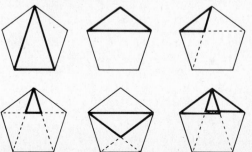

2-8 Review Exercises: *page 67*

1. Edith <u>B</u> <u>E</u> <u>L</u> <u>J</u> <u>P</u>
Place Bernie and Pierre, then Edith and Joel, and finally Lester.

2. 13 Two numbers such that one is twice the other and whose difference is 4 are 8 and 4. These were the ages 5 years ago.

3. 95¢

Number of Charities	25¢ for All but One	20¢ Each	Amount Left	
3	25 25 20	20 20 20	10¢	no
4	25 25 25 20	20 20 20 20	15¢	√

4. Ernestine, 15; Lucy, 5
Guess at Lucy's age now.

Lucy	Ernestine		
2	6	ages now	
7	11	ages in 5 years	$7 \times 2 \neq 11$
4	12	ages now	
9	17	ages in 5 years	$9 \times 2 \neq 17$
5	15	ages now	
10	20	ages in 5 years	$10 \times 2 = 20$ √

5. 220 $400 - 40 = 360$ voted for one or both
$225 + 355 = 580$ votes cast in favor
$580 - 360 = 220$ voted for both

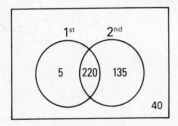

6. 10 $(2 + 4) \times 2 = 12$
$(3 + 5) \times 2 = 16$
$(1 + 2) \times 2 = 6$

7. Two solutions are shown.   Others are possible.
Q = 1; K is even.   6,382   7,435
9,382   9,435
15,764   16,870

8. 20, if all are aligned the same way in the closed carton

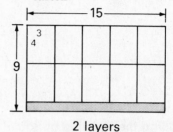

2 layers

22, if placed any way in the closed carton

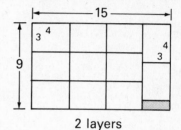

2 layers

9. 39

	Males		Females	
	Boys	Men	Girls	Women
Americans	2	1	3	4
Canadians	6	8	15	

Chapter 3.   Algebraic Expressions and Open Sentences

3-1 Translating Verbal Phrases Into Algebraic Language: *pages 70–71*

1. $y + 8$
2. $8 + y$ or $y + 8$
3. $r - 4$
4. $4 - r$
5. $7x$
6. $7x$ or $x \cdot 7$
7. $\frac{x}{10}$ or $x \div 10$
8. $\frac{10}{x}$ or $10 \div x$
9. $6d$
10. $c - 6$
11. $b + 15$
12. $\frac{1}{10}w$ or $\frac{w}{10}$
13. $b + 8$
14. $x - y$
15. xy
16. $\frac{s}{t}$ or $s \div t$
17. $12 + a$
18. $d - 5$
19. $\frac{8}{y}$ or $8 \div y$
20. $10y$ or $y \cdot 10$

21. $2c(3d)$ or $2c \cdot 3d$
22. $t + w$ or $w + t$
23. $\frac{1}{3}z$ or $\frac{z}{3}$
24. $2(p - q)$
25. $m + 4$
26. $\frac{1}{2}(L + W)$ or $\frac{L + W}{2}$
27. $5x + 2$
28. $10 - 2a$
29. $n + 2$
30. $n + 20$ or $20 + n$
31. $8 + n$ **32.** $n - 6$ **33.** $n - 2$ **34.** $3n$
35. $\frac{3}{4}n$ **36.** $4n + 3$ **37.** $10n - 2$
38. $2n - 3$
39. $4(5 + n)$ or $(n + 5) \cdot 4$
40. $L + W$ **41.** LW **42.** $L - W$
43. $\frac{W}{L}$ or $W \div L$
44. $2L + 2W$
45. $10W - 6L$

3-2 Using Letters to Represent Variables: *pages 72–74*

1. $x + 200$
2. $1,000 - d$
3. $5x$
4. $\frac{1}{2}L$ or $\dfrac{L}{2}$
5. $c + 12$
6. $100 - x$
7. $s - x$
8. $150n$
9. $39x$
10. tg
11. $45 - x$
12. $c - d$
13. $250 - y$
14. $c + 25$
15. $W + 8$
16. $2x + 3$
17. $550h$
18. $5r$
19. *a.* $100m$ *b.* $.01i$ or $\frac{1}{100}i$ *c.* $7w$ *d.* $\frac{1}{7}d$ or $\dfrac{d}{7}$
 e. $24d$ *f.* $\frac{1}{24}h$ or $\dfrac{h}{24}$ *g.* $\frac{1}{12}c$ or $\dfrac{c}{12}$ *h.* $1,000k$
20. $7w + d$
21. $\dfrac{c}{m}$ or $c \div m$
22. $15x + 18y$
23. $.45 + .09(m - 3)$
24. $.50 + .06(c - 8)$
25. $5 + .75(6) + .55(g - 9)$ or $9.50 + .55(g - 9)$

3-3 Understanding the Meaning of Some Vocabulary Used in Algebra: *pages 75–76*

1. x, y, xy
2. $3, a, 3a$
3. $5, n, 5n$
4. $7, m, n, 7m, 7n, mn, 7mn$
5. $13, x, y, 13x, 13y, xy, 13xy$
6. $11, s, t, 11s, 11t, st, 11st$
7. 8
8. $(5 + 2)$ or 7
9. $\frac{1}{2}$
10. 1
11. 1.4
12. 7
13. base m; exponent 2
14. base s; exponent 3
15. base t; exponent 1
16. base 10; exponent 6
17. base $5y$; exponent 4
18. base $(x + y)$; exponent 5
19. m^3
20. b^5
21. $4x^5$
22. πr^2
23. $a^4 b^2$
24. $7r^3 s^2$
25. $9c^3 d$
26. $(6a)^3$
27. $(x + y)^2$
28. $(a - b)^3$
29. $(b - 5)^2$
30. $(m + 2n)^4$
31. $r \cdot r \cdot r \cdot r \cdot r \cdot r$
32. $5 \cdot x \cdot x \cdot x \cdot x$
33. $x \cdot x \cdot x \cdot y \cdot y \cdot y \cdot y \cdot y$
34. $4 \cdot a \cdot a \cdot a \cdot a \cdot b \cdot b$
35. $3 \cdot c \cdot c \cdot d \cdot d \cdot d \cdot e$
36. $(3y)(3y)(3y)(3y)(3y)$

3-4 Evaluating Algebraic Expressions: *pages 77–78*

1. 40
2. 54
3. 2
4. 1.5
5. 11
6. 12
7. 6
8. 0
9. 2
10. 32
11. 60
12. 4
13. 6
14. 17
15. 9
16. 16
17. 30
18. 36
19. 35
20. 78
21. 25
22. 64
23. 16
24. 216
25. 125
26. 81
27. 1
28. 32
29. 108
30. 108
31. 6
32. 4
33. 32
34. 48
35. 192
36. 100
37. 24
38. 27,648
39. 100
40. 36
41. 100
42. 11
43. 91
44. 20
45. 48
46. 5
47. 78
48. 8
49. 33
50. 28
51. 102
52. 26
53. 24
54. 54
55. 4
56. 28
57. 28
58. 9
59. 36
60. 15
61. 192
62. 576
63. 29
64. 49
65. 488
66. 8
67. 172
68. 196
69. 644
70. 1,600
71. 2,500
72. 6,400
73. 21
74. 11
75. *a.* 10 *b.* 25 *c.* 30 *d.* 0 *e.* 100

3-5 Translating Verbal Sentences Into Formulas: *pages 79–81*

1. $l = 10m$
2. $s = c + m$
3. $p = 2l + 2w$
4. $M = \dfrac{a + b + c}{3}$
5. $A = \frac{1}{2}bh$
6. $A = s^2$
7. $V = e^3$
8. $S = 6e^2$
9. $S = 4\pi r^2$
10. $R = \dfrac{D}{T}$
11. $F = \frac{9}{5}C + 32$
12. $C = \frac{5}{9}(F - 32)$
13. $D = dQ + R$
14. $T = .08V$
15. $E = S + .02V$
16. $n = rt$
17. $n = 2rs$ or $n = rs + rs$
18. $c = 200 + t(n - 1)$
19. $c = x + 6y$
20. $c = a + 8b$
21. $D = .12N + .03(N - 25,000)$ or
 $D = 3,000 + .15(N - 25,000)$

3-6 Using Formulas for Perimeter, Area, and Volume

Evaluating Perimeter Formulas: *page 82*

1. *a.* 32 in. *b.* 10.0 m *c.* $18\frac{1}{2}$ ft. or 222 in.
 d. $19\frac{3}{4}$ ft.
2. *a.* 36 cm *b.* 14.4 m *c.* 28 ft.
3. *a.* 16 m *b.* 20.4 m *c.* 12 ft.
4. *a.* 16 cm *b.* 14 m *c.* 35 in.
5. *a.* 58 cm *b.* 28.4 m *c.* $21\frac{1}{2}$ in.
6. *a.* 44 ft. *b.* 11 cm *c.* $\frac{66}{7}$ ft. or $9\frac{3}{7}$ ft.
7. *a.* 62.8 ft. *b.* 81.64 ft. *c.* 35.168 in.

Evaluating Area Formulas: *pages 83–84*

1. *a.* 195 sq. ft. *b.* 25.50 m^2 *c.* 51 sq. ft.
 d. 4,000 cm^2 or .4 m^2
2. *a.* 96 sq. ft. *b.* 22.4 m^2 *c.* 60 sq. in.
 d. .1 m^2 or 1,000 cm^2
3. *a.* 15 m^2 *b.* 31.5 sq. in. *c.* 85 sq. ft.
 d. 165.3 cm^2
4. *a.* 625 sq. in. *b.* 81 cm^2
 c. $\frac{25}{4}$ sq. ft. or $6\frac{1}{4}$ sq. ft. *d.* 37.21 m^2
5. *a.* 30 cm^2 *b.* 39.9 m^2 *c.* 14 sq. in.
 d. 33 sq. in.
6. *a.* 99 sq. ft. *b.* 10 sq. in. *c.* 2.9 m^2

Evaluating Formulas for Volumes of Solids: *pages 85–87*

1. *a.* 140 cu. ft. *b.* 280 cm^3 *c.* 214.2 m^3
   d. 105 cu. in. *e.* 1,620 cu. in. or $\frac{15}{16}$ cu. ft.
2. *a.* 8 cu. in. *b.* 27 m^3 *c.* 512 cm^3
   d. $\frac{1}{27}$ cu. ft. *e.* 3.375 cu. in.
3. *a.* 216 cm^3 *b.* 112 cu. in.
4. *a.* 28 cu. in. *b.* 46.8 cm^3

Finding Perimeters and Areas of Geometric Figures: *pages 87–91*

1. *a.* 22 *b.* 24 | 2. *a.* .16 *b.* .0016
3. *a.* 18 *b.* 12 | 4. *a.* 16 *b.* 12
5. *a.* 90 *b.* 330 | 6. *a.* 16 *b.* 12
7. *a.* 30 *b.* 30 | 8. *a.* 27 *b.* 31.5
9. 200 cm^2 | 10. 280 sq. in.
11. 23.375 cm^2 or $23\frac{3}{8}$ cm^2
12. *a.* 5 cm *b.* 25 cm^2
13. *a.* 25 mm *b.* 625 mm^2
14. *a.* 1 ft. *b.* 1 sq. ft.
15. *a.* .5 in *b.* .25 sq. in.
16. *a.* .7 m *b.* .49 m^2
17. *a.* $x = 5, x + y = 9$ *b.* 45
18. *a.* $2x = 10, y = 4$ *b.* 40
19. *a.* $x + 1 = 6$ *b.* 36
20. *a.* $x = 5, x + y = 9, y = 4$ *b.* 28
21. *a.* $2x = 10, y = 4$ *b.* 20
22. *a.* $3x + 2 = 17, y + 1 = 5$ *b.* 85
23. *a.* $x + 3 = 8, 2x + 1 = 11$ *b.* 44
24. *a.* $y + 1 = 5, y - 1 = 3$ *b.* 15
25. *a.* $3x + 1 = 16, 2x = 10$ *b.* 80
26. *a.* $2x = 10, y + 2 = 6$ *b.* 60
27. *a.* $2x = 10$ *b.* 100
28. *a.* $\frac{y}{2} = 2, x + 7 = 12$ *b.* 24
29. *a.* $x + 3 = 8, y + 3 = 7, x + y = 9$
    b. 64
30. 27 31. 125 32. 1 33. 64
34. $\frac{27}{8}$ or $3\frac{3}{8}$ 35. 144 36. 72
37. 30,000 sq. ft.
38. *a.* 214 sq. ft. *b.* 66 ft. *c.* The amount of carpet would be the same; the amount of stripping would increase to 82 ft. *d.* The amount of carpet would be the same; the amount of stripping would increase to 96 ft.
39. 248 40. 588 41. 648 42. $28\frac{1}{2}$
43. 21 44. 18 feet wide 45. 64 sq. ft.
46. *a.* 12 ft. by 7 ft.; 84 sq. ft.
    b. 10 ft. by 8 ft. Since the area is now 80 sq. ft., there is less room.
    c. 13 ft. by $6\frac{1}{2}$ ft.

3-7 Open Sentences and Solution Sets: *pages 92–93*

1. not open 2. open 3. open
4. not open 5. open 6. open
7. x 8. y 9. r
10. 4 11. 3 12. 0
13. none 14. 0, 1, 2, 3, 4, 5
15. 3, 4, 5 16. none 17. 0, 1, 2, 3
18. 3 19. none 20. 5
21. none 22. {3} 23. {3}
24. $\varnothing$ 25. {2} 26. {10}
27. {5, 6, 7, 8, 9, 10} 28. {9, 10}
29. $\varnothing$ 30. $\{2\frac{1}{2}\}$ 31. $\{3\frac{1}{2}\}$
32. $\{4\frac{1}{2}\}$ 33. $\{4\frac{1}{2}\}$ 34. $\{4\frac{1}{2}\}$
35. $\{2, 2\frac{1}{2}\}$ 36. $\{4\frac{1}{2}\}$ 37. $\varnothing$
38. {2.3} 39. {2.1} 40. $\varnothing$
41. $\varnothing$ 42. {3} 43. {10}
44. {7, 8} 45. {3, 4} 46. {4}
47. {0, 1, 2, 3}

3-8 Review Exercises: *pages 93–94*

1. $\frac{x}{b}$ 2. $r - 4$ 3. $q - d$
4. $2g + 3$ 5. $30 - x$ 6. 26
7. 100 8. 29 9. 21
10. 4 11. 180 12. 380
13. 30 14. 64 15. $g = 1,000\,k$
16. $\frac{p}{3}$ 17. 48 cm^2 18. 29 in.
19. 168 m^2 20. {1, 3} 21. {9}
22. {1, 3, 5, 7, 9} 23. {1, 3, 5} 24. (3)
25. (2) 26. (1) 27. (3)
28. 3 pennies, 9 dimes, and 18 quarters

Chapter 4. Simple Equations and Problems

4-1 Preparing to Solve an Equation: *page 98*

1. yes 2. yes 3. no 4. yes
5. no 6. no 7. no 8. no
9. no 10. {2} 11. {7} 12. {4}
13. $\varnothing$ 14. $\varnothing$ 15. {6} 16. {4}
17. $\varnothing$ 18. $\varnothing$
19. identity 20. conditional 21. identity
22. identity 23. conditional 24. identity
25. reflexive property of equality
26. transitive property of equality
27. symmetric property of equality
28. reflexive property of equality
29. symmetric property of equality
30. transitive property of equality
31. division 32. multiplication
33. subtraction 34. addition
35. multiplication 36. division
37. division 38. subtraction
39. addition 40. subtraction
41. division 42. multiplication

43. subtraction   **44.** addition
45. subtraction   **46.** division
47. multiplication   **48.** subtraction
49. addition   **50.** addition

4-2 Solving Simple Equations by Using Addition or Subtraction Postulates: *pages 101–102*

1. $x = 8$	**2.** $m = 3$	**3.** $x = 38$
4. $y = 141$	**5.** $x = 12$	**6.** $w = 30$
7. $x = 38$	**8.** $b = 162$	**9.** $x = .7$
10. $r = .39$	**11.** $c = 1.2$	**12.** $d = 7.7$
13. $y = 1$	**14.** $t = 5\frac{1}{3}$	**15.** $m = 5$
16. $y = 20\frac{1}{4}$	**17.** $y = 7$	**18.** $t = 0$
19. $y = 11$	**20.** $d = 28$	**21.** $x = 6$
22. $t = 0$	**23.** $e = 18$	**24.** $f = 59$
25. $x = .1$	**26.** $s = .06$	**27.** $m = .6$
28. $k = 12.3$	**29.** $x = \frac{1}{2}$	**30.** $r = \frac{1}{4}$
31. $n = 3\frac{1}{2}$	**32.** $n = 12\frac{3}{5}$	**33.** $a = 13$
34. $a = 12$	**35.** $b = 9$	**36.** $d = 11$
37. $a = 21$	**38.** $r = 14$	**39.** $s = 14$
40. $t = 15$	**41.** $y = 27$	**42.** $m = 0$
43. $n = 10\frac{1}{3}$	**44.** $y = 3\frac{1}{4}$	**45.** $x = 14$
46. $m = 4$	**47.** $b = 11\frac{3}{4}$	**48.** $y = \frac{1}{8}$
49. $c = 7\frac{3}{4}$	**50.** $d = 5\frac{3}{4}$	**51.** $d = 7.3$
52. $m = 2.2$	**53.** $c = 8.8$	**54.** $p = 10.2$
55. $x = 13.5$	**56.** $z = 3.9$	**57.** $x = 46$
58. $y = 12$	**59.** $x = 6\frac{1}{2}$	**60.** $y = 2.1$
61. 14	**62.** 10	**63.** 7
64. 28	**65.** 0	

4-3 Solving Simple Equations by Using Division or Multiplication Postulates: *pages 105–106*

1. $x = 5$	**2.** $c = 9$	**3.** $d = 4$
4. $y = 12$	**5.** $c = 1$	**6.** $s = 0$
7. $p = \frac{9}{5}$	**8.** $y = 4$	**9.** $m = \frac{1}{8}$
10. $b = \frac{1}{6}$	**11.** $x = .2$	**12.** $m = .06$
13. $d = 36$	**14.** $r = 200$	**15.** $x = 27$
16. $a = 6$	**17.** $y = 1$	**18.** $b = 0$
19. $q = 3$	**20.** $y = \frac{15}{2}$ or $y = 7\frac{1}{2}$	
21. $c = 7\frac{1}{3}$ or $c = \frac{22}{3}$		**22.** $w = \frac{1}{2}$
23. $x = 0$	**24.** $a = .3$	**25.** $x = 8$
26. $x = 4$	**27.** $c = 4$	**28.** $x = 1,250$
29. $x = 900$	**30.** $z = 800$	**31.** $y = 200$
32. $c = 2,000$	**33.** $x = 2$	
34. $m = \frac{4}{3}$ or $m = 1\frac{1}{3}$	**35.** $b = 12$	
36. $x = 2$	**37.** $x = \frac{7}{4}$ or $x = 1\frac{3}{4}$	
38. $y = \frac{5}{3}$ or $y = 1\frac{2}{3}$	**39.** $x = 2$	
40. $t = 1.4$	**41.** 8	**42.** 8
43. 120	**44.** 79	**45.** 3

4-4 Writing Verbal Sentences as Equations: *pages 107–109*

1. (2)	**2.** (1)	**3.** (2)
4. (4)	**5.** (2)	**6.** (1)
7. (2)	**8.** (2)	**9.** (4)

10. $8 + n = 15$	**11.** $n - 4 = 24$
12. $12 + n = 26$	**13.** $n - 5 = 25$
14. $3n = 39$	**15.** $\dfrac{n}{4} = 16$
16. $7n = 70$	**17.** $\frac{1}{2}n - 7 = 11$
18. $2n + 7 = 27$	**19.** $2n - 5 = 25$
20. $3n + 7 = 22$	**21.** $5n - 9 = 31$
22. $100 + n = 3n$	**23.** $3n + 12 = 2n + 24$
24. $8n - 20 = 3n + 80$	**25.** $n + 2n = 34$
26. $3n - \frac{1}{2}n = 40$	

4-5 Solving Problems by Using Variables and Equations: *pages 110–111*

1. 56	**2.** 9	**3.** 53
4. 10	**5.** 15	**6.** 18
7. 14	**8.** 85	**9.** 52
10. 14	**11.** 24	**12.** 50
13. 54	**14.** 20	**15.** 400
16. $1.10	**17.** 103 kg	**18.** 12 ft.
19. 52 km/hr.	**20.** $4.50	**21.** 17.5 ft.
22. 1,203	**23.** 24	**24.** $250
25. $27.48	**26.** $15.75	**27.** 8
28. 30 m	**29.** $12	**30.** 78
31. $1,823	**32.** 96	

4-6 Solving Percent Problems: *pages 112–113*

1. 200	**2.** 48	**3.** 45
4. 30	**5.** 10	**6.** $10
7. 40	**8.** $120	**9.** 50
10. $25	**11.** $8	**12.** 700
13. 1,150	**14.** $24,850	**15.** $80
16. $16	**17.** $30	**18.** 7,000

4-7 Solving Equations by Using Several Operations: *pages 115–117*

1. $x = 10$	**2.** $a = 6$	**3.** $x = 4$
4. $y = 7$	**5.** $a = 8$	**6.** $c = 2\frac{5}{8}$
7. $x = \frac{1}{3}$	**8.** $x = 4$	**9.** $b = \frac{1}{2}$
10. $c = \frac{1}{2}$	**11.** $t = \frac{2}{3}$	**12.** $d = \frac{3}{4}$
13. $a = 32$	**14.** $c = 45$	**15.** $d = 48$
16. $x = 27$	**17.** $y = 16$	**18.** $m = 50$
19. $t = 18$	**20.** $t = 2$	**21.** $m = 1.5$
22. $x = 27$	**23.** $a = 240$	**24.** $b = 161$
25. $y = 45$	**26.** $m = 30$	**27.** $d = 2$
28. $a = 1.2$	**29.** $t = 1.4$	**30.** $x = 64$
31. $x = 81$	**32.** $y = 54$	**33.** $t = 50$
34. 5	**35.** 4	**36.** 12
37. 7	**38.** 14	**39.** 12
40. 40	**41.** 90	**42.** 162
43. 20.5	**44.** 12	**45.** 11
46. 9 cm	**47.** $.79	**48.** 12
49. 21 min.	**50.** 11 hr.	

4-8 More Practice in Solving Equations: *page 117*

1. $x = 12$
2. $b = 0$
3. $y = 9\frac{1}{4}$
4. $x = .4$
5. $x = 17$
6. $y = \frac{8}{5}$ or $y = 1\frac{3}{5}$
7. $a = 2$
8. $n = 19.6$
9. $b = 49$
10. $x = 7\frac{4}{5}$
11. $x = 10$
12. $m = 7$
13. $b = 9$
14. $x = 55$
15. $x = 2$
16. $x = 50$
17. $a = 400$
18. $x = 10\frac{3}{8}$
19. $y = 25$
20. $t = 112$
21. $x = 9\frac{1}{2}$
22. $r = \frac{1}{5}$
23. $s = 48$
24. $c = 9$
25. $x = 500$
26. $b = .2$
27. $n = 7$
28. $m = 11$
29. $x = 26$
30. $n = 40$
31. $e = 75$
32. $a = 51$
33. $x = 10\frac{8}{9}$
34. $r = 30$
35. $x = 50$
36. $t = 16$
37. $x = 10$
38. $x = \frac{3}{4}$
39. $c = 45$
40. $m = 5$
41. $y = 36$
42. $c = 2\frac{1}{2}$ or $c = 2.5$

4-9 Review Exercises: *page 118*

1. {3}
2. {5}
3. ∅
4. 30
5. 13
6. 21
7. (3)
8. (2)
9. 23
10. 8
11. 0.5
12. 9.5
13. 32
14. 9
15. 7
16. 8
17. 10
18. 25
19. $\frac{1}{4}$
20. 0
21. a. $2n - 5 = 27$ b. 16
22. a. $\frac{1}{6}n = 1\frac{1}{3}$ b. 8
23. a. $5n + 4 = 40$ b. 7.2
24. a. $.05n = 16$ b. 320
25. $270
26. $250,000

Chapter 5.   Introducing Logic

5-1 Sentences, Statements, and Truth Values: *pages 122–123*

1. yes
2. no
3. no
4. no
5. yes
6. yes
7. no
8. no
9. she
10. we
11. it
12. *y*
13. this
14. it
15. he
16. true
17. a. open b. they
18. a. false
19. a. true
20. a. open b. *x*
21. a. false
22. a. true
23. a. false
24. {Hawaii}
25. {Kansas}
26. {New York, Florida}
27. {California}
28. {New York, Florida, California, Hawaii, Kansas}
29. {12}
30. {22}
31. {18}
32. {20}
33. {2}
34. {1}
35. {1,2}
36. {1,2,3,4}
37. {4}
38. {4}
39. {15}
40. { }
41. {triangle}
42. {square, rectangle, parallelogram, rhombus}
43. {square, rhombus}
44. {square, rectangle}
45. { }
46. {triangle}
47. {trapezoid}
48. {square}

5-2 Negations and Symbols: *pages 127–129*

1. The school does not have a cafeteria.
2. It is not true that Georgia is not a city. (Georgia is a city.)
3. A school bus is not painted yellow.
4. $18 + 20 \div 2 \neq 28$
5. The measure of a right angle is not 90°.
6. $1 + 2 + 3 = 4$ (It is not true that $1 + 2 + 3 \neq 4$.)
7. There are not 100 centimeters in a meter.
8. It is not true that today is not Saturday. (Today is Saturday.)
9. a. *p* b. true
10. a. *q* b. false
11. a. $\sim q$ b. true
12. a. $\sim p$ b. false
13. a. *r* b. open
14. a. $\sim r$ b. open
15. a. $\sim q$ b. true
16. a. $\sim p$ b. false
17. a. $\sim(\sim p)$ b. true
18. a. $\sim(\sim q)$ b. false

19.

p	$\sim p$
T	F
F	T

20.

q	$\sim q$
T	F
F	T

21.

r	$\sim r$
T	F
F	T

22.

k	$\sim k$
T	F
F	T

23.

q	$\sim q$	$\sim(\sim q)$	$\sim(\sim(\sim q))$
T	F	T	F
F	T	F	T

24. a. row 2 b. row 1 c. row 2 d. row 2 e. row 1 f. row 1 g. row 2 h. row 1 i. row 2
25. a. Summer does not follow spring. b. false
26. a. Baseball is not a sport. b. false
27. a. Baseball is not a summer sport. b. false
28. a. He does not like baseball. b. open
29. a. It is not true that baseball is not a sport. b. true
30. a. It is not true that summer does not follow spring. b. true
31. a. It is not true that baseball is not a summer sport. b. true
32. a. It is not true that he does not like baseball. b. open
33. false
34. true
35. *p*
36. statement

5-3 Conjunctions: *pages 137–140*

1. $p \wedge q$
2. $p \wedge r$
3. $\sim p$
4. $\sim p \wedge r$
5. $q \wedge \sim r$
6. $\sim p \wedge \sim q$
7. $\sim r \wedge \sim p$
8. $\sim r \wedge p$
9. $\sim(p \wedge q)$
10. $\sim(q \wedge \sim p)$

11. a. $t \wedge b$ b.

t	b	$t \wedge b$
T	T	T

12. *a.* $t \wedge r$ *b.*

t	*r*	*t* ∧ *r*
T	F	F

13. *a.* $f \wedge b$ *b.*

f	*b*	*f* ∧ *b*
T	T	T

14. *a.* $f \wedge r$ *b.*

f	*r*	*f* ∧ *r*
T	F	F

15. *a.* $\sim b \wedge \sim f$ *b.*

b	*f*	~*b*	~*f*	~*b* ∧ ~*f*
T	T	F	F	F

16. *a.* $\sim r \wedge b$ *b.*

r	*b*	~*r*	~*r* ∧ *b*
F	T	T	T

17. *a.* $\sim t \wedge r$ *b.*

t	*r*	~*t*	~*t* ∧ *r*
T	F	F	F

18. *a.* $\sim(\sim b)$ *b.*

b	~*b*	~(~*b*)
T	F	T

19. *a.* $\sim(b \wedge f)$ *b.*

b	*f*	*b* ∧ *f*	~(*b* ∧ *f*)
T	T	T	F

20. *a.* $\sim(b \wedge r)$ *b.*

b	*r*	*b* ∧ *r*	~(*b* ∧ *r*)
T	F	F	T

21. false   **22.** false   **23.** true   **24.** open
25. true   **26.** open   **27.** true

28.

p	*q*	*p* ∧ *q*
T	T	T
T	F	F
F	T	F
F	F	F

29.

m	*r*	*m* ∧ *r*
T	T	T
T	F	F
F	T	F
F	F	F

30.

f	*g*	*f* ∧ *g*
T	T	T
T	F	F
F	T	F
F	F	F

31.

p	*q*	~*p*	~*q*	~*p* ∧ ~*q*
T	T	F	F	F
T	F	F	T	F
F	T	T	F	F
F	F	T	T	T

32.

p	*q*	*p* ∧ *q*	~(*p* ∧ *q*)
T	T	T	F
T	F	F	T
F	T	F	T
F	F	F	T

33.

p	*q*	~*q*	*p* ∧ ~*q*
T	T	F	F
T	F	T	T
F	T	F	F
F	F	T	F

34.

p	*q*	~*p*	~*p* ∧ *q*
T	T	F	F
T	F	F	F
F	T	T	T
F	F	T	F

35.

p	*q*	~*q*	*q* ∧ ~*q*	~(*q* ∧ ~*q*)
T	T	F	F	T
T	F	T	F	T
F	T	F	F	T
F	F	T	F	T

36.

p	*q*	~*q*	*p* ∧ ~*q*	~(*p* ∧ ~*q*)
T	T	F	F	T
T	F	T	T	F
F	T	F	F	T
F	F	T	F	T

37. *a.* {6, 7}   *b.* {5, 6}   *c.* {3, 4, 5, 6}   *d.* {0, 1}
    e. {0, 1, 2, 3}   *f.* {9, 10, 11, 12, . . .} or {*x*|*x* > 8}
    g. { } or ∅   *h.* {9, 10}
38. *a.* A banjo is a stringed instrument and a guitar is a stringed instrument.
    b. true
39. *a.* A banjo is a stringed instrument and a drum is a stringed instrument.
    b. false
40. *a.* A guitar is a stringed instrument and she plays a guitar.
    b. open
41. *a.* A banjo is a stringed instrument and a drum is not a stringed instrument.
    b. true

42. *a.* A banjo is a stringed instrument and a guitar is not a stringed instrument.
   b. false
43. *a.* A banjo is a stringed instrument and she does not play a guitar.
   b. open
44. *a.* A guitar is stringed instrument and a drum is not a stringed instrument.
   b. true
45. *a.* She does not play a guitar and a drum is a stringed instrument.
   b. false
46. *a.* A drum is not a stringed instrument and a banjo is not a stringed instrument.
   b. false
47. *a.* It is not true that a drum is a stringed instrument and a banjo is a stringed instrument.
   b. true
48. *a.* It is not true that a banjo is a stringed instrument and a guitar is a stringed instrument.
   b. false
49. *a.* It is not true that a guitar is a stringed instrument and she plays a guitar.
   b. open

50. true	**51.** false	**52.** false
53. true, true	**54.** true, false	**55.** false, true
56. true	**57.** true	**58.** true
59. false	**60.** uncertain	**61.** false
62. true	**63.** false	**64.** uncertain

65. *a.* true *b.* true *c.* false
66. *a.* true *b.* true *c.* false

5-4 Disjunctions: *pages 144–147*

1. $s \lor f$	**2.** $s \lor \sim p$	**3.** $s \land p$
4. $p \lor f$	**5.** $\sim f \land p$	**6.** $\sim s \lor f$
7. $s \lor \sim s$	**8.** $(s \land p) \lor f$	**9.** $\sim(s \lor f)$

10. $\sim(\sim s \lor \sim f)$ **11.** *a.* $m \lor k$ *b.* true
12. *a.* $c \lor l$ *b.* true
13. *a.* $c \lor m$ *b.* true
14. *a.* $\sim k \lor \sim c$ *b.* false
15. *a.* $l \lor k$ *b.* true
16. *a.* $l \land c$ *b.* false
17. *a.* $\sim(c \lor m)$ *b.* false
18. *a.* $\sim(\sim k \lor l)$ *b.* true
19. *a.* $(c \land m) \lor l$ *b.* true
20. *a.* $\sim(c \lor l)$ *b.* false

21.

p	q	$p \lor q$
T	T	T
T	F	T
F	T	T
F	F	F

22.

k	t	$k \lor t$
T	T	T
T	F	T
F	T	T
F	F	F

23.

p	r	$p \lor r$
T	T	T
T	F	T
F	T	T
F	F	F

24.

p	q	$p \lor q$	$\sim(p \lor q)$
T	T	T	F
T	F	T	F
F	T	T	F
F	F	F	T

25.

p	q	$\sim p$	$\sim p \lor q$	$\sim(\sim p \lor q)$
T	T	F	T	F
T	F	F	F	T
F	T	T	T	F
F	F	T	T	F

26.

p	q	$\sim p$	$\sim q$	$\sim p \lor \sim q$
T	T	F	F	F
T	F	F	T	T
F	T	T	F	T
F	F	T	T	T

27.

p	q	$\sim q$	$p \lor \sim q$	$q \lor (p \lor \sim q)$
T	T	F	T	T
T	F	T	T	T
F	T	F	F	T
F	F	T	T	T

28.

p	q	$\sim q$	$q \lor \sim q$	$p \lor (q \lor \sim q)$
T	T	F	T	T
T	F	T	T	T
F	T	F	T	T
F	F	T	T	T

29.

p	q	$p \lor q$	$p \land q$	$(p \lor q) \lor (p \land q)$
T	T	T	T	T
T	F	T	F	T
F	T	T	F	T
F	F	F	F	F

30. a. {0, 1, 2} b. {0, 8, 9} c. {0, 1, 2, 3}
 d. {3, 4, 5, 6} e. {0, 1, 2, 3, 4} f. ∅

31. a. Spanish is a language or homemaking is a language.
 b. true

32. a. Biology is a science or Spanish is a language.
 b. true

33. a. It's a difficult course.
 b. open

34. a. Spanish is not a language or homemaking is a language.
 b. false

35. a. It's not a difficult course.
 b. open

36. a Biology is a science or homemaking is not a language.
 b. true

37. a. Biology is not a science or Spanish is not a language.
 b. false

38. a. It is not true that Spanish is a language or homemaking is a language.
 b. false

39. a. Spanish is a language and homemaking is a language.
 b. false

40. a. Spanish is a language and biology is a science.
 b. true

41. a. It is false that biology is not a science or Spanish is a language.
 b. false

42. a. It is not the case that either Spanish is not a language or homemaking is a language.
 b. true

43. true   **44.** true   **45.** false
46. false, true   **47.** true, false   **48.** false
49. true   **50.** true   **51.** true
52. uncertain   **53.** uncertain   **54.** uncertain

5-5 Conditionals: *pages 152–155*

1. a. it rains
 b. the game is cancelled

2. a. it is 9:05 A.M.
 b. I'm late to class

3. a. it rains
 b. I do not have to water the lawn

4. a. you take the Third Avenue bus
 b. you can get to the stadium

5. a. one side of the square is $x + 2$
 b. the perimeter of the square is $4x + 8$

6. a. a polygon has exactly three sides
 b. it is a triangle

7. a. the shoe fits
 b. wear it

8. a. you have a headache
 b. you should take time out and get some rest

9. $p \rightarrow r$ **10.** $q \rightarrow r$ **11.** $\sim p \rightarrow \sim r$
12. $q \rightarrow p$ **13.** $\sim q \rightarrow \sim r$ **14.** $p \rightarrow r$
15. a. $p \rightarrow w$ b. true
16. a. $w \rightarrow p$ b. false
17. a. $w \rightarrow r$ b. true
18. a. $\sim r \rightarrow w$ b. true
19. a. $\sim p \rightarrow \sim w$ b. false
20. a. $r \rightarrow p$ b. false
21. a $(\sim r \wedge p) \rightarrow w$ b. true
22. a. $(r \wedge \sim p) \rightarrow \sim w$ b. false

23.

r	t	$r \rightarrow t$
T	T	T
T	F	F
F	T	T
F	F	T

24.

k	m	$k \rightarrow m$
T	T	T
T	F	F
F	T	T
F	F	T

25.

q	r	$q \rightarrow r$
T	T	T
T	F	F
F	T	T
F	F	T

26. true   **27.** true   **28.** true
29. true   **30.** true   **31.** false
32. false   **33.** false
34. a. If I jog, then I feel well.   b. true
35. a. If I diet, then I get hungry.   b. true
36. a. If I get hungry, then I diet.   b. false
37. a. If I do not feel well, then I jog.   b. true
38. a. If I do not feel well, then I do not jog.
 b. true
39. a. If I feel well then I do not get hungry.
 b. false
40. a. If I get hungry, then I do not diet.
 b. true
41. a. If I do not diet, then I do not get hungry.
 b. false
42. a. If I do not jog then I do not feel well.
 b. true
43. a. If I jog then I diet.
 b. false
44. a. If I jog and get hungry then I feel well.
 b. true
45. a. If I jog then I get hungry and feel well.
 b. true
46. a. If I jog or diet then I get hungry.
 b. true
47. a. If I diet then I get hungry and do not feel well.
 b. true
48. a. If I do not jog then I diet and get hungry.
 b. true

49. *a.* If I jog and get hungry then I diet.
   b. false
50. $p \rightarrow q$ **51.** $q \rightarrow p$ **52.** true, false
53. true   **54.** true   **55.** true
56. true   **57.** false   **58.** uncertain
59. uncertain   **60.** true

5-6 Review Exercises: *pages 155–156*

1. *a.* $j \rightarrow a$ *b.* true   **2.** *a.* $j \wedge w$ *b.* false
3. *a.* $w \vee j$ *b.* true
4. *a.* $a \rightarrow \sim j$ *b.* false
5. *a.* $\sim a \wedge \sim w$ *b.* false
6. *a.* at first you don't succeed
   b. you should try again
7. *a.* you are late one more time
   b. you will get a detention
8. $\sim p \rightarrow q$ **9.** $q \rightarrow p$ **10.** 6.
11. p **12.** true   **13.** false; true
14. true   **15.** false   **16.** false
17. false   **18.** true   **19.** true

20. *a.* {6, 7, 8, 9, 10}   *b.* {1, 2, 3, 4, 5}
   c. {2, 3, 5, 7}   *d.* {1, 4, 6, 8, 9, 10}
   e. {2, 3, 5, 6, 7, 8, 9, 10}   *f.* {7}   *g.* {2, 3, 5}

21.

	Peter	Carl	Ralph
Instrument	Violin	Cello	Flute
Sport	Tennis	Soccer	Baseball

1. Ralph plays baseball (clue 4).
2. The violinist who plays tennis (clue 1) is either Peter or Carl.
3. *a.* If Carl is the violinist, then Peter must play the flute (clue 3) and Ralph the cello.
   b. But then, if Ralph plays baseball and Carl plays tennis, Peter must play soccer. This contradicts clue 2.
4. Therefore, Peter plays the violin, and the other instruments and sports fall into place.

Chapter 6.   Using Logic

6-1 Compound Statements and Truth Values: *pages 159–161*

1. $p \wedge q$ **2.** $p \rightarrow q$ **3.** $p \vee q$ **4.** $\sim q$
5. (3)   **6.** (1)   **7.** (2)   **8.** (3)
9. (2)   **10.** (3)   **11.** (2)   **12.** (3)
13. *a.* Twenty-eight is a multiple of 7 and 28 is not the square of an integer.
   b. true
14. *a.* Seven is a factor of 28 or 28 is not a multiple of 7.
   b. true
15. *a.* If 28 is not a multiple of 7 then 28 is the square of an integer.
   b. true
16. *a.* It is not true that 7 is a factor of 28 and 28 is the square of an integer.
   b. true
17. *a.* Twenty-eight is the square of an integer or 7 is not a factor of 28.
   b. false
18. *a.* It is false that 28 is a multiple of 7 or 28 is the square of an integer.
   b. false
19. *a.* If 7 is not a factor of 28 then 28 is not a multiple of 7.
   b. true
20. *a.* If 28 is the square of an integer then 28 is not a multiple of 7.
   b. true
21. *a.* If 28 is a multiple of 7 and 7 is a factor of 28, then 28 is the square of an integer.
   b. false

22. *a.* If 28 is a multiple of 7 then 28 is the square of an integer or 7 is a factor of 28.
   b. true
23. *a.* If 28 is a multiple of 7 or the square of an integer then 7 is a factor of 28.
   b. true
24. *a.* If 7 is a factor of 28 then 28 is the square of an integer or a multiple of 7.
   b. true
25. true   **26.** false   **27.** false   **28.** true
29. true   **30.** true   **31.** true   **32.** true
33. false **34.** false   **35.** true   **36.** false
37. false **38.** true   **39.** true   **40.** true
41. false **42.** true   **43.** true   **44.** true

In 45 and 46, consider the conditions:
   p: She is over 21.
   q: She is unmarried.
   r: She smokes.
45. $(p \vee q) \wedge \sim r$: Any niece who smokes will not inherit, since then the conjunct $\sim r$ is false. Also Diane is eliminated because she does not satisfy $p \vee q$. Janice, Sarah, and Laurie will inherit.
46. $p \vee (q \wedge \sim r)$: Any niece over 21 will inherit, since the disjunct p is true. In addition, Sarah satisfies $q \wedge \sim r$. Judy, Janice, Sue, Sarah, and Laurie will inherit.
47. *a.* (1) 6 or any multiple of 6   (2) no values
      (3) 4 or any even number not divisible by 3
      (4) 3 or any odd number
   b. No value of x will give a true antecedent and a false consequent. Thus, $p \rightarrow q$ is true for all values of x.

1.

p	q	$p \lor q$	$\sim q$	$(p \lor q) \to \sim q$
T	T	T	F	F
T	F	T	T	T
F	T	T	F	F
F	F	F	T	T

2.

p	q	$p \land q$	$p \lor q$	$(p \land q) \to (p \lor q)$
T	T	T	T	T
T	F	F	T	T
F	T	F	T	T
F	F	F	F	T

3.

p	q	$\sim p$	$q \to \sim p$	$(q \to \sim p) \land p$
T	T	F	F	F
T	F	F	T	T
F	T	T	T	F
F	F	T	T	F

4.

p	q	$\sim p$	$\sim p \land q$	$p \lor (\sim p \land q)$
T	T	F	F	T
T	F	F	F	T
F	T	T	T	T
F	F	T	F	F

5.

p	q	$\sim p$	$p \lor \sim p$	$q \to (p \lor \sim p)$
T	T	F	T	T
T	F	F	T	T
F	T	T	T	T
F	F	T	T	T

6.

p	q	$p \to q$	$\sim q$	$(p \to q) \to \sim q$
T	T	T	F	F
T	F	F	T	T
F	T	T	F	F
F	F	T	T	T

7.

p	q	$\sim p$	$\sim p \lor q$	$p \land q$	$(\sim p \lor q) \to (p \land q)$
T	T	F	T	T	T
T	F	F	F	F	T
F	T	T	T	F	F
F	F	T	T	F	F

8.

p	q	$p \land q$	$\sim(p \land q)$	$\sim p$	$\sim q$	$\sim p \land \sim q$	$\sim(p \land q) \to (\sim p \land \sim q)$
T	T	T	F	F	F	F	T
T	F	F	T	F	T	F	F
F	T	F	T	T	F	F	F
F	F	F	T	T	T	T	T

9.

p	q	$\sim q$	$\sim q \land p$	$\sim q \to (\sim q \land p)$
T	T	F	F	T
T	F	T	T	T
F	T	F	F	T
F	F	T	F	F

10.

p	q	$p \lor q$	$\sim(p \lor q)$	$p \to \sim(p \lor q)$
T	T	T	F	F
T	F	T	F	F
F	T	T	F	T
F	F	F	T	T

11.

p	q	$p \land q$	$\sim(p \land q)$	$\sim(p \land q) \lor p$
T	T	T	F	T
T	F	F	T	T
F	T	F	T	T
F	F	F	T	T

12.

p	q	$\sim p$	$\sim p \land q$	$(\sim p \land q) \lor p$
T	T	F	F	T
T	F	F	F	T
F	T	T	T	T
F	F	T	F	F

13.

p	q	$\sim q$	$p \to \sim q$	$(p \to \sim q) \land q$
T	T	F	F	F
T	F	T	T	F
F	T	F	T	T
F	F	T	T	F

14.

p	q	~p	~q	~p∧~q	p∧q	(~p∧~q)∨(p∧q)
T	T	F	F	F	T	T
T	F	F	T	F	F	F
F	T	T	F	F	F	F
F	F	T	T	T	F	T

15. a. ~e → (e ∨ p)

b.

e	p	~e	e∨p	~e→(e∨p)
T	T	F	T	T
T	F	F	T	T
F	T	T	T	T
F	F	T	F	F

c. e is false and p is false

d. 9 or 15 or 21 or any product of odd numbers greater than 1

6-3 Biconditionals: pages 167–169

1. t ↔ r   2. n ↔ t   3. n ↔ r   4. t ↔ n   5. ~t ↔ ~n

6.

p	q	p↔q
T	T	T
T	F	F
F	T	F
F	F	T

7.

r	s	r↔s
T	T	T
T	F	F
F	T	F
F	F	T

8.

d	k	d↔k
T	T	T
T	F	F
F	T	F
F	F	T

9.

p	q	p→q
T	T	T
T	F	F
F	T	T
F	F	T

10.

p	r	~r	~r→p
T	T	F	T
T	F	T	T
F	T	F	T
F	F	T	F

11.

t	v	t∧v	(t∧v)→t
T	T	T	T
T	F	F	T
F	T	F	T
F	F	F	T

12.

b	c	b∨c	(b∨c)↔c
T	T	T	T
T	F	T	F
F	T	T	T
F	F	F	T

13.

p	t	t→p	p→t	(t→p)∧(p→t)
T	T	T	T	T
T	F	T	F	F
F	T	F	T	F
F	F	T	T	T

14.

p	q	q→p	(q→p)→q
T	T	T	T
T	F	T	F
F	T	F	T
F	F	T	F

15.

r	s	~r	~r→s	(~r→s)↔r
T	T	F	T	T
T	F	F	T	T
F	T	T	T	F
F	F	T	F	T

16. true   17. false   18. true
19. true   20. false   21. true
22. true   23. true   24. false
25. true
26. a. p ↔ q
   b. (p → q) ∧ (q → p) or p ↔ q
   c. (p → q) ∧ (q → p) or p ↔ q
   d. q ↔ p
   e. (p → q) ∨ (q → p)
27. choice e

6-4 Tautologies: pages 173–175

1. a.

p	~p	~(~p)	p↔~(~p)
T	F	T	T
F	T	F	T

   b. tautology

2. a.

p	~p	~p∧p	~(~p∧p)
T	F	F	T
F	T	F	T

   b. tautology

3. a.

p	~p	p→~p	(p→~p)↔~p
T	F	F	T
F	T	T	T

   b. tautology

4. a.

q	~q	~q→q
T	F	T
F	T	F

   b. not a tautology

5. *a.*

p	q	$\sim p$	$\sim p \lor q$	$p \lor (\sim p \lor q)$
T	T	F	T	T
T	F	F	F	T
F	T	T	T	T
F	F	T	T	T

b. tautology

6. *a.*

p	q	$p \land q$	$p \lor q$	$(p \land q) \to (p \lor q)$
T	T	T	T	T
T	F	F	T	T
F	T	F	T	T
F	F	F	F	T

b. tautology

7. *a.*

p	q	$p \lor q$	$p \land q$	$(p \lor q) \to (p \land q)$
T	T	T	T	T
T	F	T	F	F
F	T	T	F	F
F	F	F	F	T

b. not a tautology

8. *a.*

p	q	$p \lor q$	$p \to (p \lor q)$
T	T	T	T
T	F	T	T
F	T	T	T
F	F	F	T

b. tautology

9. *a.*

p	q	$\sim p$	$\sim p \land q$	$p \land (\sim p \land q)$	$\sim[p \land (\sim p \lor q)]$
T	T	F	F	F	T
T	F	F	F	F	T
F	T	T	T	F	T
F	F	T	F	F	T

b. tautology

10. *a.*

p	q	$\sim q$	$p \to \sim q$	$\sim(p \to \sim q)$	$p \land q$	$\sim(p \to \sim q) \leftrightarrow (p \land q)$
T	T	F	F	T	T	T
T	F	T	T	F	F	T
F	T	F	T	F	F	T
F	F	T	T	F	F	T

b. tautology

11.

p	q	$p \lor q$	$p \to (p \lor q)$
T	T	T	T
T	F	T	T
F	T	T	T
F	F	F	T

12.

p	q	$p \land q$	$q \land p$	$(p \land q) \leftrightarrow (q \land p)$
T	T	T	T	T
T	F	F	F	T
F	T	F	F	T
F	F	F	F	T

13.

p	$p \lor p$	$(p \lor p) \to p$
T	T	T
F	F	T

14.

p	q	$p \land q$	$(p \land q) \to q$
T	T	T	T
T	F	F	T
F	T	F	T
F	F	F	T

15.

p	q	$p \land q$	$p \lor (p \land q)$	$[p \lor (p \land q)] \leftrightarrow p$
T	T	T	T	T
T	F	F	T	T
F	T	F	F	T
F	F	F	F	T

16.

p	q	$\sim p$	$\sim p \lor q$	$p \to q$	$(\sim p \lor q) \to (p \to q)$
T	T	F	T	T	T
T	F	F	F	F	T
F	T	T	T	T	T
F	F	T	T	T	T

17.

p	q	$p \to q$	$\sim q$	$(p \to q) \wedge \sim q$	$\sim p$	$[(p \to q) \wedge \sim q] \to \sim p$
T	T	T	F	F	F	T
T	F	F	T	F	F	T
F	T	T	F	F	T	T
F	F	T	T	T	T	T

18.

p	q	$\sim p$	$\sim p \vee q$	$\sim q$	$(\sim p \vee q) \vee \sim q$	$\sim[(\sim p \vee q) \vee \sim q]$	$p \wedge q$	$\sim[(\sim p \vee q) \vee \sim q] \to (p \wedge q)$
T	T	F	T	F	T	F	T	T
T	F	F	F	T	T	F	F	T
F	T	T	T	F	T	F	F	T
F	F	T	T	T	T	F	F	T

19.

p	q	$p \vee q$	$\sim(p \vee q)$	$\sim p$	$\sim q$	$\sim p \wedge \sim q$	$\sim(p \vee q) \leftrightarrow \sim p \wedge \sim q$
T	T	T	F	F	F	F	T
T	F	T	F	F	T	F	T
F	T	T	F	T	F	F	T
F	F	F	T	T	T	T	T

20.

p	q	$\sim p$	$\sim p \vee q$	$p \wedge (\sim p \vee q)$	$p \wedge q$	$[p \wedge (\sim p \vee q)] \leftrightarrow (p \wedge q)$
T	T	F	T	T	T	T
T	F	F	F	F	F	T
F	T	T	T	F	F	T
F	F	T	T	F	F	T

21. *a.*

p	q	$\sim p$	$\sim q$	$q \to \sim p$	$\sim p \vee \sim q$	$\sim q \to \sim p$
T	T	F	F	F	F	T
T	F	F	T	T	T	F
F	T	T	F	T	T	T
F	F	T	T	T	T	T

b. $(q \to \sim p) \leftrightarrow \sim p \vee \sim q$

22. *a.*

p	q	$\sim p$	$\sim q$	$q \vee \sim p$	$p \vee \sim q$	$p \to q$
T	T	F	F	T	T	T
T	F	F	T	F	T	F
F	T	T	F	T	F	T
F	F	T	T	T	T	T

b. $(q \vee \sim p) \leftrightarrow (p \to q)$

23. *a.*

p	q	$\sim p$	$\sim q$	$\sim p \to q$	$q \wedge \sim p$	$\sim q \to p$
T	T	F	F	T	F	T
T	F	F	T	T	F	T
F	T	T	F	T	T	T
F	F	T	T	F	F	F

b. $(\sim p \to q) \leftrightarrow (\sim q \to p)$

24. *a.*

p	q	$\sim p$	$\sim q$	$p \wedge q$	$p \leftrightarrow q$	$\sim p \leftrightarrow \sim q$
T	T	F	F	T	T	T
T	F	F	T	F	F	F
F	T	T	F	F	F	F
F	F	T	T	F	T	T

b. $(p \leftrightarrow q) \leftrightarrow (\sim p \leftrightarrow \sim q)$

25. *a.*

p	q	$\sim q$	$p \to \sim q$	$p \wedge q$	$\sim(p \wedge q)$	$p \leftrightarrow \sim q$
T	T	F	F	T	F	F
T	F	T	T	F	T	T
F	T	F	T	F	T	T
F	F	T	T	F	T	F

b. $(p \to \sim q) \leftrightarrow \sim(p \wedge q)$

26. *a.*

p	q	$\sim p$	$p \to q$	$\sim p \vee q$	$(p \to q) \to (\sim p \vee q)$
T	T	F	T	T	T
T	F	F	F	F	T
F	T	T	T	T	T
F	F	T	T	T	T

b. (2)

27. *a.*

p	q	$\sim p$	$\sim q$	$p \vee \sim q$	$\sim(p \vee \sim q)$	$\sim p \wedge q$	$\sim(p \vee \sim q) \leftrightarrow (\sim p \wedge q)$
T	T	F	F	T	F	F	T
T	F	F	T	T	F	F	T
F	T	T	F	F	T	T	T
F	F	T	T	T	F	F	T

b. (1)

28. *a.*

p	q	$\sim p$	$\sim p \to q$	$p \vee q$	$(\sim p \to q) \leftrightarrow (p \vee q)$
T	T	F	T	T	T
T	F	F	T	T	T
F	T	T	T	T	T
F	F	T	F	F	T

b. (4)

29. *a.*

p	q	$\sim p$	$q \wedge \sim p$	$p \vee (q \wedge \sim p)$	$p \vee q$	$[p \vee (q \wedge \sim p)] \leftrightarrow (p \vee q)$
T	T	F	F	T	T	T
T	F	F	F	T	T	T
F	T	T	T	T	T	T
F	F	T	F	F	F	T

b. (3)

30. *a.* $l \to t$
b. $\sim t \to \sim l$

c.

l	t	$l \to t$	$\sim l$	$\sim t$	$\sim t \to \sim l$	$(l \to t) \leftrightarrow (\sim t \to \sim l)$
T	T	T	F	F	T	T
T	F	F	F	T	F	T
F	T	T	T	F	T	T
F	F	T	T	T	T	T

They are equivalences.

31.

f	s	$f \vee s$	$\sim f$	$(f \vee s) \wedge \sim f$	$[(f \vee s) \wedge \sim f] \to s$
T	T	T	F	F	T
T	F	T	F	F	T
F	T	T	T	T	T
F	F	F	T	F	T

6-5 Inverses, Converses, and Contrapositives: *pages 182–185*

1. $\sim p \rightarrow \sim q$ 2. $\sim t \rightarrow w$ 3. $m \rightarrow \sim p$
4. $p \rightarrow q$ 5. $q \rightarrow p$ 6. $\sim w \rightarrow t$
7. $p \rightarrow \sim m$ 8. $p \rightarrow q$ 9. $\sim q \rightarrow \sim p$
10. $w \rightarrow \sim t$ 11. $\sim p \rightarrow m$ 12. $p \rightarrow q$

13. If you do not use Charm face powder then you will not be beautiful.

14. If you do not buy Goal toothpaste then your children will not brush longer.

15. When you do not serve imported sparkling water then you do not have good taste.

16. The man who does not wear Cutrite clothes is not well dressed.

17. *a.* If a polygon is not a triangle then it does not have exactly three sides.
    b. true   *c.* true

18. *a.* If a polygon is not a trapezoid then the polygon does not have exactly four sides.
    b. true   *c.* false

19. *a.* If $2 \cdot 2 \neq 4$ then $2 \cdot 3 \neq 6$.   *b.* true   *c.* true

20. *a.* If $2^2 \neq 4$ then $3^2 \neq 6$.   *b.* false   *c.* true

21. If you eat Nano yogurt then you live to an old age.

22. If you care about your family then you take pictures of your family with a Blinko camera.

23. If you get good mileage then you drive a Superb car.

24. If you make a better chicken dinner then you use Dust and Roast.

25. *a.* If a number is exactly divisible by 2 then the number is even.
    b. true   *c.* true

26. *a.* If two segments are equal in measure then the two segments are each 5 cm in length.
    b. true   *c.* false

27. *a.* If $5^2 = 1^2 + 4^2$ then $5 = 1 + 4$.
    b. false   *c.* true

28. *a.* If $2(5) + 3 = 13$ then $2(5) + 3 = 10 + 3$.
    b. true   *c.* true

29. If you do not send Trademark cards then you do not care enough to send the best.

30. If you have body odor then you do not use Trickle deodorant.

31. If your teeth are not pearly white then you do not brush with Brite.

32. If you do not get a high school diploma then you do not want a good job.

33. *a.* If a quadrilateral is not a parallelogram then the opposite sides of the quadrilateral are not parallel.
    b. true   *c.* true

34. *a.* If two segments are not equal in measure then the segments are not 8 cm each.
    b. true   *c.* true

35. *a.* If $2 + 3 \neq 4$ then $1 + 2 \neq 3$.
    b. false   *c.* false

36. *a.* If a quadrilateral is not a rectangle then the angles of the quadrilateral are not all equal in measure.
    b. true   *c.* true

37. *a.* If a number is an even number then it is not prime.
    b. false   *c.* false

38. (4)   39. (4)   40. (2)   41. (3)   42. (2)

43. *a.* $\sim p \rightarrow \sim q$ *b.* $\sim q \rightarrow \sim p$
    c. They are contrapositives.
    d. The contrapositive is the converse of the inverse of the conditional (or the inverse of the converse of the conditional).

44. *a.* If today is not Friday then tomorrow is not Saturday.
    b. If tomorrow is Saturday then today is Friday.
    c. If tomorrow is not Saturday then today is not Friday.

45. *a.* If Douglas does not do well in college then he will not apply to medical school.
    b. If Douglas applies to medical school then he did well in college.
    c. If Douglas does not apply to medical school then he did not do well in college.

46. *a.* Arlette will not get a role in the play if she does not audition.
    b. If Arlette gets a role in the play then she auditioned.
    c. If Arlette does not get a role in the play then she did not audition.

47. *a.* Dorothea will not graduate from law school in January if she does not take courses this summer.
    b. If Dorothea will graduate from law school in January then she took courses this summer.
    c. If Dorothea will not graduate from law school in January then she did not take courses this summer.

48. *a.* If John is not accepted at the Culinary Institute then he does not have a chance of earning a high salary as a chef.
    b. If John has a chance of earning a high salary as a chef then he is accepted at the Culinary Institute.
    c. If John does not have a chance of earning a high salary as a chef, then he is not accepted at the Culinary Institute.

49. *a.* If a man is not honest, he steals.
    b. If a man does not steal, he is honest.
    c. If a man steals, he is not honest.

50. *a.* If Julia waters the plants then the plants will not die.
    b. If the plants die then Julia didn't water them.
    c. If the plants do not die, Julia watered them.

51. *a.* Rachel will get her allowance if she does not forget to do her chores.
    b. If Rachel does not get her allowance then she forgot to do her chores.
    c. If Rachel gets her allowance then she did not forget to do her chores.

52. (3)   53. (3)   54. (2)

55. *a.* If he lives in California then Eddie lives in San Francisco.
    b. uncertain
    c. If Eddie does not live in San Francisco then he does not live in California.
    d. uncertain
    e. If he does not live in California then Eddie does not live in San Francisco.
    f. true
56. *a.* If a number is divisible by 3 then it is divisible by 12.
    b. uncertain
    c. If a number is not divisible by 12 then it is not divisible by 3.
    d. uncertain
    e. If a number is not divisible by 3 then it is not divisible by 12.
    f. true
57. *a.* If I am ill then I have the flu.
    b. uncertain
    c. If I do not have the flu then I am not ill.
    d. uncertain
    e. If I am not ill then I do not have the flu.
    f. true
58. *a.* If three pens cost 87 cents then one pen costs 29 cents.
    b. true
    c. If one pen does not cost 29 cents then three pens do not cost 87 cents.
    d. true
    e. If three pens do not cost 87 cents then one pen does not cost 29 cents.
    f. true
59. *a.* If a quadrilateral has four congruent sides then it is a rhombus.
    b. true
    c. If a quadrilateral is not a rhombus then it does not have four congruent sides.
    d. true
    e. If a quadrilateral does not have four congruent sides then it is not a rhombus.
    f. true

Note that in 58–59, the original statements are biconditionals. Thus, the converse and the inverse have the same truth value as the original.

60. *a.* Alex loves computers if he will learn how to write programs.
    b. uncertain
    c. If Alex does not love computers then he will not learn how to write programs.
    d. uncertain
    e. Alex does not love computers if he will not learn how to write programs.
    f. true

6-6 Drawing Conclusions: *pages 189–190*

1. true   2. true
3. true   4. cannot be determined
5. cannot be determined   6. true
7. false   8. cannot be determined
9. true   10. cannot be determined
11. I pass the course.   12. We played hockey.
13. *x* is not prime.
14. Parallelogram *ABCD* does not contain a right angle.
15. $x \geq 10$ 16. $2x = 2; x = 1$
17. 2 is a prime.
18. 3 has exactly two factors.
19. no conclusion   20. no conclusion
21. It is not July.   22. It is October.
23. I study Spanish.
24. *x* is even and a prime
25. *x* is not even *or* *x* is not a prime *or* *x* is neither even nor a prime.

6-7 Review Exercises: *pages 190–191*

1. *a.* If there is one even prime, then 2 is not a prime.
   b. false
2. *a.* If 4 is a prime, then 2 is a prime and there is one even prime. *b.* true
3. *a.* 2 is not a prime or 4 is not a prime. *b.* true
4. *a.* If there is one even prime, then 2 is a prime or 4 is a prime. *b.* true
5. *a.* $q \rightarrow p$ *b.* $\sim p \rightarrow \sim q$ *c.* $\sim q \rightarrow \sim p$
6. (4)   7. (2)   8. (2)   9. (1)
10. (2)   11. (2)   12. (4)   13. (2)

14. *a.*

p	q	$\sim q$	$p \rightarrow \sim q$	$(p \rightarrow \sim q) \wedge p$	$[(p \rightarrow \sim q) \wedge p] \rightarrow \sim q$
T	T	F	F	F	T
T	F	T	T	T	T
F	T	F	T	F	T
F	F	T	T	F	T

b. Yes
c. The statement is always true, shown by the last column of *T*'s in the truth table.

15. *a.*

p	q	$p \wedge q$	$\sim(p \wedge q)$	$\sim p$	$\sim q$	$\sim p \vee \sim q$	$\sim(p \wedge q) \leftrightarrow (\sim p \vee \sim q)$
T	T	T	F	F	F	F	T
T	F	F	T	F	T	T	T
F	T	F	T	T	F	T	T
F	F	F	T	T	T	T	T

b. Yes. The statement is always true (all T in the last column).

16. *a.*

p	q	$p \rightarrow q$	$\sim(p \rightarrow q)$	$\sim(p \rightarrow q) \vee q$	$p \leftrightarrow [\sim(p \rightarrow q) \vee q]$
T	T	T	F	T	T
T	F	F	T	T	T
F	T	T	F	T	F
F	F	T	F	F	T

b. No. The truth values vary for the statement, as seen in the last column of the truth table.

17. (3) **18.** $\triangle ABC$ is not isosceles. **19.** Virginia, Kay, Janice

Chapter 7. Signed Numbers

7-1 Extending the Number Line: *page 194*

1-3. Graphs
4. true; $^+5$ is to the right of $^+2$
5. true; $^-3$ is to the left of 0
6. false; $^-7$ is to the right of $^-1$
7. true; $^-1\frac{3}{4}$ is to the right of $^-1\frac{7}{8}$
8. $^-4 < {}^+8$ 9. $^-6 < {}^-3$
10. $^-1\frac{1}{2} < {}^+1\frac{1}{2}$ 11. $^-4 < {}^-2 < {}^+3$
12. $^-2 < 0 < {}^+8$ 13. $^-3\frac{1}{2} < {}^+2\frac{1}{2} < {}^+6$
14. $^+7 > {}^-4$ 15. $^+12 > {}^-12$
16. $0 > {}^-1\frac{1}{2}$ 17. $^+5 > {}^+3 > {}^-3$
18. $0 > {}^-1 > {}^-5$ 19. $^+3\frac{1}{2} > {}^-1.5 > {}^-2\frac{1}{2}$
20. $^+2$ 21. $^-4$
22. $^+.6$ 23. true
24. true 25. false
26. false 27. true
28. false
29. *a.* $(^+2 < {}^+5) \wedge (^+5 < {}^+7)$
b. $(^-3 < 0) \wedge (0 < {}^+9)$
c. $(^-8 > {}^-10) \wedge (^-10 > {}^-12)$
30. *a.* false *b.* true *c.* false *d.* false *e.* true
31. 1 or $^+1$ 32. $^-1$
33. *a.* no
b. the number line extends indefinitely to the right

34. *a.* no
b. the number line extends indefinitely to the left

7-2 Graphing the Solution Set of an Open Sentence Involving One Variable on a Number Line: *pages 197–199*

1-20. Graphs
21. (3) 22. (3) 23. (4) 24. (1)
25. (4) 26. (2) 27. (4) 28. (1)
29. (2)
30-37. Graphs

7-3 The Opposite of a Directed Number: *pages 200–201*

1. -8 2. 8 or $+8$ 3. $-3\frac{1}{2}$ 4. 6.5 or $+6.5$
5. -19 6. -14 7. 0 8. 0
9. $^-7$ 10. $-\frac{3}{4}$ 11. -5 12. -14
13. 10 14. 7 15. -4 16. 0
17. false 18. true
19. false (opposite of 0 is 0)
20. true 21. false 22. true 23. true
24. true 25. true 26. true

7-4 The Absolute Value of a Number: *page 202*

1. *a.* 3 *b.* −3 2. *a.* 5 *b.* 5
3. *a.* 18 *b.* −18 4. *a.* 13 *b.* 13
5. *a.* 20 *b.* 20 6. *a.* $1\frac{1}{2}$ *b.* $-1\frac{1}{2}$
7. *a.* $3\frac{3}{4}$ *b.* $3\frac{3}{4}$ 8. *a.* $1\frac{1}{2}$ *b.* $1\frac{1}{2}$
9. *a.* 2.7 *b.* −2.7 10. *a.* 1.4 *b.* 1.4
11. true 12. true 13. false 14. true
15. false 16. true 17. true 18. false
19. 12 20. 6 21. 10 22. 5
23. 0 24. 10 25. 14 26. 5
27. 0 28. 8 29. 9 30. 0
31. 7 32. −2 33. −6 34. true
35. false 36. false 37. true 38. false
39. true 40. true 41. false

7-5 Adding Signed Numbers on a Number Line: *pages 204–205*

1. +7 2. +14 3. −6 4. −8
5. +3 6. +3 7. −1 8. +2
9. 0 10. 0 11. 0 12. +4
13. −6 14. +6 15. −8 16. +9
17. −2 18. −4 19. 0
20. temperature rose 7° or +7 21. 18
22. lost 3 yd. or −3 23. $230
24. dropped $\frac{3}{4}$ or $-\frac{3}{4}$ 25. positive
26. negative 27. *a.* yes *b.* yes
28. The sum will have the same sign as the sign of the number with the larger absolute value.
29. no
30. *a.* yes
   b. $(-2) + (-3) = -5$ (If any two negative numbers are added, the sum will be smaller than either of the numbers.)

7-6 Addition of Signed Numbers: *pages 209–211*

1. +10 2. +13 3. −37 4. −45
5. +2 6. −2 7. +4 8. −7
9. −12 10. +6 11. −5 12. +4
13. −9 14. 0 15. 0 16. +24
17. −66 18. −30 19. +8 20. −9
21. $+18\frac{1}{4}$ 22. $-8\frac{1}{2}$ 23. $-13\frac{2}{3}$ 24. $+2\frac{3}{4}$
25. −7.8 26. +8.3 27. −16.3 28. +2.3
29. +2.5 30. $-1\frac{3}{4}$ 31. −6 32. +25
33. +23 34. −18 35. −28 36. 0
37. +54 38. −17 39. 0 40. +6
41. −20 42. 0 43. 0 44. −6.1
45. +12 46. +12 47. 0 48. −26
49. +4 50. −6 51. 0 52. +10
53. −8 54. +2 55. 0 56. −4
57. −4 58. +2 59. 0 60. −12
61. −*b* 62. *y* 63. +4 64. −3
65. −10 66. −5 67. $+\frac{8}{7}$ or $+1\frac{1}{7}$
68. 0 69. −9 70. 12 71. −4
72. −6 73. 14 74. 2

75. commutative property of addition
76. addition property of opposites
77. addition property of zero
78. property of the opposite of a sum
79. associative property of addition
80. false 81. true 82. true 83. true

7-7 Subtraction of Signed Numbers: *pages 214–215*

1. +6 2. +7 3. −2 4. −8
5. −4 6. −14 7. +4 8. +16
9. +6 10. +45 11. +13 12. +140
13. −8 14. −92 15. −12 16. −86
17. +10 18. −7 19. +20 20. 0
21. −11 22. 0 23. +51 24. −54
25. −62 26. −12 27. 0 28. +15
29. +2.2 30. +14.5 31. −10.6 32. −1.3
33. +3 34. $+4\frac{1}{2}$ 35. +10 36. $-10\frac{1}{2}$
37. −11 38. +13 39. +30 40. −1.7
41. +1.5 42. −17.5 43. 25 44. 27
45. 3 46. 9 47. −12 48. 19
49. −26 50. −5 51. +3 52. −8.5
53. +3.7 54. $-1\frac{7}{8}$ 55. $+\frac{9}{2}$ 56. +20
57. −41 58. −28 59. 0 60. $7\frac{1}{2}$
61. 0
62. *a.* +3° *b.* +28° *c.* −12° *d.* −16°
63. +110 meters 64. 185 65. 114°
66. .25 km 67. *a.* false *b.* false
68. *a.* no *b.* yes; if $x = y$ *c.* They are opposites. *d.* no
69. *a.* false *b.* false 70. no

7-8 Multiplication of Signed Numbers: *pages 219–220*

1. +24 2. +7 3. +105 4. −32
5. −120 6. −144 7. 0 8. +100
9. −192 10. 0 11. +225 12. −135
13. −3.6 14. −20 15. +4 16. −9
17. $+\frac{1}{6}$ 18. −36 19. +2 20. +12
21. −1 22. +24 23. −56 24. −60
25. 0 26. −120 27. 0 28. +16
29. +9 30. +125 31. −64 32. −125
33. +1 34. $+\frac{1}{4}$ 35. $+\frac{1}{4}$ 36. $+\frac{8}{27}$
37. $-\frac{27}{125}$ 38. $-\frac{1}{64}$ 39. $+\frac{1}{625}$
40. 5(9) + 5(7) 41. −4*x* + (−4*y*)
42. 6[−3 + (−5)] 43. 7 (*a* + *b*)
44. 8[5 + (−3)] = 8 · 5 + 8 · (−3)
45. commutative property of multiplication
46. associative property of multiplication
47. distributive property
48. distributive property
49. *a.* distributive property of multiplication over addition
   b. commutative property of addition
   c. associative property of addition
   d. addition property of zero
   e. commutative property of multiplication
50. *a.* true *b.* true 51. yes

52. *a.*

a	*b*	*ab*
+5	+2	+10
+5	−2	−10
−5	+2	−10
−5	−2	+10

b. $p \leftrightarrow q$
(Other answers are possible.)
c. + corresponds to T
− corresponds to F

7-9 Division of Signed Numbers: *pages 224–225*

1. $\frac{1}{6}$ **2.** $-\frac{1}{5}$ **3.** $\frac{1}{9}$ **4.** $-\frac{1}{7}$
5. 1   **6.** −1   **7.** 5   **8.** −10
9. $\frac{4}{3}$ **10.** $-\frac{3}{2}$ **11.** $\frac{1}{x}$ **12.** $\frac{1}{x}$
13. +5   **14.** +7   **15.** −2   **16.** −3
17. −25   **18.** −6   **19.** +1   **20.** −1
21. 0   **22.** −13   **23.** −7   **24.** +5
25. −4   **26.** undefined   **27.** −13
28. 0   **29.** $-\frac{1}{2}$ **30.** $+\frac{2}{3}$
31. $+\frac{5}{4}$ or $+1\frac{1}{4}$ **32.** $-\frac{9}{2}$ or $-4\frac{1}{2}$
33. $-\frac{8}{3}$ or $-2\frac{2}{3}$ **34.** $-\frac{17}{2}$ or $-8\frac{1}{2}$
35. $-\frac{25}{2}$ or $-12\frac{1}{2}$ **36.** $+\frac{9}{2}$ or $+4\frac{1}{2}$
37. 0   **38.** $+\frac{5}{9}$ **39.** $-\frac{3}{7}$ **40.** −2.1
41. +32   **42.** −3   **43.** −8   **44.** +5
45. undefined   **46.** −36   **47.** $-\frac{1}{8}$
48. $+\frac{9}{8}$ or $1\frac{1}{8}$ **49.** *a.* 2   *b.* 2
50. $\frac{1}{x-5}$; 5   **51.** $\frac{1}{x+3}$; −3
52. $\frac{1}{2x-1}$, $\frac{1}{2}$ **53.** $\frac{1}{3x+1}$; $-\frac{1}{3}$
54. *a.* false   *b.* false
55. *a.* no
b. yes; $(+2) \div (-2) = (-2) \div (+2)$;
$x \div y = y \div x$ whenever $|y| = |x|$
c. reciprocals
d. no
56. *a.* false   *b.* false   **57.** no
58. *a.* true   *b.* true   **59.** yes
60. *a.* 0   *b.* +1 or 1   *c.* −3   *d.* $-\frac{1}{6}$ *e.* 1 or −1

7-10 Using Signed Numbers in Evaluating Algebraic Expressions: *pages 226–227*

1. −48   **2.** −30   **3.** −48   **4.** −40
5. +24   **6.** −1   **7.** −4   **8.** −3
9. −10   **10.** +36   **11.** +64   **12.** −27
13. −25   **14.** −9   **15.** +1   **16.** +32
17. −75   **18.** −108   **19.** +36   **20.** +2
21. −100   **22.** 384 or +384
23. 450 or +450   **24.** −54   **25.** +54
26. −2   **27.** −4   **28.** −9
29. 9 or +9   **30.** −2   **31.** 18 or +18

32. −10   **33.** 62 or +62   **34.** 12 or +12
35. 78 or +78   **36.** 20 or +20   **37.** 21 or +21
38. −43   **39.** 88 or +88   **40.** 65 or +65
41. 9 or +9   **42.** −8   **43.** 98 or +98
44. 27 or +27   **45.** 49 or +49   **46.** 9 or +9
47. −4   **48.** −21   **49.** 34 or +34
50. 10 or +10   **51.** 28 or +28   **52.** 0
53. 13   **54.** 0   **55.** *a.* 32   *b.* 64
56. *a.* 12   *b.* 36   **57.** *a.* 1   *b.* 4
58. $-\frac{2}{3}$ **59.** +3   **60.** −2   **61.** +24
62. $-\frac{3}{5}$ or −.6

7-11 Using the Additive Inverse in Solving Equations: *page 228*

1. $x = 18$ **2.** $y = 4$ **3.** $t = 26$
4. $c = 16$ **5.** $x = -2$ **6.** $x = -4$
7. $n = -3$ **8.** $y = -9$ **9.** $r = -14$
10. $c = 2$ **11.** $d = 4$ **12.** $s = -4$
13. $x = -.4$ **14.** $w = 1.9$ **15.** $y = -.4$
16. $s = -1$ **17.** $n = -1\frac{1}{2}$ **18.** $x = -2\frac{2}{3}$
19. $n = 1\frac{1}{4}$ **20.** $y = -3\frac{1}{4}$ **21.** $\{-5\}$
22. $\{-6\}$ **23.** $\{0\}$

7-12 Using the Multiplicative Inverse in Solving Equations: *pages 229–230*

1. $\{5\}$ **2.** $\{-3\}$ **3.** $\{-7\}$
4. $\{-\frac{5}{2}\}$ or $\{-2\frac{1}{2}\}$ **5.** $\{-5\}$ **6.** $\{-1.1\}$
7. $\{7\}$ **8.** $\{-\frac{1}{18}\}$ **9.** $\{-18\}$
10. $\{18\}$ **11.** $\{-50\}$ **12.** $\{-16\}$
13. $\{-5.4\}$ **14.** $\{\frac{5}{4}\}$ or $\{1\frac{1}{4}\}$ **15.** $\{-1\}$
16. $\{-1\}$ **17.** $\{-\frac{1}{3}\}$ **18.** $\{-45\}$
19. $\{-6\}$ **20.** $\{\frac{2}{3}\}$ **21.** $\{-100\}$
22. $\{-50\}$ **23.** $\{0\}$

7-13 Review Exercises: *pages 230–231*

1. +7   **2.** −13   **3.** −54   **4.** −14
5. +62   **6.** +1.3   **7.** −42   **8.** −104
9. +.9   **10.** −3   **11.** +7   **12.** $-\frac{1}{4}$
13. false   **14.** true   **15.** false   **16.** false
17. true   **18.** false   **19.** 22   **20.** −1
21. +1   **22.** −16   **23.** −51   **24.** +15
25. −32   **26.** +.6   **27.** −240   **28.** +6
29. 0   **30.** $+\frac{1}{9}$ **31–36.** Graphs
37. (3)   **38.** 2   **39.** −3   **40.** 36
41. 144   **42.** −4   **43.** 20   **44.** −6
45. −24   **46.** −9   **47.** 5   **48.** −36
49. 3   **50.** −15   **51.** −2   **52.** $x = 11$
53. $y = 15$ **54.** $z = -8$ **55.** $r = 10$
56. $a = 14$ **57.** $x = -4$ **58.** $q = 25$
59. $b = -16$
60. *a.* −15   *b.* 8   *c.* no

Chapter 8. Operations with Monomials

8-1 Adding Like Monomials: *pages 234–235*

1. $+15c$
2. $+7t$
3. $-10a$
4. $-15r$
5. $0 \cdot w$ or 0
6. $-4ab$
7. $+15c$
8. $-61r$
9. $-13t$
10. $+13c$
11. $-.3m$
12. $0 \cdot e$ or 0
13. $+11x^2$
14. $-61y^2$
15. $+6d^2$
16. $1.3y^3$
17. $-\frac{2}{3}c^4$
18. $0 \cdot r^3$ or 0
19. $14rs$
20. $-7mn$
21. $+1xyz$ or xyz
22. $-.4cd$
23. $0 \cdot xy$ or 0
24. $+12(x + y)$
25. $+13a^2b$
26. $-4xy^2$
27. $-2x^2$
28. $+13rst$
29. $0 \cdot xy^2$ or 0
30. $5c^2d^2$
31. $0 \cdot (r + s)$ or 0
32. $+7x$
33. $-4y$
34. $+6c$
35. $0 \cdot m$ or 0
36. $-3x^2$
37. $5y^2$
38. a. $16y$ b. $24y$ c. $19y$ d. $7.6y$ e. $8\frac{1}{2}y$ f. $19\frac{1}{2}y$
39. a. $15x$ b. $24m$ c. $13a$ d. $23\frac{3}{4}y$
40. $3a$ 41. $4x$ 42. $6s$ 43. $3\frac{1}{2}x$ 44. $6p$

8-2 Subtracting Like Monomials: *pages 236–237*

1. $+6x$
2. $+3c$
3. $-1ab$ or $-ab$
4. $+4cd^2$
5. $+2x$
6. $-4y$
7. $-2xy$
8. $-4a^2b^2$
9. $+18c$
10. $-11x$
11. $-16xyz$
12. $+7z$
13. $+5x^2$
14. $+6m$
15. $0 \cdot m$ or 0
16. $+8d$
17. $-7.4x$
18. $0 \cdot r$ or 0
19. $+10d^2$
20. $-9t^3$
21. $-2.2y^3$
22. $+4(m + n)$
23. $-2cd$
24. $+1mn$ or mn
25. $-11rs$
26. $-10ab$
27. $+1.3cd$
28. $-2(x + y)$
29. $+1y^2z^2$ or y^2z^2
30. $-7xy^2$
31. $+7r$
32. $+20s$
33. $-28n$
34. $0 \cdot t$ or 0
35. $+8x$
36. $-8x$
37. $+12x^2$
38. $-10y^2$
39. $+3ab$
40. $-15xy$
41. $-6rs^2$
42. $-2x^2y$
43. $-6x$
44. $+5x$
45. $+3xy^2$
46. $+7x$
47. $+4x$
48. $+4d$
49. $-11z$
50. $+13xy$
51. $8x$
52. $7y$
53. $17k$
54. $\frac{1}{3}x$
55. $5c$
56. $8bc$
57. $2.4d$
58. $3\frac{1}{2}x$
59. $4p$
60. $8d$

8-3 Multiplying Powers of the Same Base: *pages 239–240*

1. a^5
2. b^7
3. c^7
4. d^{10}
5. r^{11}
6. t^4
7. r^6
8. s^8
9. e^{10}
10. z^{11}
11. x^5
12. a^7
13. s^9
14. y^6
15. t^{14}
16. x^2
17. a^3
18. b^5
19. c^6
20. e^{10}
21. 2^5 or 32
22. 3^7
23. 5^6 or $15,625$
24. 4^4 or 256
25. 2^{10} or 1024
26. x^6
27. a^8
28. y^8
29. y^{10}
30. z^{14}
31. x^4y^6
32. a^4b^8
33. r^3s^3
34. $2^6 \cdot 3^6$
35. $5^4 \cdot 2^{12}$

36. x^{3a}
37. y^{c+2}
38. c^{r+2}
39. x^{m+1}
40. $(3y)^{a+b}$
41. true
42. false
43. false
44. false
45. true
46. true
47. false
48. true
49. x^3
50. x^2y
51. z^2y or yz^2

8-4 Multiplying a Monomial by a Monomial: *pages 241–242*

1. $12x^5$
2. $15w^2$
3. $+3t^3$
4. $-25d^6$
5. $-18d^6$
6. $-108c^2$
7. $-12a$
8. $+24b$
9. $+30y$
10. $20ab$
11. $+16rs$
12. $-42xyz$
13. $-3xy$
14. $-6ab$
15. $+1xyz$ or xyz
16. $-15abc$
17. $-35rst$
18. $+12cde$
19. $-18xycd$
20. $-60smcd$
21. $-20a^4$
22. $+18x^7$
23. $-140y^5$
24. $-90r^7$
25. $+12z^3$
26. $-40y^6$
27. $-72z^8$
28. $-24x^6y^5$
29. $-35a^5b^3$
30. $-8a^3b^5$
31. $-16r^5s^2$
32. $-72c^2d^2$
33. $-225x^2y^4$
34. $-4x^3$
35. $+49a^2$
36. $+.25x^2$
37. $-8x^6$
38. $+\frac{4}{25}r^4s^4$
39. $+36x^2y^2$
40. $2x^6y^2$
41. $80x^3$
42. $-40x^2y^6$
43. $15y^2$
44. $15xy$
45. $24c^2d^3$
46. $4x^2$
47. $\frac{1}{4}y^2$
48. $9x^2y^2$
49. $25x^4$
50. $40x^3$
51. $40x^2$
52. $40xyz$
53. $2bad$ or $2abd$
54. w^3
55. $27x^3$
56. $125y^3$
57. $\frac{1}{8}k^3$
58. (3)
59. (3)
60. (3)
61. $175xy$
62. $40z^2$
63. $10n$

8-5 Dividing Powers of the Same Base: *page 244*

1. x^6
2. a^5
3. b^4
4. c
5. 1
6. d^2
7. e^6
8. m^8
9. n
10. 1
11. x^7
12. y^6
13. z^9
14. t^4
15. 1
16. 2^3 or 8
17. 10^2 or 100
18. 3^2 or 9
19. 5^2 or 25
20. 10^3 or $1,000$
21. x^{3a}
22. y^{8b}
23. r^{c-d}
24. s^{x-2}
25. 1
26. 2^{a-b}
27. 2^5 or 32
28. 5^3 or 125
29. 10
30. 1
31. 1
32. 6^8 or $1,679,616$
33. false
34. true
35. false

8-6 Dividing a Monomial by a Monomial: *pages 245–246*

1. $9x$
2. $-2x^2y^2$
3. $-6y^8$
4. $-10a^3$
5. $-3a^2$
6. $-3c$
7. -1
8. $-4c$
9. $6e$
10. $-2d$
11. $+2$
12. $9x^4$
13. $-4c^2$
14. $-x^2$
15. $-7c^2b$
16. $+8x$
17. $-3y$
18. -7
19. -3
20. $3y$
21. 50 miles per hour
22. $10b$ hours
23. $4y^2$
24. $5x^2$
25. $3y^2$
26. x^3
27. $12xy$

8-7 Nonpositive Integral Exponents: *page 248*

1. $\dfrac{1}{10^4}$ 2. $\dfrac{1}{2}$ or $\dfrac{1}{2^1}$ 3. $\dfrac{1}{(\frac{2}{3})^2}$ or $(\frac{3}{2})^2$

4. $\dfrac{1}{m^6}$ 5. $\dfrac{1}{r^3}$ 6. 1

7. 1   8. 1   9. 1

10. $\frac{1}{9}$ 11. $\frac{1}{16}$ 12. $-\frac{1}{6}$

13. -1 14. $\frac{1}{10}$ 15. $\frac{1}{100}$

16. $\frac{1}{1,000}$ 17. $\frac{1}{10,000}$ 18. $\frac{4}{100}$ or $\frac{1}{25}$

19. $\frac{1.5}{1,000}$ or $\frac{3}{2,000}$ or .0015   20. $1\frac{1}{36}$

21. $1\frac{1}{27}$ 22. 10^3 or 1,000   23. 3^{-6} or $\dfrac{1}{3^6}$

24. 10^2 or 100   25. 3^4 or 81

26. 4^{-2} or $\dfrac{1}{4^2}$ or $\dfrac{1}{16}$ 27. 3^6

28. a^4 29. x^{-4} or $\dfrac{1}{x^4}$ 30. m^{-5} or $\dfrac{1}{m^5}$

31. t^{-8} or $\dfrac{1}{t^8}$ 32. a^{-12} or $\dfrac{1}{a^{12}}$ 33. x^0 or 1

34. 6   35. $5\frac{1}{2}$

8-8 Expressing Large Numbers in Scientific Notation: *pages 250–251*

1. 10^5 2. 10^9 3. 10^{12}
4. 10,000,000   5. 10,000,000,000
6. 10,000,000,000,000
7. 1,000,000,000,000,000
8. 300,000   9. 400,000,000
10. 600,000,000,000,000
11. 9,000,000,000   12. 13,000
13. 8,300,000,000,000   14. 1,270
15. 61,400,000,000
16. 4×10^2 17. 6×10^3 18. 3×10^4
19. 4×10^5 20. 7×10^6 21. 3×10^8
22. 8×10^7 23. 2×10^{10} 24. 2
25. 2   26. 3   27. 4
28. 3   29. 5   30. 6
31. 8   32. 8.4×10^3 33. 2.7×10^4
34. 5.4×10^7 35. 3.2×10^8 36. 6.75×10^3
37. 8.16×10^4 38. 4.53×10^5 39. 3.75×10^8
40. *a.* 6×10^7 *b.* 60,000,000
41. *a.* 1.2×10^{14} *b.* 120,000,000,000,000
42. *a.* 2×10^{10} *b.* 20,000,000,000
43. *a.* 3×10^6 *b.* 3,000,000
44. 2×10^9 45. 3×10^{10} 46. 2.6×10^{13}
47. 9.5×10^{12} 48. 1.2×10^{22}

49. 2,000,000,000   50. 240,000
51. 1,800,000,000,000,000,000,000,000
52. 5,900,000,000,000,000,000,000,000

8-9 Expressing Small Numbers in Scientific Notation: *pages 252–253*

1. 10^{-2} 2. 10^{-5} 3. 10^{-8} 4. 10^{-10}
5. .000001   6. .00000001
7. .000000000000001   8. .00000000000000001
9. .004   10. .000000007
11. .0000000008   12. .0000000000009
13. .00012   14. .000036
15. .000000000074   16. .0000000000000314
17. 2×10^{-3} 18. 5×10^{-4} 19. 3×10^{-6}
20. 9×10^{-8} 21. -2 22. -5
23. -8 24. -11 25. -3
26. -7 27. 5.2×10^{-3} 28. 6.1×10^{-4}
29. 3.9×10^{-6} 30. 1.4×10^{-8} 31. 1.56×10^{-1}
32. 3.81×10^{-3} 33. 7.63×10^{-5}
34. 9.17×10^{-7} 35. *a.* 6×10^{-3} *b.* .006
36. *a.* 7.5×10^{-5} *b.* .000075
37. *a.* 3×10^{-7} *b.* .0000003
38. *a.* 2×10^3 *b.* 2,000
39. 4×10^{-3} 40. 1×10^{-6} 41. 5×10^{-13}
42. 8×10^{-4} 43. 6.5×10^{-5} 44. 1.67×10^{-24}
45. .06   46. .00000002   47. .0013
48. .00000000000000000000000166

8-10 Review Exercises: *pages 254–255*

1. $5r^2$ 2. $4bc$ 3. $10w$
4. $36k^2$ 5. $-a^3m^6$ 6. $-24mg^2$
7. $3t$ 8. $40t^2$ 9. $\frac{5}{8}$
10. $-12x^4y^5$ 11. $-9y^2$ 12. $20y^4$
13. $-5bx^5$ 14. x^{b+4} 15. $-4c$
16. $\dfrac{1}{8^2} = \dfrac{1}{64}$ 17. $\dfrac{1}{k^6}$ 18. $\dfrac{1}{10^3} = \dfrac{1}{1,000}$
19. $(\frac{5}{2})^2 = \frac{25}{4}$ 20. $\dfrac{2}{x^4}$ 21. $\frac{1}{3}$
22. 1   23. 100   24. $\frac{1}{144}$
25. *a.* $22x$ *b.* $24x^2$
26. *a.* $2h$ *b.* $\frac{1}{4}h^2$
27. $16px$ 28. $4x^3$ 29. $16w^3$
30. 10   31. $-4py$ 32. 5.8×10^3
33. 1.42×10^7 34. 6×10^{-5} 35. 2.77×10^{-6}
36. 40,000   37. .003   38. 390,000,000
39. .000103   40. (3)   41. (2)
42. (3)   43. (2)   44. (3)
45. (4)   46. (3)   47. (1)
48. 1:06 P.M.

Chapter 9.   Operations with Polynomials

9-1 Adding Polynomials: *pages 259–261*

1. 2   2. 5   3. 3
4. 1   5. no degree   6. 3
7. 2   8. 3   9. 4

10. 0   11. binomial   12. monomial
13. trinomial   14. none of these
15. *a.* $2x^2 - 3x + 5$ *b.* $5 - 3x + 2x^2$ *c.* 2
16. *a.* $y^4 + y^3 - 9$ *b.* $-9 + y^3 + y^4$ *c.* 4
17. *a.* $x^4 - \frac{1}{2}x^3 + 6$ *b.* $6 - \frac{1}{2}x^3 + x^4$ *c.* 4

18. *a.* $a^4 + 2a^2 - 3a$ *b.* $-3a + 2a^2 + a^4$ *c.* 4
19. $7c + 11d$
20. $10y + 9w$
21. $5x + 3y$
22. $-a + 5b$
23. $7r - 3s + 10t$
24. $-2m + 8p$
25. $5x^2 - 2x - 2$
26. $3x^2 - 6x$
27. $11x + 12y$
28. $13a - 3b$
29. $-10m - 4n$
30. $-6ab$
31. $18x - 40y + 5z$
32. $-3x^2 - 15x - 21$
33. $+2a^2 - 7b^2$
34. $-2x^2 + x + 8$
35. c^2
36. $1.2 + .4z + .8z^2$
37. $13a + 3$
38. $11b - 6$
39. $7 - c$
40. -4
41. $3r + s$
42. $14d^2 - 4d$
43. $11x - 2$
44. 0
45. $-15y + 7$
46. $3a + 7b$
47. $2x^2$
48. $9y^2 + 3y - 4$
49. $x^3 + x^2 - 9$
50. $-5d^2 + 9d + 2$
51. $x - 15$
52. $x^3 - 4x^2 - 3x$
53. $-2y^2 - y + 16$
54. $6c^2 - 2$
55. $2x^2 - 10xy - 3y^2$
56. *a.* $6x$
   b. 5 (any positive number)
   c. -2 (any negative number or zero)
57. *a.* $8x + 4$
   b. 3 (any positive number)
   c. -1 (any negative number or zero)
58. *a.* $4x - 6$
   b. 4 (any number greater than 3)
   c. 0 (any number less than or equal to 3)
59. *a.* $4x - 10$
   b. 10 (any number greater than 8)
   c. 5 (any number less than or equal to 8)
60. *a.* $8x - 8$
   b. 2 (any number greater than $\frac{4}{3}$)
   c. 1 (any number less than or equal to $\frac{4}{3}$)
61. *a.* $4x - 20$
   b. 10 (any number greater than 6)
   c. 5 (any number less than or equal to 6)
62. *a.* $4x - 20$
   b. 4 (any number less than or equal to 5)
63. *a.* $6x - 6$
   b. 3 (any number less than or equal to 4)
64. *a.* $6x - 12$
   b. 2 (any number less than or equal to $\frac{5}{2}$)
65. *a.* $5x - 2$
   b. $\frac{1}{2}$ (any number less than or equal to $\frac{1}{2}$)
66. *a.* $12x + 20$ *b.* $16x - 4$ *c.* $4x^2 + 16x - 12$
   d. $4x^2 + 8xy + 4y^2$
67. $14x - 30$ 68. $12x - 3$ 69. $4x + 8$
70. $2h - 40$ 71. $3b + 11$ 72. $5x - 3$

9-2 Subtracting Polynomials: pages 263–264

1. $-9x - 6$
2. $5x - 3$
3. $6x + 6y$
4. $-2x^2 + 3x - 2$
5. $y^2 - 5y + 4$
6. $-7ab + 3bc$
7. $6a + 3b$
8. $b + 2c$
9. $-3d + 14e$
10. $12x - 11y$
11. $-r$
12. $-8a + 6b$
13. $-3rs$
14. $8xy - 10cd$

15. $-2x^2 - 4x + 7$
16. $8y^2 - 7$
17. $4a^2 + 3ab$
18. $4a + 6b - 3c$
19. $3x^2 - 5x - 6$
20. $5 - 2d$
21. $12y - 14$
22. $-7x + 14$
23. $-a - b$
24. $7c + 9d$
25. $4x^2 + 9x - 16$
26. $-8x - 1$
27. $3x - 5$
28. $-2x + 4$
29. $-2z + 2$
30. $3m - 6$
31. n
32. $-5c$
33. $c + 6c^2$
34. $16r + 6s$
35. $-7x - 8$
36. $-5d + 2c$
37. 0
38. $a - b$
39. $-4x^2 - 12x + 12$
40. $-6c + 6$
41. $24 - 6x$
42. $8x + 4$
43. $x^2 + 10x - 4$
44. $2x^2 - 3x - 3$
45. $-7a^2 + 18a + 7$
46. $y^2 + 2y - 4$
47. $3x + 6y$
48. $-2a - 2b$
49. $4x^2 + 8x - 9$
50. $3r^2 - 6r + 1$
51. $8m - 3$
52. $13x - 12y + 12z$
53. $-x^2 + 9x - 19$
54. $2y^2 + 4y$
55. $7x^2 - 16x + 10$
56. $-2c^2 - 3c + 4$
57. $3a^2 + 6ab - 3b^2$
58. *a.* 10 *b.* $3x + 2y$
59. $x^2 - 7$
60. *a.* 3 *b.* $3x + 8$
61. $2c$
62. $6x^2 - 9x - 12$
63. $-4x^2 + 8$
64. $3x^2 - 7x - 5$
65. $6y + 6$
66. $5c^2 - 9c + 12$

9-3 Multiplying a Polynomial by a Monomial: page 265

1. $18c + 9d$
2. $-20m + 30n$
3. $-16a - 12b$
4. $20x - 2y$
5. $8m - 48n$
6. $-32r + 2s$
7. $-12c + 10d$
8. $20x^2 + 24x$
9. $5d^3 - 15d^2$
10. $-75c^3 + 20c^4$
11. $m^2n + mn^2$
12. $-a^2b + ab^2$
13. $15a^3b - 21ab^3$
14. $-6r^7s^4 + 3r^3s^7$
15. $20ad - 30cd + 40bd$
16. $-16x^2 + 24x + 40$
17. $3x^3y + 3x^2y^2 + 3xy^3$
18. $-10r^4s^2 + 15r^3s^3 - 20r^2s^4$
19. $10x - 15$
20. $15y^2 - 21y$
21. $6b^2 + 4b$
22. $(9x - 21)$ miles
23. $(3xy - 6y)$ dollars
24. $3w^2 - 2w$

9-4 Using Multiplication to Simplify Algebraic Expressions Containing Symbols of Grouping: pages 266–267

1. $5d + 5$
2. $6 - 4c$
3. $14x - 3$
4. $-2x + 8$
5. $17a - 12$
6. $25 - 12e$
7. $6 + 4e$
8. b
9. $4b + 4$
10. $3 - 5t$
11. $2 + 8s$
12. $-6x + 21$
13. $10x^2 - 6x$
14. $24y - 6y^2$
15. $13x - 11$
16. $-c + 2d$
17. $3a - 7a^2$
18. $6b$
19. $29x + 14$
20. $5x - 3y$
21. $-18x^2 + 11x$
22. $-2y$
23. $7x^2 + 37xy + 4y^2$
24. $-2c^2 + 4cd - 12d^2$
25. $7a^2b - 5abc + b^2c$
26. 0
27. $49x - 14$
28. $-8y + 16$
29. $-24x^2 - 20x$
30. 0
31. *a.* $12x^2 - 24x$ *b.* $2x^2 + 4x$ *c.* $10x^2 - 28x$
32. $(12x - 18)$ dollars
33. $(5x - 35)$ dollars
34. $(5x - 35)$ dollars
35. $(8x - 19)$ dollars

9-5 Multiplying a Polynomial by a Polynomial: *pages 269–270*

1. $a^2 + 5a + 6$ **2.** $c^2 + 7c + 6$
3. $x^2 - 8x + 15$ **4.** $d^2 - 11d + 30$
5. $d^2 + 6d - 27$ **6.** $x^2 + 5x - 14$
7. $m^2 - 4m - 21$ **8.** $z^2 + 3z - 40$
9. $f^2 + 2f - 80$ **10.** $t^2 + 9t - 90$
11. $b^2 - 18b + 80$ **12.** $w^2 - 6w - 91$
13. $30 + 11y + y^2$ **14.** $48 - 14e + e^2$
15. $72 + 6r - r^2$ **16.** $x^2 - 25$
17. $y^2 - 49$ **18.** $a^2 - 81$
19. $2x^2 - 11x - 6$ **20.** $2c^2 - 14c + 20$
21. $6a^2 + 29a + 9$ **22.** $15y^2 - 11y + 2$
23. $4x^2 - 9$ **24.** $9d^2 - 64$
25. $x^2 + 2xy + y^2$ **26.** $a^2 - 2ab + b^2$
27. $a^2 - b^2$ **28.** $a^2 + 5ab + 6b^2$
29. $6c^2 - cd - d^2$ **30.** $x^2 - 16y^2$
31. $6z^2 + 7wz - 20w^2$ **32.** $18x^2 + 17xy - 15y^2$
33. $15kr + 20ks + 6mr + 8ms$
34. $9x^2 - 16y^2$ **35.** $r^4 + 3r^2 - 10$ **36.** $x^4 - y^4$
37. $x^3 + 5x^2 + 11x + 10$ **38.** $4c^3 - 4c^2 - 5c - 1$
39. $15 - 16d - d^2 + 2d^3$ **40.** $c^3 + 8$
41. $6x^3 - 13x^2 + 9x - 2$
42. $12x^3 - 7x^2y - 8xy^2 + 3y^3$
43. $3x^4 - 10x^3 + 9x^2 - 14x + 4$
44. $6x^3 + 13x^2 - 19x - 12$
45. $x^4 + x^3 - 21x^2 + 13x - 2$
46. $x^3 + 12x^2 + 48x + 64$
47. $a^3 + 15a^2 + 75a + 125$
48. $x^3 - 3x^2y + 3xy^2 - y^3$
49. $2x^3 - 7x^2 + 16x - 15$
50. $8x^3 + 26x^2 - x - 12$
51. $x^3 + 3x^2y + 3xy^2 + y^3$
52. $a^3 - ab^2$ **53.** $5x - 14$ **54.** $12x^2 - 6$
55. $-2x + 3$ **56.** $14x + 2$ **57.** $y^2 - 33y - 8$
58. $14y + 7$ **59.** $r^2 - 2rs - r + s$ **60.** $a^3 - 8a$
61. $(2x - 5)(x + 7) = 2x^2 + 9x - 35$
62. $(11x - 8)(3x + 5) = 33x^2 + 31x - 40$
63. $(x + 100)(2x + 3) = 2x^2 + 203x + 300$
64. *a.* $x^2 + 5x + 6$
   b.

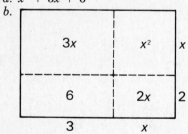

65. *a.* $x^2 + 11x + 30$
   b.

66. *a.* $10x^2 + 31x + 15$
   b.

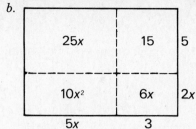

67. *a.* $9x^2 + 6x + 1$
   b.

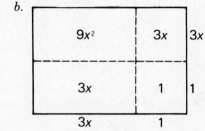

68. *a.* $2x^2 + 5xy + 3y^2$
   b.

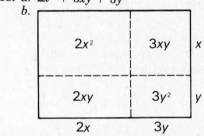

69. *a.* $6x^2 + 23xy + 20y^2$
   b.

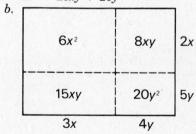

9-6 Dividing a Polynomial by a Monomial: *pages 271–272*

1. $2x + 4y$ **2.** $2r - 3s$ **3.** $2x + 1$
4. $m + n$ **5.** $t - 1$ **6.** $-6a + 3b$
7. $-2c^2 + 3d^2$ **8.** $m + 8$ **9.** $1 + rt$
10. $-y + 5$ **11.** $3d^2 + 2d$ **12.** $4x + 3$
13. $3r^3 + 2r$ **14.** $4t^3 - 2t^2$ **15.** $-3y^6 + 2y^3$
16. $-2a + 1$ **17.** $3b - 4a$ **18.** $c - 3d$
19. $r + h$ **20.** $3a + 6b$ **21.** $-2a^2 + 1$
22. $y^5 - 3y + 5$ **23.** $2a^2 + 3a - 1$
24. $-4y^2 - 2y + 1$ **25.** $-3r^2s^2 - 4rs + 1$

26. $4y + 3$ **27.** $3c^2 - 2c + 1$

28. $b - 2c$ **29.** $-y^2 + y - 1$

30. $3x^2 - 2x + 1$ **31.** $2d^2 - 1.5d + 1$

9-7 Dividing a Polynomial by a Polynomial: *page 274*

1. $b + 2$ **2.** $y + 1$

3. $m - 7$ **4.** $w - 3$

5. $y + 3 + \dfrac{10}{y + 17}$ **6.** $m + 12 + \dfrac{33}{m - 5}$

7. $x - 2$ **8.** $3t - 8$ **9.** $5r - 8$

10. $3c - 4$ **11.** $11 + x$ **12.** $6 + m$

13. $x + 8$ **14.** $2y - 7$ **15.** $x + 3$

16. $x - 9$ **17.** $y + 2$

9-8 Review Exercises: *pages 274–275*

1. *a* $4x^2 + 2bx$

b.
$$\begin{aligned} 12 + 18 + 3 &= 33 \\ 4 - 30 - 3 &= -29 \\ \hline 16 - 12 \quad\quad &= 4 \end{aligned}$$

2. $3c - 11d$ **3.** $2y^2 + 6y + 8$

4. $-r + 2s - 16t$ **5.** $2m^2 - m - 21$

6. $5k - r$ **7.** $-p^2 - 7$

8. $x + 2$ **9.** $3x - 4$

10. $x^2 - 4$ **11.** $b^2 - 9b + 18$

12. $2h^2 - 9h - 5$ **13.** $y^2 + 8y + 16$

14. $2m + 8$

15. $-3a^3x + 12a^2x^2 + 15ax^3$

16. $3w^2 - 4w + 1$ **17.** $2ab$

18. $4y^2 + 4y - 3$

19. *a.* $4x + 20$ *b.* $x^2 + 10x + 25$

20. $x - 12$ **21.** $3y + 5$

22. (2) **23.** (1)

24. (2) **25.** $(6k^2 - 8k)$ miles

26. $(5x - 1)$ cents **27.** $(24x - 40)$ cents

28. 3 (Note that the units place has 4 digits in a recurring pattern: 7, 9, 3, 1, 7, 9, . . . $(27)^{24}$ has a units digit of 1, and $(27)^{27}$ has 3 in the units place.)

29. 4 or -4

Chapter 10. First-Degree Equations and Inequalities in One Variable

10-1 Using Both the Additive and Multiplicative Inverses in Solving Equations: *pages 277–279*

1. $x = 4$ **2.** $y = 2$ **3.** $c = -16$

4. $y = -5$ **5.** $x = 14$ **6.** $x = -9$

7. $x = -14$ **8.** $t = 6$

9. $x = 2\frac{1}{2}$ or $x = 2.5$

10. $y = -\frac{1}{2}$ or $y = -.5$

11. $z = 18$ **12.** $y = -5$ **13.** $m = 33$

14. $r = -25$ **15.** $x = 20$ **16.** $r = -6$

17. $x = -4$ **18.** $x = -2$ **19.** $x = 10$

20. $y = 4$ **21.** $x = 2$ **22.** $\{-4\}$

23. $\{5\}$ **24.** $\{108\}$ **25.** $\{4\}$

26. $2x + 8$ **27.** $3x - 12$ **28.** $4(x + 3)$

29. $3(x + 5)$ **30.** $2(x + 5)$ **31.** $10(2x - 10)$

32. *a.* $10 - x$ *b.* $25 - x$ *c.* $36 - x$ *d.* $50 - x$ *e.* $100 - x$ *f.* $3,000 - x$

33. $S - x$ **34.** $S - l$ **35.** -8

36. 11 **37.** 60 **38.** 35

39. 45 **40.** 13 **41.** 3.5

10-2 Solving Equations That Have the Variable in Both Members: *pages 281–282*

1. $x = 2$ **2.** $x = 4$ **3.** $c = 7$

4. $y = -10$ **5.** $d = -12$ **6.** $y = -8$

7. $m = 40$ **8.** $y = 9$ **9.** $x = -18$

10. $x = 96$ **11.** $a = 20$ **12.** $c = -27$

13. $x = 9$ **14.** $m = -50$ **15.** $c = -8$

16. $r = 10$ **17.** $y = 11$ **18.** $x = -7$

19. $x = 0$ **20.** $x = 7$ **21.** $y = 4$

22. $c = 7$ **23.** $d = -18$ **24.** $y = -17$

25. $m = -\frac{1}{2}$ **26.** $x = 10$ **27.** $b = 2$

28. $t = 15$ **29.** $n = -1$ **30.** $y = -3$

31. $x = 13$ **32.** $x = 3$ **33.** $a = 20$

34. $c = -5$ **35.** $x = 11$ **36.** $d = -13$

37. $m = 9$ **38.** $z = -1$ **39.** 5

40. 8 **41.** -7 **42.** 5

43. 22 **44.** 4 **45.** 8

46. 6 **47.** 25 **48.** 8

49. 9

10-3 Solving Equations Containing Parentheses: *pages 284–285*

1. $x = 13$ **2.** $x = 25$

3. $x = \frac{3}{5}$ or $x = .6$

4. $c = 20$ **5.** $x = -4$ **6.** $x = -13$

7. $x = 2$ **8.** $y = 19$ **9.** $c = 4$

10. $c = -2$ **11.** $y = 4$ **12.** $c = 7$

13. $t = 3$ **14.** $x = 3$ **15.** $m = 5$

16. $x = 3$ **17.** $x = 3$ **18.** $a = -17$

19. $b = 9$ **20.** $c = 3$ **21.** $r = 2$

22. $y = 6$ **23.** $x = 11$ **24.** $z = \frac{6}{7}$

25. $b = 4$ **26.** $m = \frac{7}{3}$ or $m = 2\frac{1}{3}$

27. $v = 5$ **28.** $r = 1$ **29.** $a = 2$

30. $r = 5$ **31.** $x = 7$ **32.** $x = 4$

33. 30, 35 **34.** 18, 20 **35.** 10, 30

36. 7 **37.** 32, 56 **38.** 52, 92

39. 12, 33 **40.** 8, 23 **41.** 6, 19

42. 7, 15 **43.** 2, 4, 4 **44.** 19, 18, 31

10-4 Consecutive Integer Problems

Preparing to Solve Consecutive Integer Problems: *page 286*

1. *a.* 3, 4, 5, 6, 7 *b.* consecutive

2. *a.* $-3, -2, -1, 0, 1$ *b.* consecutive

3. *a.* −1, 1, 3, 5, 7   *b.* consecutive odd
4. *a.* 15, 16, 17, 18   *b.* 31, 32, 33, 34
   c. −10, −9, −8, −7 *d.* −2, −1, 0, 1
   e. $y, y + 1, y + 2, y + 3$
   f. $2y + 1, 2y + 2, 2y + 3, 2y + 4$
   g. $3y − 2, 3y − 1, 3y, 3y + 1$
5. *a.* 8, 10, 12, 14   *b.* 26, 28, 30, 32
   c. −20, −18, −16, −14 *d.* −4, −2, 0, 2
   e. $y, y + 2, y + 4, y + 6$
   f. $2y, 2y + 2, 2y + 4, 2y + 6$
   g. $2y − 6, 2y − 4, 2y − 2, 2y$
6. *a.* 9, 11, 13, 15   *b.* 35, 37, 39, 41
   c. −15, −13, −11, −9 *d.* −3, −1, 1, 3
   e. $y, y + 2, y + 4, y + 6$
   f. $2y + 1, 2y + 3, 2y + 5, 2y + 7$
   g. $2y − 1, 2y + 1, 2y + 3, 2y + 5$
7. *a.* even *b.* odd
8. *a.* even *b.* odd
9. *a.* even *b.* odd
10. *a.* odd *b.* even
11. *a.* even *b.* odd *c.* even
12. even   13. odd   14. even

Solving Consecutive Integer Problems: *page 288*

1. *a.* 30, 31 *b.* 17, 18 *c.* 45, 46 *d.* 62, 63
   e. −9, −8 *f.* −41, −40
2. *a.* 5, 6, 7 *b.* 15, 16, 17 *c.* 32, 33, 34
   d. −1, 0, 1 *e.* −5, −4, −3
   f. −20, −19, −18
3. 57, 58, 59, 60
4. *a.* 10, 12 *b.* 18, 20 *c.* 72, 74 *d.* 102, 104
   e. −6, −4 *f.* −18, −16
5. *a.* 2, 4, 6 *b.* 14, 16, 18 *c.* 50, 52, 54
   d. 84, 86, 88 *e.* −8, −6, −4
   f. −22, −20, −18
6. 12, 14, 16, 18
7. *a.* 9, 11, 13 *b.* 13, 15, 17 *c.* 51, 53, 55
   d. 203, 205, 207 *e.* −11, −9, −7
   f. −37, −35, −33
8. 25, 27, 29, 31   9. 19, 20, 21
10. 64, 65, 66, 67   11. 21, 23
12. 20, 22   13. 14, 15, 16
14. 25, 26, 27   15. 10, 12, 14
16. 19, 20   17. 9, 11, 13, 15
18. 15, 17, 19
19. no; the sum of three consecutive even integers must be a multiple of 3
20. no; the sum of three consecutive odd integers must be a multiple of 3

10-5 Finding the Value of a Variable in a Formula: *pages 289–290*

1. $c = 35$
2. *a.* $s = 5$ *b.* $s = 8$ *c.* $s = 1.6$
3. *a.* $w = 20$ *b.* $w = 4$
4. *a.* $h = 6$ *b.* $h = 8$
5. $w = 8$

6. *a.* $w = 3$ *b.* $w = 8\frac{1}{2}$
7. *a.* $l = 11$ *b.* $l = 7.7$
8. $b = 20$ cm   9. $a = 6.4$ cm
10. $h = 6$ 11. $b = 14$ cm
12. *a.* 40 *b.* 80
13. \$750
14. *a.* $C = 35°$ *b.* $C = 20°$ *c.* $C = 15°$
    d. $C = 0°$ *e.* $C = 100°$ *f.* $C = −25°$
15. 11.6 cm   16. *a.* 9 cm *b.* 6 cm
17. *a.* 7 cm *b.* 49 cm^2
18. *a.* $\frac{3}{4}$ in. *b.* $\frac{9}{16}$ sq. in.
19. *a.* 4.2 cm *b.* 17.64 cm^2
20. *a.* $\frac{1}{2}$ ft. *b.* $\frac{1}{4}$ sq. ft.

10-6 Perimeter Problems

Preparing to Solve Perimeter Problems: *page 291*

1. *a.* $7x + 2$ *b.* $8x − 10$ *c.* $7x + 2$
   d. $12x − 8$
2. *a.* $2x, 6x$ *b.* $x + 4, 4x + 8$
   c. $2x − 5, 6x − 10$ *d.* $2x + 3, 6x + 6$
3. $3x + 15$ 4. $8x − 4$
5. $10x + 15$ 6. $12x − 18$
7. *a.* $4x − 8$ *b.* $3x − 6$ *c.* $2x − 4$

Solving Perimeter Problems: *pages 292–293*

1. 9 cm, 27 cm   2. 12 cm, 30 cm
3. 19 in., 21 in., 33 in.   4. 30 cm
5. 14 m, 19 m   6. 34 yd., 31 yd.
7. 16 m, 57 m   8. 36 ft., 78 ft.
9. 20   10. 6, 7, 7
11. 32 in., 64 in.   12. 6 ft., 10 ft.
13. 8 m
14. hexagon is 18 in., square is 12 in.

10-7 Solving Equations That Have Variables in the Answers: *pages 294–295*

1. $x = \dfrac{b}{5}$ 2. $x = \dfrac{8}{s}$ 3. $y = \dfrac{s}{r}$

4. $y = \dfrac{t}{3}$ 5. $y = \dfrac{5}{c}$ 6. $y = \dfrac{m}{h}$

7. $x = r − 5$ 8. $x = 7 − a$ 9. $y = d − c$

10. $x = k − 4$ 11. $y = 9 − d$ 12. $x = \dfrac{p + q}{3}$

13. $x = r + 2$ 14. $y = 7 + a$ 15. $x = d + c$

16. $x = \dfrac{r + e}{3}$ 17. $y = \dfrac{4 + d}{c}$ 18. $x = \dfrac{c − b}{a}$

19. $x = \dfrac{s}{r}$ 20. $y = \dfrac{t − r}{s}$

21. $x = \dfrac{m − 2n}{2}$ or $x = \dfrac{m}{2} − n$ 22. $x = 2c$

23. $x = 9b$ **24.** $x = c$ **25.** $x = \dfrac{c + 5}{b}$

26. $y = \dfrac{a - 6}{b}$ **27.** $y = \dfrac{t - s}{r}$ **28.** $x = \dfrac{6d}{ab}$

29. $x = s$ **30.** $x = 15$ **31.** $x = 6a$

32. $x = 2a$

10-8 Transforming Formulas: pages 296–297

1. $h = \dfrac{A}{6}$ **2.** $h = \dfrac{36}{b}$ **3.** $s = \dfrac{P}{4}$

4. $t = \dfrac{D}{r}$ **5.** $l = \dfrac{V}{wh}$ **6.** $r = \dfrac{p}{b}$

7. $B = \dfrac{A}{H}$ **8.** $l = \dfrac{A}{w}$ **9.** $h = \dfrac{V}{lw}$

10. $h = \dfrac{V}{4b}$ **11.** $p = \dfrac{i}{rt}$ **12.** $B = \dfrac{400}{H}$

13. $h = \dfrac{2A}{b}$ **14.** $H = \dfrac{3V}{B}$ **15.** $g = \dfrac{2S}{t^2}$

16. $c = l + s$ **17.** $l = \dfrac{P - 2w}{2}$ or $l = \dfrac{P}{2} - w$

18. $C = \dfrac{5}{9}(F - 32)$ or $C = \dfrac{5F - 160}{9}$

19. $a = \dfrac{2S}{n} - l$ or $a = \dfrac{2S - nl}{n}$

20. $H = \dfrac{A}{B}$ **21.** $b = P - 2a$

22. $a = \dfrac{P - b - c}{2}$ or $a = \dfrac{P - (b + c)}{2}$

23. a. $W = \dfrac{144}{LH}$ b. 8   **24.** a. $h = \dfrac{2A}{b}$ b. 6

25. a. $C = \dfrac{5}{9}(F - 32)$ or $C = \dfrac{5F - 160}{9}$ b. 35

26. a. $L = \dfrac{P - 2W}{2}$ or $L = \dfrac{P}{2} - W$ b. 19

27. $A = 4h^2$ **28.** $A = 2b^2$

10-9 Properties of Inequality: pages 299–300

1. >	**2.** <	**3.** >
4. >	**5.** >	**6.** >
7. <	**8.** <	**9.** >
10. <	**11.** >	**12.** <
13. <	**14.** >	**15.** >, >
16. <, <	**17.** <, <	**18.** >, >
19. <, <	**20.** >, >	**21.** <, <
22. <	**23.** >	**24.** <
25. >	**26.** always	**27.** always
28. sometimes	**29.** never	**30.** always
31. sometimes	**32.** never	**33.** always

10-10 Finding and Graphing the Solution Sets of Inequalities: pages 300–304

1-51 require graphs.

1. $x > 6$	**2.** $z < 10$	**3.** $y > 2\frac{1}{2}$
4. $x < 5$	**5.** $x > 3$	**6.** $y > 2$
7. $d > 2\frac{3}{4}$	**8.** $c < -4$	**9.** $y \geq 8$
10. $d \geq 3$	**11.** $t > 2$	**12.** $x \leq 6$
13. $y \geq 5$	**14.** $h \geq -2\frac{1}{2}$	**15.** $y > -4$
16. $y > -3$	**17.** $x < 2$	**18.** $r \leq -10$
19. $x > 6$	**20.** $z \leq -9$	**21.** $x > 2$
22. $y \leq -3$	**23.** $z \geq 2$	**24.** $y \geq -10$
25. $z \leq -4$	**26.** $x > 3$	**27.** $y \geq 6$
28. $x > -6$	**29.** $y \geq -1$	**30.** $x > 2$
31. $y \geq 2$	**32.** $c > -2$	**33.** $d \leq 3.5$
34. $x > 1$	**35.** $y \leq 5.6$	**36.** $x > -6$
37. $x > 6$	**38.** $y < 2$	**39.** $x \leq -3$
40. $x > 2$	**41.** $c \leq -27$	**42.** $x \geq -24$
43. $x > 5$	**44.** $x > -10$	**45.** $x > 3$
46. $m \geq 1.5$	**47.** $r > -2$	**48.** $y \geq -9$
49. $x \geq -2$	**50.** $x < \frac{9}{8}$	**51.** $y \geq -4$
52. (2)	**53.** (4)	**54.** (3)
55. (2)	**56.** $x > 1$	**57.** $x < -1$
58. $x \leq 2$	**59.** $x \geq -3$	

10-11 Solving Verbal Problems by Using Inequalities

Preparing to Solve Problems Involving Inequalities: page 305

1. $x \leq 15$	**2.** $y \geq 4$
3. $x \leq 50$	**4.** $x > 50$
5. $3y \leq 30$	**6.** $5x + 2x \geq 70$
7. $4x - 6 \leq 54$	**8.** $2x + 1 \geq 13$
9. $3x(x + 1) < 35$	**10.** $\{x \mid x > 10\}$
11. $\{x \mid x < 10\}$	**12.** $\{x \mid x < 12\}$
13. $\{x \mid x > 40\}$	**14.** $\{x \mid x < 50\}$
15. $\{x \mid x < 21\}$	**16.** $\{x \mid x > 12\}$

Solving Problems Involving Inequalities: pages 307–308

1. 13   **2.** any number less than 14 ($n < 14$)
3. 39 lb., 117 lb.

4. $450	**5.** 165	**6.** $25
7. 16	**8.** 10 m	**9.** 65 cm
10. $150	**11.** 24, 26	**12.** 4

13. $6.01
14. a. 30 min. b. 45 min. c. 90 min.

10-12 Review Exercises: pages 308–309

1. $x = 23$	**2.** $m = -6$	**3.** $c = \frac{1}{2}$
4. $x = 7$	**5.** $d = 20$	**6.** $b = -64$
7. $p = 50$	**8.** $z = 13$	**9.** $w = 5$
10. $w = 15$	**11.** $h = 4$	**12.** $y = -1$
13. $z = -2$	**14.** $b = -2$	**15.** $x = 2$

16. $x = b + c - a$ **17.** $x = \dfrac{b - a}{c}$

18. $x = \dfrac{c + a}{b}$ **19.** $x = \dfrac{2b}{a + c}$ **20.** $h = \dfrac{2A}{b}$

21. $w = 3.5$ **22.** 68   **23.** 3

24-31. Graphs (Some also require solving an inequality.)

24. $x < 3$ **25.** $x \le -4$ **26.** $x > -3$

27. $x \ge -1$

31. $5 \le x < 9$ **32.** always   **33.** sometimes

34. always   **35.** never   **36.** (1)

37. (1)   **38.** (3)   **39.** 5, 23

40. $-9, -19$ **41.** 6.5 ft. by 24.5 ft.

42. 4, 5, 6   **43.** 7, 9, 11, 13

44. 15 min., 35 min., 70 min.   **45.** 8

Chapter 11.   Geometry

11-1   Points, Lines, and Planes: *page 313*

1. line LM (no endpoints)
2. line segment LM (endpoints are L and M)
3. ray LM (endpoint is L)
4. the distance between L and M
5. T and Q or R and S
6. $\overline{SR}, \overline{SP}, \overline{ST}, \overline{SQ}, \overline{PT}, \overline{PQ}, \overline{TQ}$
7. $\overrightarrow{TQ}$ and $\overrightarrow{TR}$ (or $\overrightarrow{TP}$ or $\overrightarrow{TS}$)
8. $\overrightarrow{TP}$ or $\overrightarrow{TR}$ or $\overrightarrow{TS}$
9. no   10. *a.* two   *b.* one   *c.* none

11-2   Angles, Angle Measures, and Perpendicularity: *page 316*

1. *a.* 60   *b.* acute   2. *a.* 120   *b.* obtuse
3. *a.* 40   *b.* acute   4. *a.* 60   *b.* acute
5. *a.* 120   *b.* obtuse
6–11. Student drawings
12. *a.* $\angle BOA$ or $\angle AOB$ *b.* $\angle y$
    c. $\angle x$ or $\angle y$ ($\angle BOA$ or $\angle COB$)   *d.* $\angle COA$
13. *a.* 180   *b.* 270   *c.* 30   *d.* 150
14. 30   15. 120   16. 180
17. 15   18. 12 o'clock

11-3   Pairs of Angles: *pages 321–324*

1. 50   2. 65   3. 45
4. 20.5   5. $2\frac{2}{3}$ 6. $90 - m$
7. $90 - d$ 8. y 9. $80 - x$
10. $110 - x$ 11. 15, 75   12. 20, 70
13. 65, 25   14. 20, 70   15. 30, 60
16. 80   17. 75   18. 35
19. 41   20. 140   21. 111
22. 90   23. 70   24. $12\frac{1}{2}$
25. $180 - m$ 26. $180 - c$ 27. $180 - 2y$
28. t 29. $140 - x$ 30. 45, 135
31. 120, 60   32. 105, 75   33. 50, 130
34. 60, 120   35. 110   36. 140
37. 130   38. (3)   39. 30
40. 65   41. 90   42. 128.4
43. $175\frac{1}{2}$ 44. 25   45. 60
46. 72
47. m$\angle FGH = 90$; m$\angle HGI = 28$
48. m$\angle JLN = 42$; m$\angle MLK = 90$; m$\angle KLO = 42$; m$\angle JLO = 138$
49. m$\angle HKI = 56$; m$\angle HKG = 124$; m$\angle GKJ = 146$
50. m$\angle PMO = 90$; m$\angle OML = 50$
51. m$\angle RSQ = 90$; m$\angle QST = 90$; m$\angle TSU = 91$
52. m$\angle VWY = 91$; m$\angle YWX = 89$; m$\angle XWZ = 91$

53. m$\angle ABD = 70$; m$\angle DBE = 70$
54. m$\angle FKJ = 40$; m$\angle FKG = 40$; m$\angle GKH = 100$; m$\angle JKI = 140$
55. m$\angle CEB = 20$; m$\angle BED = 160$; m$\angle CEA = 160$
56. m$\angle RQS = 60$; m$\angle SQT = 120$; m$\angle PQT = 150$
57. m$\angle LRP = 50$; m$\angle LRQ = 130$; m$\angle PRM = 130$
58. m$\angle FEB = 10$; m$\angle CEF = 80$; m$\angle AEF = 170$

11-4   Angles and Parallel Lines: *pages 329–330*

1. *a.* m$\angle 1$ = m$\angle 5$ = m$\angle 7$ = 80; m$\angle 2$ = m$\angle 4$ = m$\angle 6$ = m$\angle 8$ = 100
   b. m$\angle 1$ = m$\angle 3$ because they are vertical angles; m$\angle 3$ = m$\angle 5$ because they are alternate interior angles; m$\angle 5$ = m$\angle 7$ because they are vertical angles; $\angle 2$ and $\angle 3$ are a linear pair of angles and are supplementary; m$\angle 2$ = m$\angle 4$ because they are vertical angles; m$\angle 4$ = m$\angle 6$ because they are alternate interior angles; m$\angle 6$ = m$\angle 8$ because they are vertical angles
2. *a.* m$\angle 6$ = m$\angle 8$ = m$\angle 4$ = m$\angle 2$ = 150; m$\angle 7$ = m$\angle 5$ = m$\angle 3$ = m$\angle 1$ = 30
   b. m$\angle 6$ = m$\angle 8$ because they are vertical angles; m$\angle 6$ = m$\angle 4$ because they are alternate interior angles; m$\angle 4$ = m$\angle 2$ because they are vertical angles; $\angle 6$ and $\angle 7$ are a linear pair and are supplementary; m$\angle 7$ = m$\angle 5$ because they are vertical angles; m$\angle 5$ = m$\angle 3$ because they are alternate interior angles; m$\angle 3$ = m$\angle 1$ because they are vertical angles
3. *a.* m$\angle 5$ = m$\angle 7$ = m$\angle 3$ = m$\angle 1$ = 60; m$\angle 6$ = m$\angle 8$ = m$\angle 4$ = m$\angle 2$ = 120
   b. m$\angle 5$ = m$\angle 7$ because they are vertical angles; m$\angle 5$ = m$\angle 3$ because they are alternate interior angles; m$\angle 3$ = m$\angle 1$ because they are vertical angles; $\angle 5$ and $\angle 6$ are a linear pair and are supplementary; m$\angle 6$ = m$\angle 8$ because they are vertical angles; m$\angle 6$ = m$\angle 4$ because they are alternate interior angles; m$\angle 4$ = m$\angle 2$ because they are vertical angles
4. *a.* m$\angle 1$ = m$\angle 3$ = m$\angle 5$ = m$\angle 7$ = 75; m$\angle 2$ = m$\angle 4$ = m$\angle 6$ = m$\angle 8$ = 105
   b. same reasons as in 1*b*
5. m$\angle 1$ = 150; m$\angle 2$ = 30; m$\angle 3$ = 150; m$\angle 6$ = 140; m$\angle 7$ = 40; m$\angle 8$ = 140; m$\angle 9$ = 40; m$\angle 10$ = 110; m$\angle 11$ = 30

6. m∠1 = m∠3 = m∠5 = m∠7 = 80;
   m∠2 = m∠4 = m∠6 = m∠8 = 100
7. m∠2 = m∠4 = m∠6 = m∠8 = 110;
   m∠1 = m∠3 = m∠5 = m∠7 = 70
8. m∠2 = m∠4 = m∠6 = m∠8 = 124;
   m∠1 = m∠3 = m∠5 = m∠7 = 56
9. m∠1 = m∠3 = m∠5 = m∠7 = 130;
   m∠2 = m∠4 = m∠6 = m∠8 = 50
10. measure of each angle is 90°
11. never
12. sometimes (if they lie in the same plane)
13. always   14. always
15. sometimes   16. sometimes
17. ∠1 ≅ ∠3 because they are corresponding
    angles
    ∠3 ≅ ∠2 because they are vertical angles
    ∠1 ≅ ∠2 by substitution
    m∠1 = m∠2 because congruent angles have
    equal measures

11-5 Geometric Figures: *page 332*

1. *a.* 4, 6, 7, 8 *b.* 4, 7, 8
2. *a.* C, S *b.* A, R *c.* B, T
3. *a.* 1, 3, 5, 8, 10 *b.* 3 *c.* 1 *d.* 5 *e.* 8 *f.* 10
4. *a.* 6 *b.* 4 *c.* 3 *d.* 8 *e.* 5
5. *a.* rectangle, quadrilateral
   b. square, quadrilateral
   c. hexagon
   d. octagon

11-6 The Triangle

The Sum of the Measures of the Angles of a Triangle: *pages 335–336*

1. yes   2. no   3. yes   4. 80
5. 60   6. 43.2   7. 74   8. 60
9. *a.* no *b.* no
   c. no; the sum of the measures would be
   greater than 180°
10. 90°
11. congruent; the sum of the measures of the three
    angles must be 180°
12. 20°, 60°, 100°
13. 18°, 72°, 90° 14. 35°, 65°, 80° 15. 35°, 75°, 70°
16. *a.* m∠x = 60, m∠y = 30, m∠z = 90 *b.* right
17. *a.* m∠R = 60, m∠S = 90, m∠T = 30
    b. right
18. *a.* m∠K = 60, m∠L = 60, m∠M = 60
    b. equiangular

The Exterior Angle of a Triangle: *pages 338–339*

1. *a.* ∠BCD *b.* ∠A and ∠B
2. *a.* ∠ACE *b.* ∠A and ∠B

3. *a.* ∠CBF *b.* ∠A and ∠C
4. *a.* ∠BAG *b.* ∠B and ∠C
5. *a.* ∠ABH *b.* ∠A and ∠C
6. 110°   7. 65°   8. 70°   9. 27°
10. 60°   11. x = 30   12. x = 30   13. x = 12
14. m∠F = 40
15. The measure of an exterior angle at M is 130°.
16. 120°   17. 90°   18. (3)
19. *a.* 360° *b.* yes

The Isosceles Triangle: *pages 341–342*

1. *a.* legs, $\overline{LN}$ and $\overline{MN}$; base, $\overline{LM}$;
   vertex angle, ∠N; base angles, ∠L and ∠M
   b. legs, $\overline{OP}$ and $\overline{OQ}$; base, $\overline{PQ}$;
   vertex angle, ∠O; base angles, ∠P and ∠Q
   c. legs, $\overline{RT}$ and $\overline{RS}$; base, $\overline{ST}$;
   vertex angle, ∠R; base angles, ∠T and ∠S
   d. legs, $\overline{XY}$ and $\overline{XZ}$; base, $\overline{YZ}$;
   vertex angle, ∠X; base angles, ∠Y and ∠Z
2. *a.* isosceles   *b.* ∠A and ∠C
   c. because they are opposite sides of equal measure (base angles of an isosceles triangle are
   congruent)
3. *a.* 70°   *b.* $\overline{RT} ≅ \overline{ST}$
   c. because they are opposite angles of equal
   measure
   d. isosceles
4. Drawings
5. *a.* no   *b.* no
   c. because the second base angle would be
   equal in measure and a triangle cannot have
   two right or obtuse angles (because the sum
   of the measures of the angles of the triangle
   would be greater than 180°)
6. *a.* 20° *b.* 70° *c.* 96° *d.* 135° *e.* 77°
7. *a.* 70° *b.* 65° *c.* 52° *d.* 40° *e.* $57\frac{1}{2}°$
8. 45°   9. 12°, 84°, 84° 10. 90°, 45°, 45°
11. 36°, 36°, 108° 12. 55°, 55°, 70° 13. 64°, 58°, 58°
14. 22°, 79°, 79°
15. *a.* m∠A = 40, m∠B = 70, m∠C = 70
    b. isosceles
16. 130°   17. 50°   18. 30°
19. *a.* true
    b. Two sides of a triangle are equal in measure
    if the angles opposite these sides are equal
    in measure. Or: If two angles of a triangle
    are equal in measure, then the sides oppo-
    site these sides are equal in measure.
    c. true
    d. Two sides of a triangle are equal in measure
    if and only if the angles opposite these sides
    are equal in measure.
    e. true

11-7 Congruent Triangles: *pages 348–350*

1. *b* and *d*   2. *c* and *e*   3. *a* and *c*
4. *a.* yes
   b. copies have the same size and shape (corresponding sides and angles will be congruent)

5. *a.* similar
   b. lengths should be in proportion and angles congruent
6*a*–8*a*. Drawings
6. *b.* △*ABC* ≅ △*FED*; s.a.s. ≅ s.a.s.
   (Note that △*ABC* ≇ △*DEF*
   because $\overline{AB}$ ≇ $\overline{DE}$ and $\overline{BC}$ ≇ $\overline{EF}$.)
7. *b.* △*ABC* ≅ △*FED*; a.s.a. ≅ a.s.a.
   (Note that △*ABC* ≇ △*DEF*
   because $\overline{AB}$ ≇ $\overline{DE}$ and ∠*A* ≇ ∠*D*.)
8. *b.* △*ABC* ≅ △*DEF*; a.s.a. ≅ a.s.a.
9. the congruent angle may not have been the included angle in both triangles
10. *a.* △*ABC* ≅ △*VTS* by a.s.a. ≅ a.s.a.
   △*DEF* ≅ △*QPR* by s.a.s. ≅ s.a.s.
   △*JKL* ≅ △*YXZ* by a.s.a. ≅ a.s.a.
   b. for △*ABC* and △*VTS*:
   ∠*A* ≅ ∠*V*, ∠*B* ≅ ∠*T*, ∠*C* ≅ ∠*S*
   $\overline{AB}$ ≅ $\overline{VT}$, $\overline{BC}$ ≅ $\overline{TS}$, $\overline{AC}$ ≅ $\overline{VS}$
   or
   ∠*A* ≅ ∠*T*, ∠*B* ≅ ∠*V*, ∠*C* ≅ ∠*S*
   $\overline{AB}$ ≅ $\overline{VT}$, $\overline{BC}$ ≅ $\overline{VS}$, $\overline{AC}$ ≅ $\overline{TS}$
   for △*DEF* and △*QPR*:
   ∠*D* ≅ ∠*Q*, ∠*E* ≅ ∠*P*, ∠*F* ≅ ∠*R*
   $\overline{DE}$ ≅ $\overline{QP}$, $\overline{EF}$ ≅ $\overline{PR}$, $\overline{DF}$ ≅ $\overline{QR}$
   for △*JKL* and △*YXZ*:
   ∠*J* ≅ ∠*Y*, ∠*K* ≅ ∠*X*, ∠*L* ≅ ∠*Z*
   $\overline{JK}$ ≅ $\overline{YX}$, $\overline{KL}$ ≅ $\overline{XZ}$, $\overline{JL}$ ≅ $\overline{YZ}$
11. *a.* s.a.s. ≅ s.a.s.
   b. m∠*RTS* = m∠*R'T'S'* = 60
12. *a.* a.s.a. ≅ a.s.a.   *b.* *BC* = *B'C'* = 3.4 m
13. *a.* equal   *b.* a.s.a. ≅ a.s.a.   *c.* equal
   d. *BA* = *CD* = 35 cm
14. *a.* △*ABE* ≅ △*CBE*; s.a.s. ≅ s.a.s.
   b. *AE* = *CE* = 25 ft.
15. *a.* s.s.s. ≅ s.s.s.   *b.* *x* = 20

11-8 The Quadrilateral: *pages 354–355*

1. *a.* If a polygon is a trapezoid, it is a quadrilateral; true
   b. If a polygon is a quadrilateral, it is a trapezoid; false (not always true)
   c. If a polygon is not a trapezoid, it is not a quadrilateral; false (not always true)
   d. If a polygon is not a quadrilateral, it is not a trapezoid; true
2. *a.* If a polygon is a rectangle, it is a parallelogram; true
   b. If a polygon is a parallelogram, it is a rectangle; false (not always true)
   c. If a polygon is not a rectangle, it is not a parallelogram; false (not always true)
   d. If a polygon is not a parallelogram, it is not a rectangle; true
3. *a.* If a polygon is a rhombus, it is a parallelogram; true
   b. If a polygon is a parallelogram, it is a rhombus; false (not always true)
   c. If a polygon is not a rhombus, it is not a parallelogram; false (not always true)

d. If a polygon is not a parallelogram, it is not a rhombus; true
4. *a.* If a polygon is a rhombus, it is a square; false (not always true)
   b. If a polygon is a square, it is a rhombus; true
   c. If a polygon is not a rhombus, it is not a square; true
   d. If a polygon is not a square, it is not a rhombus; false (not always true)
5. *a.* If a polygon is a parallelogram, it is a square; false (not always true)
   b. If a polygon is a square, it is a parallelogram; true
   c. If a polygon is not a parallelogram, it is not a square; true
   d. If a polygon is not a square, it is not a parallelogram; false (not always true)
6. *a.* If two angles are opposite angles of a parallelogram, they are congruent; true
   b. If two angles are congruent, they are opposite angles of a parallelogram; false (not always true)
   c. If two angles are not opposite angles of a parallelogram, they are not congruent; false (not always true)
   d. If two angles are not congruent, they are not opposite angles of a parallelogram; true
7. *a.* *x* = 50
   b. m∠*A* = 110, m∠*B* = 50, m∠*C* = 120, m∠*D* = 80
8. *a.* *x* = 90
   b. m∠*E* = 90, m∠*F* = 90, m∠*G* = 70, m∠*H* = 110
9. *a.* *x* = 60
   b. m∠*K* = 60, m∠*L* = 50, m∠*M* = 130, m∠*N* = 120
10. *a.* *x* = 45
   b. m∠*Q* = 55, m∠*R* = 105, m∠*S* = 110, m∠*T* = 90
11. *AB* = *DC* = 14
12. m∠*A* = 110, m∠*B* = 70, m∠*C* = 110, m∠*D* = 70
13. *BC* = *AD* = 11   14. 20°   15. 42
16. 18
17. *a.* *PR* = *TS* = 4, *RS* = 7, *PT* = 11
   b. m∠*P* = m∠*T* = 60,
   m∠*TSR* = m∠*SRP* = 120
18. *a.* 360°   *b.* 360°   *c.* yes

11-9 Transformations

Line Reflection: *page 358*

1.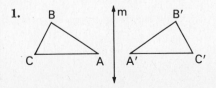

2.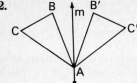

3.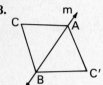

4.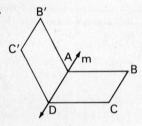

5.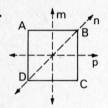

Line Symmetry: *page 360*

1.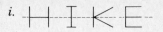

A B C D E H I K
M O T U V W X Y

2. *b, c, f, g, h, j.* none

a. M O M

d. O T T O

e. B O O K

i. H I K E

k. O H H O

l. C H O K E D

3. *a.*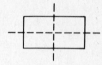

b. two

4. *a.*

b. three

5. *a.*

b. none

6. *a.*

b. one

7. *a.*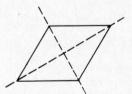

b. two

238

8. *a.*

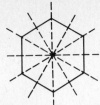

    b. six

9. *a.*

    b. none (unless the trapezoid is isosceles)

10. *a.*

    b. none

11. *a.*

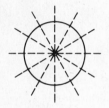

    b. infinitely many (any line through the center)

12. *a.*

    b. eight

13. *a.*

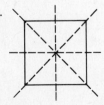

    b. four

14. *a.*

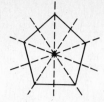

    b. five

Point Reflection: *page 362*

1. *a.*

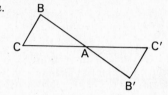

  b.

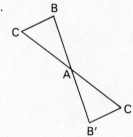

  c.

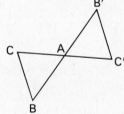

  d.

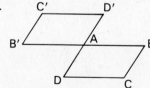

2. *a.* D   *b.* $\dfrac{B}{}$ *c.* $\dfrac{E}{}$ *d.* $\dfrac{A}{}$
    e. C   *f.* $\overline{DE}$ *g.* $\overline{DB}$ *h.* $\overline{AC}$

Point Symmetry: *page 363*

1.

2. *a, b, d, e, f, i, l.* no point symmetry

c. SIS   g. u•n

h. NO•ON

j. SWIMS

k. OH•HO

3. point symmetry (as shown) in rectangle, parallelogram, rhombus, regular hexagon, circle, regular octagon, square

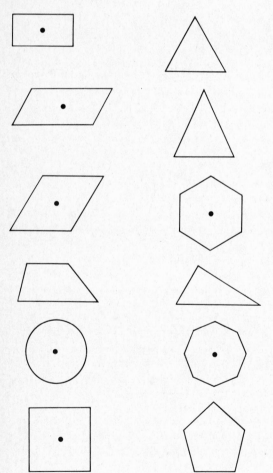

4. yes 5. no 6. yes 7. no 8. no 9. yes

Translation: *page 364*

1. *a.* P *b.* H *c.* O *d.* L *e.* K
2. *a.* I *b.* A *c.* N *d.* K *e.* F
3. *a.* no *b.* yes, *F* *c.* yes, *E* *d.* no

Rotation: *pages 365–366*

1. *a.* D *b.* E *c.* F *d.* J *e.* K *f.* A *g.* B
2. *a.* J *b.* K *c.* L *d.* D *e.* E *f.* G *g.* H
3. rectangle *a.* yes *b.* 180°
   equilateral triangle *a.* yes *b.* 120°
   parallelogram *a.* yes *b.* 180°
   isosceles triangle *a.* no
   rhombus *a.* yes *b.* 180°
   regular hexagon *a.* yes *b.* 60°
   trapezoid *a.* no
   scalene triangle *a.* no
   circle *a.* yes *b.* symmetric for *any* rotation
   regular octagon *a.* yes *b.* 45°
   square *a.* yes *b.* 90°
   regular pentagon *a.* yes *b.* 72°

General Exercises: *page 366*

4. yes, point symmetry (equivalent to 180° rotational symmetry)
5. *a.* B *b.* E *c.* $\overline{BO}$ *d.* ∠FCO
6. *a.* C *b.* G *c.* $\overline{CO}$ *d.* ∠FBO
7. *a.* D *b.* H *c.* $\overline{DO}$ *d.* ∠GCO
8. *a.* G *b.* C *c.* $\overline{OG}$ *d.* ∠COG
9. (3)

11-10   Review Exercises: *pages 366–368*

1. 135   2. 50   3. 90   4. 55   5. 70
6. 73   7. 24   8. 70
9. *a.* m∠A = 50; m∠R = 80; m∠T = 50 *b.* (2)
10. 119   11. 64   12. 52   13. 9
14. 70   15. N; S; Z   16. (3)   17. (3)
18. (4)   19. (3)
20. *a.* x *b.* 30 *c.* 1. 30 2. 120 3. 150
21. *a.* s.a.s. ≅ s.a.s. *b.* 4 *c.* C *d.* $\overrightarrow{BD}$
22. 13
23. 30   Using the same upper vertex for all, and 3 different altitudes:
    base 1 segment wide, 4(3) = 12;
       2 segments wide, 3(3) = 9;
       3 segments wide, 2(3) = 6;
       4 segments wide, 1 (3) = 3.
    12 + 9 + 6 + 3 = 30

Chapter 12. Ratio and Proportion

12-1 Ratio: *pages 371–372*

1. *a.* $\frac{36}{12}$ *b.* 36:12   2. *a.* $\frac{48}{24}$ *b.* 48:24
3. *a.* $\frac{40}{25}$ *b.* 40:25   4. *a.* $\frac{2}{3}$ *b.* 2:3
5. *a.* $\frac{5}{4}$ *b.* 5:4
6. *a.* $\frac{1}{4}$ or 1:4 *b.* $\frac{8}{1}$ or 8:1 *c.* $\frac{3}{7}$ or 3:7
   d. $\frac{4}{3}$ or 4:3 *e.* $\frac{3}{2}$ or 3:2 *f.* 2:1
   g. 1:3 *h.* 1:1 *i.* 12:5
   j. 3:5 *k.* 3:2 *l.* 1:4
   m. 3:5 *n.* x:y *o.* 3:1
7. *a.* 2 *b.* 3 *c.* 1.5 *d.* 2.5 *e.* $\frac{5}{3}$
8. 10   9. $\frac{1}{8}$
10. *a.* yes *b.* no *c.* no *d.* yes *e.* yes *f.* no
11. *a.* $\frac{2}{3} = \frac{6}{9} = \frac{50}{75}$ *b.* 10:8 = 20:16 = 50:40
12. *a.* 2:4 = 3:6 = 4:8
    b. 2:10 = 3:15 = 4:20
    c. 6:2 = 9:3 = 12:4
    d. 8:2 = 12:3 = 16:4
    e. 6:8 = 9:12 = 12:16
    f. 4:6 = 6:9 = 8:12
13. *a.* 1:1 *b.* 1:1
14. *a.* 3:1 *b.* 3:1 *c.* 1:2 *d.* 3:1 *e.* 24:1
15. *a.* 5:1 *b.* 3:4 *c.* 1:2 *d.* 3:5
    e. 150:7 *f.* 4:1 *g.* 3:250 *h.* 3:100 *i.* 1:4
16. *a.* 3:1 *b.* 6:1 *c.* 12:1 *d.* 3:1 *e.* 2:1
    f. 1:4 *g.* 4:1 *h.* 12:1 *i.* 4:1
17. *a.* 90:162 or 5:9 *b.* 5
18. *a.* 6:4 or 3:2 *b.* 3
19. $1\frac{1}{2}:1\frac{3}{4}$ or 6:7   20. 10:5 or 2:1
21. b:(b + g)   22. 2x:10x or 1:5
23. *a.* 3x and 4x *b.* 5x and 3x *c.* x and 4x
    d. x and 2x *e.* 3x and 5x
24. *a.* x, 2x, 3x *b.* 3x, 4x, 5x *c.* x, 3x, 4x
    d. 2x, 3x, 5x

12-2 Using a Ratio to Express a Rate: *pages 373–374*

1. 2:1 (2 apples per person)
2. 8:1 (8 patients per nurse)
3. .5:1 ($.50 per liter)
4. 6:1 (6 cents per gram)
5. 3:1 (3 ounces per dollar)
6. .62:1 (.62 miles per kilometer)
7. 3   8. 8 cents   9. 62
10. *a.* 3.5 *b.* 3.3 *c.* giant size
11. Sue   12. Ronald

12-3 Solving Verbal Problems Involving Ratios: *pages 375–376*

1. 40, 30   2. 100, 60   3. 42, 30   4. 48, 12
5. 12 cm, 20 cm   6. 12 cm, 12 cm, 10 cm
7. 275 boys, 250 girls   8. 12 cm, 16 cm, 20 cm
9. 132 cm, 48 cm   10. 36°, 54°   11. 80°, 100°
12. m∠1 = m∠3 = m∠5 = m∠7 = 60; m∠2 = m∠4 = m∠6 = m∠8 = 120

13. *a.* 40°, 40°, 100° *b.* isosceles   14. 84°, 48°, 48°
15. 20°, 80°, 80°   16. $70, $30   17. 9, 21
18. 12, 20   19. 21, 27
20. $7\frac{1}{2}$ liters of water, 5 liters of acid
21. 25 in., 25 in., 15 in.

12-4 Proportion: *pages 379–381*

1. yes	2. no	3. no	4. no
5. yes	6. yes	7. 4	8. 30
9. 24	10. 28	11. 20	12. 5
13. 36	14. 12	15. 9	16. 15
17. 18	18. 4	19. 3	20. 7
21. 36	22. 8	23. 3	24. $\frac{bc}{a}$
25. 6r	26. $\frac{2mr}{s}$	27. $\frac{12}{20}$	28. $\frac{25}{60}$
29. $\frac{20}{50}$	30. $\frac{36}{12}$	31. 29	32. $\frac{12}{9}$
33. $\frac{12}{19}$	34. 24		

12-5 Direct Variation: *pages 383–385*

1. 4   2. 40   3. $\frac{1}{9}$ 4. 4   5. $\frac{3}{2}$
6. $\frac{17}{2}$ 7. $\frac{4}{5}$ 8. $\frac{53}{50}$ 9. $\frac{3}{2}$
10. yes, p = 3s   11. yes, c = 2n   12. no
13. yes, d = 20t   14. yes, y = −3x   15. no
16. A = 10, h = 5, A = 5h
17. S = 12, h = 10, S = $\frac{3}{2}$h
18. W = 4, L = 14, L = 2W
19. no; the ratio $\frac{R}{T}$ is not constant
20. yes; the ratio $\frac{T}{D}$ is constant
21. yes; the ratio $\frac{e}{i}$ is constant
22. no; the ratio $\frac{b}{h}$ is not constant
23. *a.* directly
    b. The cost of 9 articles will be 3 times as much.
    c. C is doubled.
24. *a.* directly
    b. The rectangle having an 8-in. length will have 2 times the area.
    c. A is tripled.
25. 360
26. Y = 140	27. h = 3	28. N = 15
29. $4.45	30. $30.80	31. 5 lb.
32. 140	33. 420	34. 1,620
35. 170	36. $5\frac{1}{2}$ hr.	37. 7.65 kg
38. $2\frac{1}{2}$	39. $8.25	40. $1,320
41. 5.6 km	42. $21.00	43. $4\frac{1}{4}$ in.
44. 25	45. $\frac{dn}{p}$	46. $\frac{qh}{d}$

12-6 Percent and Percentage Problems: pages 387–389

1. .72	**2.** 9	**3.** 7.2	**4.** 10
5. 33.6	**6.** 7.5	**7.** 16	**8.** 24
9. 27	**10.** 200	**11.** 80	**12.** 200
13. 72	**14.** 36	**15.** 160	**16.** 81
17. 62	**18.** 50%	**19.** 30%	**20.** 60%
21. 80%	**22.** $33\frac{1}{3}$%	**23.** 100%	**24.** 150%
25. $\frac{1}{2}$% or .5%		**26.** 25%	**27.** 30

28. a. $1.92 b. $25.92 **29.** 90
30. $8,000,000 **31.** $814.50 **32.** 6 kg
33. 52,464 **34.** 16
35. $120 (before the 20% discount)

36. $3,500	**37.** $120	**38.** 25%
39. 5%	**40.** $78	**41.** $1.80
42. $3,000	**43.** 8%	**44.** 20%
45. $37\frac{1}{2}$%	**46.** $60	

12-7 Similar Polygons: pages 391–393

1. no; corresponding sides are not in proportion
2. no; corresponding angles are not congruent
3. yes; corresponding sides are in proportion and corresponding angles are congruent
4. yes; corresponding sides are in proportion and corresponding angles are congruent
5. no; corresponding sides may not be in proportion
6. no; corresponding angles may not be congruent and corresponding sides may not be in proportion
7. no; corresponding angles may not be congruent
8. 9 cm   9. 12 cm   10. $5\frac{1}{2}$ in.
11. $BC = 6, A'B' = 8, B'C' = 12, C'D' = 8$
12. $XY = 15, YZ = 20, X'Y' = 7\frac{1}{2}, Y'Z' = 10, W'Z' = 7\frac{1}{2}$
13. $B'C' = 5, A'C' = 6$
14. $RT = 8, ST = 10, R'T' = 16, S'T' = 20$

12-8 Similar Triangles; Dilation: pages 398–402

1. $\angle A$ and $\angle E$, $\angle B$ and $\angle F$, $\angle C$ and $\angle D$; $\overline{AB}$ and $\overline{EF}$, $\overline{BC}$ and $\overline{FD}$, $\overline{CA}$ and $\overline{DE}$
2. $\angle L$ and $\angle Q$, $\angle M$ and $\angle P$, $\angle N$ and $\angle R$; $\overline{LM}$ and $\overline{QP}$, $\overline{MN}$ and $\overline{PR}$, $\overline{NL}$ and $\overline{RQ}$
3. $\angle R$ and $\angle Y$, $\angle S$ and $\angle Z$, $\angle T$ and $\angle X$; $\overline{RS}$ and $\overline{YZ}$, $\overline{ST}$ and $\overline{ZX}$, $\overline{TR}$ and $\overline{YX}$
4. $\angle J$ and $\angle R$, $\angle K$ and $\angle Q$, $\angle L$ and $\angle P$; $\overline{JK}$ and $\overline{RQ}$, $\overline{KL}$ and $\overline{QP}$, $\overline{LJ}$ and $\overline{PR}$
5–6. Drawings
7. a. yes b. corresponding angles are congruent
8. $\triangle ABC \sim \triangle STR$ and $\triangle DEF \sim \triangle ZXY$; corresponding angles are congruent
9. $\triangle ACB \sim \triangle MNL$; corresponding angles are congruent
10. 2 cm
11. a. yes b. corresponding angles are congruent c. 4.5 cm

12. $DF = 8, EF = 10$
13. a. corresponding angles are congruent b. 8
14. 12   15. 4.5
16. a. yes b. corresponding angles are congruent c. 16 ft.
17. 3 m   18. 30 ft.
19. a. yes; corresponding angles are congruent b. 8 m
20. 75 ft.
21. a. corresponding angles are congruent b. (1) 150 m   (2) 90 m
22. a. $OA' = 48, OB' = 72$ b. $OA' = 18, OB' = 27$ c. $OA' = 16, OB' = 24$
23. a. 3 b. $\frac{6}{5}$ c. $\frac{5}{2}$ 24. 16
25. $m\angle ACB = m\angle AC'B'$ because they are right angles. $\angle A$ is an angle in both triangles and so the second pair of corresponding angles are equal in measure. $\triangle ABC \sim \triangle AB'C'$ because two triangles are similar if two angles of one are equal in measure to two corresponding angles of the other.
26. 6 in.   27. 20 m   28. 5:4
29. a. 24 m b. 864 m^2 c. 384 m^2 d. 480 m^2
30. a. C' b. $B'C' = 12, AC' = 16, AB' = 20$

12-9 Ratios of Perimeters and of Areas of Similar Polygons

The Ratio of Perimeters: pages 405–406

1. a. 5:2 b. $BC = 12.5$ in.; $CA = 15$ in. c. 5:2
2. a. 1:3 b. $A'B' = 24$ in.; $B'C' = 36$ in.; $C'D' = 12$ in. c. 1:3
3. (4)   4. (3)   5. (3)   6. 81
7. 90   8. 9   9. 24 mm   10. 25 in., 40 in.

The Ratio of Areas: pages 407–408

1. a. $\frac{3}{1}$ b. $\frac{9}{1}$ 2. a. $\frac{4}{1}$ b. $\frac{16}{1}$
3. a. $\frac{1}{2}$ b. $\frac{1}{4}$ 4. a. $\frac{1}{4}$ b. $\frac{1}{16}$
5. a. $\frac{6}{5}$ b. $\frac{36}{25}$ 6. a. $\frac{10}{3}$ b. $\frac{100}{9}$
7. 242 cm^2 8. 25:81   9. 13.5 sq. ft.
10. a. 2:1 b. 4:1
11. a. 4:5 b. 16:25
12. a. 2:1 b. 3:1 c. no; all sides are not in proportion d. 6:1

12-10 Review Exercises: pages 408–410

1. 6:7	**2.** 2 to 3	**3.** 3 to 5	**4.** 1 to 2
5. 165	**6.** 500	**7.** 5	**8.** 3
9. 5	**10.** 6	**11.** 8 and 32	**12.** (3)
13. (3)	**14.** (1)	**15.** 300	**16.** 125%

17. .07
18. a. $HJ = 11\frac{1}{4}$ in.; $GJ = 7\frac{1}{2}$ in. b. $\frac{4}{3}$ c. $\frac{4}{3}$ d. $\frac{16}{9}$
19. 1,700   20. 21
21. a. $\angle A$ and $\angle T$, $\angle B$ and $\angle R$, $\angle C$ and $\angle S$ b. $\overline{AB}$ and $\overline{TR}$, $\overline{BC}$ and $\overline{RS}$, $\overline{CA}$ and $\overline{ST}$ c. 6

22. 16
23. *a.* 8 *b.* 5 *c.* 8 *d.* 16 *e.* 10 *f.* 20
24. 25
25. *a.* yes, by a.a. $\cong$ a.a. (m$\angle C$ = 65° and
m$\angle F$ = 45°) *b.* 3

26. *a.* a.a. $\cong$ a.a. *b.* 5 in.
c. **1.** 9 sq. in. **2.** 25 sq. in. **3.** 16 sq. in.
27. 4 days **28.** 50

Chapter 13. Special Products and Factoring

13-1 Understanding the Meaning of Factoring: *pages 413–414*

1. yes   **2.** no   **3.** yes   **4.** no
5. yes   **6.** no   **7.** yes   **8.** no
9. no   **10.** no   **11.** $5 \cdot 7$ **12.** $2 \cdot 3^2$
13. $2^4 \cdot 3^2$ **14.** $7 \cdot 11$ **15.** 2^7 **16.** $2^4 \cdot 5^2$
17. $2 \cdot 101$ **18.** $3 \cdot 43$ **19.** $2 \cdot 5 \cdot 59$ **20.** $2^2 \cdot 79$
21. 1, 2, 13, 26
22. 1, 2, 5, 10, 25, 50
23. 1, 2, 3, 4, 6, 9, 12, 18, 36
24. 1, 2, 4, 8, 11, 22, 44, 88
25. 1, 2, 4, 5, 10, 20, 25, 50, 100
26. 1, 2, 11, 22, 121, 242
27. *a.* 72 *b.* 18 *c.* -8 *d.* 4 *e.* -3
28. *a.* $12xy$ *b.* $6y^2$ *c.* $3x^2y^2$ *d.* $-4y^3$ *e.* $2y^2$
29. 5   **30.** 4   **31.** 7   **32.** 6
33. 25   **34.** 36   **35.** 8   **36.** 1
37. 4   **38.** 6   **39.** $2r$ **40.** $2x$
41. $5x$ **42.** $7c^2d$ **43.** $9xy^2z$ **44.** $25m^3n$
45. $6ac^2$ **46.** ab **47.** xyz **48.** 1

13-2 Factoring Polynomials Whose Terms Have a Common Monomial Factor: *pages 415–416*

1. $2(a + b)$ **2.** $5(c + d)$
3. $8(m + n)$ **4.** $3(x - y)$
5. $7(l - n)$ **6.** $6(R - r)$
7. $b(x + y)$ **8.** $s(r - t)$
9. $x(c - d)$ **10.** $4(x + 2y)$
11. $3(m - 2n)$ **12.** $6(2t - r)$
13. $5(3c - 2d)$ **14.** $6(2x - 3y)$
15. $9(2c - 3d)$ **16.** $8(x + 2)$
17. $6(x - 3)$ **18.** $4(2x - 3)$
19. $7(y - 1)$ **20.** $4(2 - y)$
21. $6(1 - 3c)$ **22.** $y(y - 3)$
23. $x(2x + 5)$ **24.** $3x(x - 2)$
25. $x(32 + x)$ **26.** $r(s^2 - 2)$
27. $a(x - 5b)$ **28.** $3y^2(y^2 + 1)$
29. $5x(2 - 3x^2)$ **30.** $2x(1 - 2x^2)$
31. $p(1 + rt)$ **32.** $s(1 - r)$
33. $h(b + c)$ **34.** $\pi(r^2 + R^2)$
35. $\pi r(r + l)$ **36.** $\pi r(r + 2h)$
37. $4(x^2 + y^2)$ **38.** $3(a^2 - 3)$
39. $5(x^2 + 1)$ **40.** $3ab(b - 2a)$
41. $5xy(2 - 3xy)$ **42.** $7r^2s(3rs - 2)$
43. $2(x^2 + 4x + 2)$ **44.** $3(x^2 - 2x - 10)$
45. $a(y - 4w - 12)$ **46.** $c(c^2 - c + 2)$
47. $2m(a + 2b + c)$ **48.** $3a(3b^2 - 2b - 1)$
49. $5xyz(3x^2y^2z^2 - 1)$ **50.** $4a^2b^2c^2(2a^2c + 3)$
51. $14m^2n^3(2m^2 - 5n)$ **52.** $2(L + W)$
53. $5(x + y)$ **54.** $6(3x + 1)$
55. $x(x + 2)$ **56.** $2x^2(2x + 3)$

13-3 Squaring a Monomial: *page 417*

1. a^4 **2.** b^6 **3.** d^{10}
4. r^2s^2 **5.** m^4n^4 **6.** x^6y^4
7. $9x^4$ **8.** $25y^8$ **9.** $81a^2b^2$
10. $100x^4y^4$ **11.** $144c^2d^6$ **12.** $\frac{9}{16}a^2$
13. $\frac{25}{49}x^2y^2$ **14.** $\frac{49}{64}a^4b^4$ **15.** $\frac{x^2}{36}$
16. $\frac{16x^4}{25}$ **17.** $.64x^2$ **18.** $.25y^4$
19. $.01x^2y^2$ **20.** $.36a^4b^2$
21. *a.* $16x^2$ *b.* $100y^2$ *c.* $\frac{4}{9}x^2$
d. $2.25x^2$ *e.* $9x^4$ *f.* $16x^4y^4$

13-4 Multiplying the Sum and Difference of Two Terms: *page 418*

1. $x^2 - 64$ **2.** $y^2 - 100$ **3.** $m^2 - 16$
4. $n^2 - 81$ **5.** $100 - a^2$ **6.** $144 - b^2$
7. $c^2 - d^2$ **8.** $r^2 - s^2$ **9.** $9x^2 - 1$
10. $25c^2 - 16$ **11.** $64x^2 - 9y^2$ **12.** $25r^2 - 49s^2$
13. $x^4 - 64$ **14.** $9 - 25y^4$ **15.** $a^2 - \frac{1}{4}$
16. $r^2 - .25$ **17.** $.09 - m^2$ **18.** $a^2b^2 - 64$
19. $r^6 - 4s^8$ **20.** $a^4 - 625$ **21.** $x^4 - 81$
22. $a^4 - b^4$ **23.** $x^2 - 49$ **24.** $4x^2 - 9$
25. $c^2 - d^2$ **26.** $4a^2 - 9b^2$

13-5 Factoring the Difference of Two Squares: *pages 419–420*

1. $(y)^2 - (8)^2$ **2.** $(2r)^2 - (b)^2$
3. this is not a difference
4. 7 is not the square of an integer
5. $(3n)^2 - (4m)^2$ **6.** $(c)^2 - (3d)^2$
7. $(p)^2 - (\frac{3}{5}q)^2$ **8.** $(4a^2)^2 - (5b^3)^2$
9. $(m)^2 - (3)^2$ **10.** $(a + 2)(a - 2)$
11. $(b + 5)(b - 5)$ **12.** $(c + 10)(c - 10)$
13. $(r + 4)(r - 4)$ **14.** $(s + 7)(s - 7)$
15. $(t + 9)(t - 9)$ **16.** $(3 + x)(3 - x)$
17. $(12 + c)(12 - c)$ **18.** $(11 + m)(11 - m)$
19. $(4a + b)(4a - b)$ **20.** $(5m + n)(5m - n)$
21. $(d + 2c)(d - 2c)$ **22.** $(r^2 + 3)(r^2 - 3)$
23. $(x^2 + 8)(x^2 - 8)$ **24.** $(5 + s^2)(5 - s^2)$
25. $(10x + 9y)(10x - 9y)$ **26.** $(8e + 3f)(8e - 3f)$
27. $(rs + 12)(rs - 12)$ **28.** $(w + \frac{1}{8})(w - \frac{1}{8})$
29. $(s + \frac{1}{10})(s - \frac{1}{10})$ **30.** $(\frac{1}{9} + t)(\frac{1}{9} - t)$
31. $(7x + \frac{1}{3})(7x - \frac{1}{3})$
32. $\left(\frac{2}{5} + \frac{7d}{9}\right)\left(\frac{2}{5} - \frac{7d}{9}\right)$
33. $\left(\frac{1}{3}r + \frac{8s}{11}\right)\left(\frac{1}{3}r - \frac{8s}{11}\right)$
34. $(x + .8)(x - .8)$ **35.** $(y + 1.2)(y - 1.2)$

36. $(.2 + 7r)(.2 - 7r)$ 37. $(.4m + 3)(.4m - 3)$
38. $(9n + .1)(9n - .1)$ 39. $(.9x + y)(.9x - y)$
40. $(8ab - cd)(8ab + cd)$
41. $(5rs - 3tu)(5rs + 3tu)$
42. $(9mn + 7xy)(9mn - 7xy)$
43. $(7m^2 + 8n^2)(7m^2 - 8n^2)$
44. $(5x^3 + 11y^5)(5x^3 - 11y^5)$
45. $(x^2y^4 - 12a^3b^5)(x^2y^4 + 12a^3b^5)$
46. $(x + 2)(x - 2)$ 47. $(y + 3)(y - 3)$
48. $(t + 7)(t - 7)$ 49. $(t + 8)(t - 8)$
50. $(2x + y)(2x - y)$
51. a. $c^2 - d^2$ b. $(c + d)(c - d)$
52. a. $4x^2 - y^2$ b. $(2x + y)(2x - y)$
53. a. $x^2 - y^2$ b. $(x + y)(x - y)$
54. $(5a + 2b)(5a - 2b)$ 55. $(3x + 4y)(3x - 4y)$

13-6 Finding the Product of Two Binomials: *page 422*

1. $x^2 + 8x + 15$ 2. $y^2 + 11y + 18$
3. $18 + 9d + d^2$ 4. $x^2 - 15x + 50$
5. $y^2 - 10y + 9$ 6. $24 - 11c + c^2$
7. $x^2 + 5x - 14$ 8. $y^2 + 7y - 44$
9. $m^2 - 13m - 30$ 10. $n^2 - 17n - 60$
11. $45 - 4t - t^2$ 12. $2x^2 + 3x + 1$
13. $3x^2 + 17x + 10$ 14. $3c^2 - 16c + 5$
15. $3m^2 - 16m - 12$ 16. $y^2 + 16y + 64$
17. $Z^2 - 8Z + 16$ 18. $y^2 + 10y + 25$
19. $1 - 2t + t^2$ 20. $4x^2 + 4x + 1$
21. $9x^2 - 12x + 4$ 22. $14x^2 - x - 3$
23. $6y^2 + 13y + 6$ 24. $10Z^2 - 31Z + 15$
25. $4y^2 + 12y + 9$ 26. $9x^2 + 24x + 16$
27. $4x^2 - 20x + 25$ 28. $12t^2 + 13t - 14$
29. $25y^2 - 40y + 16$ 30. $10t^2 + 17t + 3$
31. $10c^2 - 19cd + 6d^2$ 32. $12a^2 - 5ab - 3b^2$
33. $25a^2 - 49b^2$ 34. $25a^2 + 70ab + 49b^2$
35. $35a^2 + 74ab + 35b^2$ 36. $35a^2 + 24ab - 35b^2$
37. a. $x^2 + 9x + 20$ b. $2x^2 + x - 3$
38. a. $x^2 + 12x + 36$ b. $x^2 - 4x + 4$
    c. $4x^2 + 4x + 1$ d. $9x^2 - 12x + 4$

13-7 Factoring Trinomials of the Form $ax^2 + bx + c$: *pages 426–427*

1. $(a + 2)(a + 1)$ 2. $(c + 5)(c + 1)$
3. $(x + 7)(x + 1)$ 4. $(r + 11)(r + 1)$
5. $(m + 4)(m + 1)$ 6. $(y + 5)(y + 7)$
7. $(x + 8)(x + 3)$ 8. $(a + 9)(a + 2)$
9. $(16 + c)(1 + c)$ 10. $(x + 1)^2$
11. $(z + 5)^2$ 12. $(a - 7)(a - 1)$
13. $(a - 5)(a - 1)$ 14. $(x - 2)(x - 3)$
15. $(x - 10)(x - 1)$ 16. $(y - 4)(y - 2)$
17. $(5 - y)(3 - y)$ 18. $(x - 6)(x - 4)$
19. $(c - 10)(c - 4)$ 20. $(x - 12)(x - 4)$
21. $(x - 7)^2$ 22. $(x - 2)(x + 1)$
23. $(x - 7)(x + 1)$ 24. $(y + 5)(y - 1)$
25. $(z - 13)(z + 1)$ 26. $(c - 5)(c + 3)$
27. $(c + 7)(c - 5)$ 28. $(x - 9)(x + 2)$
29. $(z + 12)(z - 3)$ 30. $(x - 16)(x + 3)$
31. $(x - 8)^2$ 32. $(2x + 1)(x + 2)$
33. $(2x + 3)(x + 2)$ 34. $(3x + 4)(x + 2)$
35. $(4x + 1)^2$ 36. $(2x + 3)(x - 1)$

37. $(3x + 5)(x - 1)$ 38. $(2x - 3)(x + 2)$
39. $(2x - 5)(2x - 1)$ 40. $(5a - 2)(2a - 1)$
41. $(9y + 2)(2y - 3)$ 42. $(x + 2y)(x + y)$
43. $(r - 5s)(r + 2s)$ 44. $(3a - b)(a - 2b)$
45. $(4x + 3y)(x - 2y)$ 46. $(x + 6)(x + 3)$
47. $(x - 7)(x - 2)$ 48. $(y - 8)(y + 3)$
49. $(x + 7)(x + 1)$ 50. $(x + 6)(x + 3)$
51. $(3x + 5)(x + 3)$ 52. $(x + 5)$
53. $(9x + 1)$ 54. $(2x + 3)$

13-8 Factoring Completely: *page 428*

1. $2(a + b)(a - b)$ 2. $6(x + y)(x - y)$
3. $4(x + 1)(x - 1)$ 4. $a(x + y)(x - y)$
5. $c(m + n)(m - n)$ 6. $s(t + 1)(t - 1)$
7. $2(x + 3)(x - 3)$ 8. $2(x + 4)(x - 4)$
9. $3(x + 3y)(x - 3y)$ 10. $2(3m + 2)(3m - 2)$
11. $3(2a + 3b)(2a - 3b)$ 12. $7(3c + 1)(3c - 1)$
13. $x(x + 2)(x - 2)$ 14. $y(y + 5)(y - 5)$
15. $z(z + 1)(z - 1)$ 16. $a(2a + b)(2a - b)$
17. $c(2c + 7)(2c - 7)$ 18. $d(3b + 1)(3b - 1)$
19. $4(a + 3)(a - 3)$
20. $(x^2 + 1)(x + 1)(x - 1)$
21. $(y^2 + 9)(y + 3)(y - 3)$
22. $\pi(R + r)(R - r)$ 23. $\pi(c + d)(c - d)$
24. $4(5x + 3y)(5x - 3y)$
25. $a(x + 2)(x + 1)$ 26. $3(x + 1)^2$
27. $4(r - 4)(r + 3)$ 28. $x(x + 5)(x + 2)$
29. $2(2x + 1)(x - 2)$ 30. $y(a + 5)^2$
31. $d(d - 4)^2$ 32. $2a(x - 3)(x + 2)$
33. $ab(x + 1)(x - 1)$
34. $z^2(z^2 + 1)(z + 1)(z - 1)$
35. $x^2(4 + y^2)(2 + y)(2 - y)$
36. $(x^2 + 2)(x + 1)(x - 1)$
37. $(a + 3)(a - 3)(a + 1)(a - 1)$
38. $(y + 3)(y - 3)(y + 2)(y - 2)$
39. $2(x^2 + 6x + 4)$ 40. $5(x^2 + 1)^2$
41. $b(2a + 1)(a + 3)$ 42. $4(2x - 1)^2$
43. $25(x + 2y)^2$ 44. $2(3m + 2)^2$
45. $(4a + b)(3a - 2b)$

13-9 Review Exercises: *page 429*

1. $2 \cdot 5 \cdot 5 \cdot 5$ 2. $4a$ 3. $8a^2bc^2$
4. $9g^6$ 5. $16x^8$ 6. $.04c^4y^2$
7. $x^2 + 4x - 45$ 8. $y^2 - 14y + 48$
9. $a^2b^2 - 16$ 10. $3d^2 - 5d - 2$
11. $4w^2 + 4w + 1$ 12. $2x^2 + 11cx + 12c^2$
13. $3(2x + 9b)$ 14. $y(3y + 10)$
15. $(m + 9)(m - 9)$ 16. $(x + 4h)(x - 4h)$
17. $(x - 5)(x + 1)$ 18. $(y - 2)(y - 7)$
19. $(8b - 3)(8b + 3)$ 20. $(11 + k)(11 - k)$
21. $(x - 4)(x - 4)$ 22. $(a + 3)(a - 10)$
23. $(x - 6)(x - 10)$ 24. $16(y + 1)(y - 1)$
25. $(x + 8b)(x - 2b)$ 26. $(2x + y)(x - 5y)$
27. $3x(x + 2)(x - 4)$ 28. $k^2 - 225$
29. $16e^2z^2 - 4ez^3$ 30. $6x^2 - 13x + 6$
31. $64m^2 + 16m + 1$ 32. $3x + 5$
33. $(15a - 2)(4a + 3)$
34. 121; 11 persons (The size of the group must be a multiple of 60, plus 1.)

244

Chapter 14. Fractions, and First-Degree Equations and Inequalities Involving Fractions

14-1 The Meaning of an Algebraic Fraction: page 431

1. 0   2. 0   3. 0   4. 5   5. 8   6. 2
7. -2 8. $\frac{1}{2}$ 9. $-\frac{1}{2}$
10. $+2, -2$ 11. $\frac{c}{5}$ 12. $\frac{98}{p}$
13. $\frac{10x + 20}{y}$ 14. $\frac{m}{60}$ 15. $\frac{4x + 2y}{4}$

14-2 Reducing Fractions to Lowest Terms: pages 434–435

1. $\frac{1}{3}$ 2. $\frac{3}{4}$ 3. $\frac{2c}{3d}$ 4. $\frac{9}{10}$ 5. $\frac{a}{c}$ 6. $\frac{a}{2b}$
7. $\frac{5}{9}$ 8. $\frac{1}{2}$ 9. $3x$
10. $\frac{1}{5x^2}$ 11. $\frac{3}{4a}$ 12. $\frac{y}{3x}$
13. $-\frac{3ab}{2c}$ 14. $\frac{2x}{9}$ 15. $-\frac{2}{3}$
16. $\frac{1}{9xy}$ 17. $\frac{3x + 6}{4}$ or $\frac{3(x + 2)}{4}$
18. $\frac{4y - 6}{3}$ 19. $\frac{x - 7}{5}$ 20. $m + 5$
21. $\frac{a + b}{3x}$ 22. $\frac{a - 2}{a}$ 23. $\frac{4a - b}{a}$
24. $\frac{2x + 3y}{4}$ 25. $\frac{6b + 10}{3b^2}$ 26. $\frac{x}{x + 2}$
27. $\frac{d}{d + 2}$ 28. $\frac{y}{y + x}$ 29. $\frac{a}{3a - b}$
30. $\frac{2}{r - 3s}$ 31. 4   32. $\frac{x - 3}{3}$
33. $\frac{x + 1}{5}$ 34. -1 35. $-\frac{1}{b + 3}$
36. $\frac{2}{s + r}$ 37. $-\frac{4 + a}{2}$ 38. $-\frac{x + y}{3}$
39. $-\frac{2b}{b + 3}$ 40. $\frac{r + 2}{3}$ 41. $\frac{x + 3}{x - 4}$
42. $\frac{x - 1}{x + 2}$ 43. $\frac{3}{y - 1}$ 44. $\frac{x}{x - 1}$
45. $\frac{x + 5}{x + 3}$ 46. $\frac{a + 2}{a + 3}$ 47. $\frac{a}{a - 1}$
48. $\frac{2(x - 5)}{x + 3}$ 49. $\frac{r + 1}{r + 3}$ 50. $\frac{12 - x}{x - 3}$
51. $\frac{2x - 1}{x - 3}$ 52. $\frac{3(x - 2)}{x + 2}$ 53. $\frac{x - 3y}{x + 5y}$
54. $\frac{2(3c - 4d)}{(2c - 3d)}$

14-3 Multiplying Fractions: pages 437–438

1. $\frac{5}{9}$ 2. 20   3. $10x$
4. $5d$ 5. $\frac{5x^2}{9}$ 6. $\frac{8}{mn}$
7. $\frac{6}{5}$ 8. $\frac{y}{x}$ 9. $\frac{4m}{3}$
10. $\frac{2}{s}$ 11. $2m$ 12. $\frac{6a^2b}{c}$
13. $\frac{x + 2}{12}$ 14. $\frac{a^2(a + 3)}{90}$ 15. $\frac{y(x - y)}{5x}$
16. $\frac{b^2(3a - 1)}{3}$ 17. $(b - 1)^2$
18. $\frac{(x + 1)(x - 1)^2}{5x}$ or $\frac{(x^2 - 1)(x - 1)}{5x}$
19. $\frac{r}{5}$ 20. $\frac{2s}{3}$ 21. $\frac{4}{x}$
22. $\frac{1}{3(x - 1)}$ 23. $2(a + 3)$ 24. $\frac{7(x + 1)}{x + 2}$
25. $\frac{a - b}{a + b}$ 26. $-\frac{4b^2(a - 2)}{a + 2}$
27. $\frac{5}{2}$ 28. $\frac{x + 5}{3y}$ 29. $\frac{y - 3}{c}$
30. $\frac{3(2a - 3)}{5(a - 3)}$ 31. $\frac{x + 5}{2x - 3}$ 32. $\frac{10}{3(x - 2)}$
33. 2   34. $\frac{1}{x(x - 2)}$ 35. $-\frac{1}{2}$
36. $-5(d - 5)$ 37. -1 38. $-\frac{(a + 6)^2}{36 + a^2}$
39. 5

14-4 Dividing Fractions: pages 439–440

1. $\frac{1}{6}$ 2. $\frac{3}{5}$ 3. 16
4. $\frac{1}{3}$ 5. $\frac{2}{35}$ 6. $\frac{acd}{4b}$
7. $\frac{y^4}{x^2}$ 8. $\frac{ab}{4c}$ 9. $\frac{32x(x + 1)}{27}$
10. $\frac{9(y + 3)}{10y}$ 11. $\frac{4b^2(a^2 - 1)}{a^2}$ 12. $2(x + 1)$
13. $2x(x - 4)$ 14. $\frac{2a - 3}{2}$ 15. $\frac{b(b - 3)}{2(b - 2)}$
16. $\frac{1}{4(a + b)}$ 17. $\frac{3}{4(y - 1)}$ 18. $\frac{x - 2}{28x}$
19. $\frac{3}{5}$ 20. $-\frac{1}{3}$ 21. $2(3 - y)$
22. $\frac{1}{2}$ 23. x 24. $-\frac{1}{2}$
25. $-\frac{a + b}{a - b}$ 26. $0, \pm 1$

14-5 Adding or Subtracting Fractions That Have the Same Denominator: pages 441–442

1. $\frac{5}{8}$

2. $\frac{1}{5}$

3. $\frac{5}{x}$

4. $\frac{5}{2c}$

5. $\frac{5x}{4}$

6. $\frac{8y}{5}$

7. $\frac{2c - 3d}{5}$

8. $\frac{x - y + z}{2}$

9. $\frac{x + y}{a}$

10. $\frac{5r - 2s}{t}$

11. $\frac{15}{8x}$

12. $\frac{1}{y}$

13. $\frac{11a}{4x}$

14. $\frac{7b}{3y}$

15. $\frac{7c}{3d}$

16. $\frac{6}{5c}$

17. $\frac{5x + 7}{2}$

18. $\frac{3x + 4}{4x}$

19. $\frac{3x - 5}{3}$

20. $\frac{a - 3}{4a}$

21. $\frac{8}{x + 2}$

22. $\frac{1}{a - b}$

23. $\frac{r + x}{y - 2}$

24. 1

25. 2

26. $\frac{1}{y + 2}$

27. $\frac{10x - 2}{3x + 2}$

28. $\frac{4c + 2}{2c - 3}$

29. 1

30. 1

31. $\frac{2x + 1}{x + 3}$

32. $\frac{1}{x - 1}$

33. $a + b$

34. $x - y$

35. 2

36. $\frac{2}{a + b}$

37. $\frac{4}{r - 3}$

38. $\frac{2m - 1}{m + 2}$

	$A + B$	$A - B$	$A \cdot B$	$A \div B$
39.	$\frac{15}{y}$	$\frac{9}{y}$	$\frac{36}{y^2}$	4
40.	$\frac{x}{2}$	$\frac{x}{4}$	$\frac{3x^2}{64}$	3
41.	$\frac{r + p}{t}$	$\frac{r - p}{t}$	$\frac{rp}{t^2}$	$\frac{r}{p}$
42.	$\frac{6k}{x}$	$\frac{k}{x}$	$\frac{35k^2}{x^2}$	$\frac{7}{5}$

14-6 Adding or Subtracting Fractions That Have Different Denominators: pages 445–448

1. 6

2. 30

3. $4x$

4. $24r$

5. xyz

6. $60x^2y^2$

7. $15x(x + y)$

8. $12a(a + b)$

9. $12(y + z)$

10. $(x^2 - 9)$

11. $\frac{19}{6}$

12. $\frac{17}{15}$

13. $\frac{61}{12}$

14. $\frac{33}{100}$

15. $\frac{11}{12}$

16. $\frac{5}{8}$

17. $\frac{1}{6}$

18. $\frac{29}{12}$

19. $\frac{5x}{6}$

20. $\frac{2d}{15}$

21. $\frac{x}{6}$

22. $-\frac{2y}{15}$

23. $\frac{9ab}{20}$

24. $\frac{31x}{20}$

25. $\frac{a}{12}$

26. $\frac{2a + b}{14}$

27. $\frac{15}{4x}$

28. $-\frac{1}{8x}$

29. $\frac{3a}{8b}$

30. $\frac{b + a}{ab}$

31. $\frac{2b - 5a^2}{a^2b}$

32. $\frac{z + x}{xyz}$

33. $\frac{5t + 9r}{rst}$

34. $\frac{2cx - 3ay}{6abc}$

35. $\frac{9c + 2a - 3b}{abc}$

36. $\frac{y^2 + 3xy - 5x^2}{x^2y^2}$

37. $\frac{3a - 5}{6}$

38. $\frac{-x + 44}{15}$

39. $\frac{7y - 6}{20}$

40. $\frac{a - 5b}{12}$

41. $\frac{4x + 9}{4x}$

42. $\frac{5d + 21}{4d}$

43. $\frac{b - 8}{10b}$

44. $\frac{19 - 8b}{20b}$

45. $\frac{12y^2 - 17y - 12}{12y^2}$

46. $\frac{3c^2 - 8c + 1}{2c^2}$

47. $\frac{9x}{5}$

48. $\frac{7(x - 1)}{6}$

49. $\frac{6(x - 2)}{7}$

50. $\frac{2x + 5}{12}$

51. $\frac{2(x - 5)}{15}$

52. $\frac{17}{3}$

53. $\frac{39}{4}$

54. $\frac{5x + 1}{x}$

55. $\frac{9s - 7}{s}$

56. $\frac{m^2 + 1}{m}$

57. $\frac{5d^2 - 7}{5d}$

58. $\frac{a + bc}{b}$

59. $\frac{3x + 8}{x + 1}$

60. $\frac{6x - 6y - 4}{x - y}$

61. $\frac{7b + 7c + 2a}{b + c}$

62. $\frac{t^2 + t + 1}{t + 1}$

63. $\frac{s^2 - s - 1}{s - 1}$

64. $\frac{3x + 5y}{x + y}$

65. $\frac{4y - 4}{y - 2}$

66. $\frac{9c - 22}{c - 3}$

67. $\frac{6x - 8y}{x - y}$

68. $\frac{a^2 + 2a + 2}{a + 1}$

69. $\frac{x^2 - 3x - 15}{x + 3}$

70. $\frac{2x^2 + 3x - 7}{x + 2}$

71. $\frac{17}{2(x - 3)}$

72. $\frac{33}{4(y + 1)}$

73. $\frac{17}{5(3a - 1)}$

74. $\frac{29}{6(x - 2)}$

75. $\frac{5x}{8(x - 1)}$

76. $\frac{-2}{(2x - 3y)}$

77. $\frac{a + 2b}{2(a - 2b)}$

78. $\frac{17x - 8}{6(x + 1)}$

79. $\frac{11x + 23}{12(2x - 1)}$

80. $\frac{2x}{(x + 5)(x - 5)}$

81. $\frac{3y - 60}{(y + 4)(y - 4)}$

82. $\frac{26 - 3a}{(a + 3)(2 - a)}$

83. $\frac{10x - 6}{x(x - 2)}$

84. $\frac{7c - 16}{c(c + 8)}$

85. $\frac{a^2 + ab + b^2}{b(a - b)}$

86. $\dfrac{3y + 14}{(y + 3)(y - 3)}$ **87.** $\dfrac{-5y + 26}{(y + 4)(y - 4)}$

88. $\dfrac{9 - 3a - 3b}{(a + b)(a - b)}$ **89.** $\dfrac{y - 4}{(y + 2)(y - 2)}$

90. $\dfrac{-x + 24}{3(x + 6)(x - 6)}$ **91.** $\dfrac{9b + 3a}{ab(a - b)}$

92. $\dfrac{2y^2 + 11y - 30}{3(y - 3)(y + 4)}$ **93.** $\dfrac{x^2 + 3x + 3}{(x + 2)^3}$

94. $\dfrac{9a^2 + 7a + 5}{(a - 1)(a + 3)(a + 2)}$

95. $\dfrac{2r + 19}{(r + 2)(r - 2)(r + 5)}$

96. $\dfrac{x^2 + xy - 2y^2 - 18x + 3y}{3(x + 4y)(x - y)}$

97. $\dfrac{-a^2 - 2a - 2}{(a - 5)(a + 3)(a - 2)}$

14-7 Solving Equations Containing Fractional Coefficients:
pages 451–454

1. $x = 21$ **2.** $t = 108$ **3.** $x = 25$
4. $n = 49$ **5.** $x = 16$ **6.** $m = 29$
7. $y = \frac{1}{10}$ **8.** $z = .04$ **9.** $t = 3.1$
10. $r = 40$ **11.** $t = .3$ **12.** $a = 24$
13. $r = -13$ **14.** $y = 6$ **15.** $x = \frac{3}{2}$
16. $m = 30$ **17.** $x = 4$ **18.** $y = 9$
19. $x = 1$ **20.** $x = 21$ **21.** $r = 12$
22. $t = \frac{15}{2}$ or $t = 7.5$ **23.** $r = 2$
24. $t = 9$ **25.** $a = 24$ **26.** $y = 1$
27. $y = 12$ **28.** $t = 15$ **29.** $m = 3$
30. $x = 2$ **31.** $y = 330$ **32.** $x = 10.4$
33. $x = 40$ **34.** $c = 20$ **35.** $y = 15$
36. $x = 20$ **37.** $y = 1.3$ **38.** $c = 150$
39. $m = 12$ **40.** $x = 23$ **41.** $x = 180$
42. $y = 1,000$ **43.** $x = 395$ **44.** $x = -20$
45. $x = 48$ **46.** $x = 31$ **47.** $x = 1,500$
48. $x = 600$ **49.** $x = 700$ **50.** $x = 40$
51. 30 **52.** 100 **53.** 30
54. 60 **55.** 13, 14 **56.** 19, 21
57. 12, 12, 18 **58.** 6, 18 **59.** 21, 35
60. 30, 60 **61.** 60, 90
62. 1st = 30 ft.; 2nd = 40 ft.; 3rd = 10 ft.; 4th = 20ft.
63. Sam, 6; father, 36 **64.** Robert, 24; father, 48
65. 52 **66.** $8
67. 20 passengers **68.** 27
69. 4 nickels, 12 dimes **70.** 6
71. 12 nickels, 17 dimes
72. 3 dimes, 10 quarters
73. 80 student tickets, 96 full-price tickets
74. No. Let $x =$ number of dimes
$.10x + .25(2x) = 4.50$
$x =$ fraction
75. Yes, 15 of each type of coin gives a total of $6.
76. $1,500 at 7%, $1,900 at 8%
77. $1,750 at 10%, $250 at 11%

14-8 Solving Inequalities Containing Fractional Coefficients: *pages 456–458*

1–20 also require graphs
1. $x > 9$ **2.** $y < 15$ **3.** $c > 6$
4. $x \le 5$ **5.** $y \ge 12$ **6.** $y < -1$
7. $t \ge -40$ **8.** $x \ge -6$ **9.** $x > 4\frac{4}{9}$
10. $y \ge -1\frac{2}{3}$ **11.** $x > 12$ **12.** $x \le 6$
13. $d < 1$ **14.** $c \ge 2\frac{1}{3}$ **15.** $m \ge 3$
16. $x < 18$ **17.** $x > 2$ **18.** $y < 9$
19. $r \le 24$ **20.** $t \ge 17$ **21.** 18
22. 38 **23.** 133 **24.** 113
25. 10, 25 **26.** 24, 20
27. 51 (Let $x =$ number of calls. Then, $15 + .10x > 20$.)
28. 51 (Let $x =$ number of calls. Then, $17 + .10(x - 20) > 20$.)
29. 8 cans of vegetables
30. 4 nickels **31.** Rhoda, 18; Alice, 27
32. Mary, 16; Bill, 20 **33.** $1,200
34. $11.96
35. 81 (Let $x =$ original number. Then, $\frac{2}{3}(\frac{2}{3}x + 3) + 6 < 45$, and $x < 83$.)

14-9 Solving Fractional Equations:
pages 460–461

1. $x = 2$ **2.** $y = 5$ **3.** $x = \frac{1}{2}$
4. $b = -4$ **5.** $x = 3$ **6.** $x = 30$
7. $y = -7$ **8.** $y = -8$ **9.** $x = 2$
10. $y = 3$ **11.** $c = \frac{1}{2}$ **12.** $x = \frac{1}{2}$
13. $x = 3$ **14.** $y = 8$ **15.** $c = 2$
16. $y = 3$ **17.** $x = 1$ **18.** $x = 2$
19. x cannot equal 0
20. $4(a + 1) \ne 5(a + 1)$ since $a + 1$ cannot equal 0
21. x cannot equal 0
22. $x = 3$ **23.** $x = 4$ **24.** $x = 4$
25. $a = -\frac{1}{3}$ **26.** $z = 1$ **27.** $r = \frac{1}{5}$
28. $y = 3$ **29.** $a = -10$ **30.** $m = 2$
31. $y = -\frac{1}{2}$ **32.** no solution
33. 4 **34.** $\frac{1}{3}$ **35.** 3
36. 84 **37.** $\frac{1}{7}$ **38.** $\frac{12}{20}$
39. 48

14-10 Equations and Formulas Involving Several Variables: *page 462*

1. $x = 5t$ **2.** $x = cd$ **3.** $x = 3ab$

4. $x = \dfrac{3b}{4}$ **5.** $x = \dfrac{ab}{3}$ **6.** $x = 9b$

7. $x = \dfrac{r}{t}$ **8.** $x = \dfrac{t}{k}$ **9.** $x = 44b$

10. $x = \dfrac{a + b}{c}$ **11.** $x = \dfrac{dr}{m}$ **12.** $x = 15a$

13. $n = \dfrac{360}{C}$ **14.** $I = \dfrac{E}{R}$ **15.** $t = \dfrac{s}{v}$

16. $m = \dfrac{Fgr}{v^2}$ **17.** $R = \dfrac{L}{AV}$

18. $C = \frac{5}{9}(F - 32)$ 19. $a = \frac{2S}{t^2}$

20. $t = \frac{A - p}{pr}$ 21. 30   22. 6

14-11   Review Exercises: *pages 462–464*

1. $\frac{x}{10}$ 2. 4   3. $\frac{2}{3}$

4. $\frac{2}{d}$ 5. $x^2 - 12$ 6. $\frac{2y - 3}{2}$

7. $\frac{2x}{3}$ 8. $x - 1$ 9. $12c$

10. $\frac{5}{6b}$ 11. $\frac{2m}{3}$ 12. $\frac{10}{k}$

13. $\frac{7ax}{12}$ 14. $\frac{8}{9y}$ 15. $\frac{5z - 2x}{xyz}$

16. $\frac{4w + 7}{3w}$ 17. $\frac{2x + 2}{x}$ 18. $\frac{14x - 11}{25x^2}$

19. $2b$ 20. 2   21. 15
22. 11   23. 12   24. 7
25. 6   26. no solution

27. $\frac{S}{2\pi h}$ 28. $\frac{a}{n}$ 29. $\frac{C}{2\pi}$

30. $\frac{1}{2}$ 31. 2   32. $\frac{13 - y}{20}$

33. $\frac{x + 5}{3(x - 5)}$ 34. $\frac{5c + 3}{24}$ 35. $\frac{3}{1 + 3a}$

36. $\frac{12}{16}$ 37. $1,920   38. 25

39. $23.10   40. 90 points

Chapter 15. Probability

15-1   Empirical Probability: *pages 471–473*

1. *a.* $P(2) = \frac{1}{4}$

b.

Barbara	29	100	$\frac{29}{100} = .290$
Tom	60	200	$\frac{60}{200} = .300$
Ann	79	300	$\frac{79}{300} = .263$
Eddie	102	400	$\frac{102}{400} = .255$
Cathy	126	500	$\frac{126}{500} = .252$

c. yes; cumulative relative frequency is approaching .250 or $\frac{1}{4}$

2. $P(5) = \frac{1}{6}$ 3. P(any heart) $= \frac{1}{4}$
4. $P(7) = \frac{1}{10}$ 5. P(black) $= \frac{2}{5}$
6. $\frac{4}{26}$ or $\frac{2}{13}$ 7. $P(4) = \frac{1}{4}$
8–13. Answers will vary.

15-2   Theoretical Probability: *pages 477–479*

1. *a.* $\{H, T\}$ *b.* P(head) $= \frac{1}{2}$ *c.* P(tail) $= \frac{1}{2}$
2. *a.* (1) 3 (2) $\frac{1}{6}$ *b.* (1) 2, 4, 6, (2) $\frac{3}{6} = \frac{1}{2}$
   c. (1) 1, 2 (2) $\frac{2}{6} = \frac{1}{3}$
   d. (1) 1, 3, 5 (2) $\frac{3}{6} = \frac{1}{2}$
   e. (1) 4, 5, 6 (2) $\frac{3}{6} = \frac{1}{2}$
   f. (1) 3, 4, 5, 6   (2) $\frac{4}{6} = \frac{2}{3}$
3. *a.* (1) 3 (2) $\frac{1}{5}$ *b.* (1) 2, 4 (2) $\frac{2}{5}$
   c. (1) 1, 2 (2) $\frac{2}{5}$ *d.* (1) 1, 3, 5 (2) $\frac{3}{5}$
   e. (1) 4, 5 (2) $\frac{2}{5}$ *f.* (1) 3, 4, 5 (2) $\frac{3}{5}$
4. *a.* $\frac{1}{52}$ *b.* $\frac{4}{52} = \frac{1}{13}$ *c.* $\frac{13}{52} = \frac{1}{4}$ *d.* $\frac{26}{52} = \frac{1}{2}$ *e.* $\frac{1}{52}$
   f. $\frac{13}{52} = \frac{1}{4}$ *g.* $\frac{4}{52} = \frac{1}{13}$ *h.* $\frac{2}{52} = \frac{1}{26}$ *i.* $\frac{2}{52} = \frac{1}{26}$
   j. $\frac{12}{52} = \frac{3}{13}$
5. *a.* $\frac{1}{4}$ *b.* $\frac{1}{2}$ *c.* $\frac{1}{3}$
6. *a.* $\frac{2}{5}$ *b.* $\frac{1}{5}$ *c.* $\frac{2}{10} = \frac{1}{5}$ *d.* $\frac{4}{10} = \frac{2}{5}$ *e.* $\frac{3}{12} = \frac{1}{4}$
   f. $\frac{2}{100} = \frac{1}{50}$

7. $\frac{2}{4} = \frac{1}{2}$ 8. *a.* $\frac{16}{30} = \frac{8}{15}$ *b.* $\frac{14}{30} = \frac{7}{15}$
9. *a.* $\frac{1}{168}$ *b.* $\frac{1}{210}$
10. *a.* $\frac{2}{5}$ *b.* $\frac{3}{6} = \frac{1}{2}$ *c.* $\frac{3}{8}$ *d.* $\frac{4}{11}$
11. *a.* $\frac{3}{8}$ *b.* $\frac{4}{8} = \frac{1}{2}$ *c.* $\frac{3}{8}$ *d.* $\frac{5}{8}$ *e.* $\frac{3}{8}$ *f.* $\frac{6}{8} = \frac{3}{4}$
    g. $\frac{7}{8}$ *h.* $\frac{3}{8}$ *i.* $\frac{5}{8}$ *j.* $\frac{3}{8}$
12. *a.* It is not equally likely that a person be born in each state. (State populations are not the same.)
    b. It is not equally likely that a person be born in each month. (September has 30 days; some months have 31 days.)
    c. Point up and point down are not equally likely.
    d. It is not equally likely that a person attend a religious service each day.

15-3   Evaluating Simple Probabilities: *pages 484–486*

1. *a.* { }, {H}, {T}, {H, T}
   b. P(neither H nor T) $= 0$
   $P(H) = \frac{1}{2}$
   $P(T) = \frac{1}{2}$
   P(either H or T) $= 1$
2. *a.* (1) {5} (2) $\frac{1}{7}$ *b.* (1) {2, 4, 6} (2) $\frac{3}{7}$
   c. (1) {1, 2, 3, 4} (2) $\frac{4}{7}$
   d. (1) {1, 3, 5, 7} (2) $\frac{4}{7}$ *e.* (1) {6, 7} (2) $\frac{2}{7}$
   f. (1) {2, 3, 4, 5, 6, 7} (2) $\frac{6}{7}$
3. *a.* $\frac{5}{7}$ *b.* $\frac{2}{3}$ *c.* $\frac{3}{8}$ *d.* 1 *e.* 0
   f. 1 *g.* (1) { } (2) 0
   h. (1) {1, 2, 3, 4, 5, 6, 7} (2) 1
4. *a.* $\frac{1}{6}$ *b.* $\frac{3}{6} = \frac{1}{2}$ *c.* $\frac{2}{6} = \frac{1}{3}$ *d.* 0 *e.* $\frac{4}{6} = \frac{2}{3}$
   f. 1 *g.* 0 *h.* 0 *i.* 1
5. *a.* 0 *b.* 1 *c.* $\frac{4}{6} = \frac{2}{3}$ *d.* 0 *e.* 1 *f.* 0
6. *a.* $\frac{4}{52} = \frac{1}{13}$ *b.* $\frac{13}{52} = \frac{1}{4}$ *c.* 0 *d.* 0 *e.* 1
   f. $\frac{13}{52} = \frac{1}{4}$ *g.* 0 *h.* 0 *i.* 0
7. *a.* .6 *b.* .4 *c.* 1 *d.* 0
8. *a.* 10% *b.* 50% *c.* 40% *d.* 100% *e.* 0%
9. *a.* $\frac{3}{5}$ *b.* $\frac{2}{5}$ *c.* $\frac{1}{5}$ *d.* 0 *e.* $\frac{2}{5}$ *f.* 0 *g.* 0 *h.* $\frac{1}{5}$
   i. $\frac{2}{5}$ *j.* 1 *k.* 0 *l.* 1

10. *a.* $\frac{3}{6} = \frac{1}{2}$ *b.* 0 *c.* 0 *d.* $\frac{3}{6} = \frac{1}{2}$
e. $\frac{1}{6}$ *f.* 0 *g.* 1
11. 8   12. 12 boys, 9 girls
13. 18 caramels, 12 nut clusters
14–15. Answers will vary.
16. Probability is never greater than 1, which represents certainty.
17. Probability is never less than 0, which represents an impossibility.
18. This is a certainty with probability 1 or 100%.
19. *a.* (1) $\{E_1, E_2\}$ (2) $\frac{2}{5}$
b. (1) $\{S_1, S_2, S_3, S_4\}$ (2) $\frac{4}{11}$
c. (1) $\{I, A, E\}$ (2) $\frac{3}{8}$
d. (1) $\{E_1, E_2, E_3, I\}$ (2) $\frac{4}{7}$
e. (1) $\{S, P, R, Y\}$ (2) 1

15-4 The Probability of *A and B: page 489*

1. *a.* $\frac{2}{6} = \frac{1}{3}$ *b.* $\frac{1}{6}$ *c.* $\frac{1}{6}$ *d.* 0 *e.* $\frac{3}{6} = \frac{1}{2}$ *f.* 0
2. *a.* $\frac{2}{52}$ *b.* $\frac{2}{52} = \frac{1}{26}$ *c.* $\frac{1}{52}$ *d.* $\frac{2}{52} = \frac{1}{26}$
e. $\frac{1}{52}$ *f.* 0 *g.* $\frac{1}{52}$ *h.* $\frac{2}{52} = \frac{1}{26}$ *i.* $\frac{6}{52} = \frac{3}{26}$
3. *a.* $\frac{2}{4} = \frac{1}{2}$ *b.* $\frac{1}{4}$ *c.* $\frac{1}{4}$ *d.* 1 *e.* $\frac{3}{4}$
4. *a.* $\frac{7}{12}$ *b.* $\frac{5}{12}$ *c.* $\frac{4}{12} = \frac{1}{3}$ *d.* $\frac{8}{12} = \frac{2}{3}$
e. $\frac{3}{12} = \frac{1}{4}$ *f.* $\frac{2}{12} = \frac{1}{6}$ *g.* $\frac{2}{12} = \frac{1}{6}$ *h.* $\frac{5}{12}$
i. 0 *j.* $\frac{2}{12} = \frac{1}{6}$

15-5 The Probability of *A or B:*
pages 494–495

1. *a.* $\frac{1}{5}$ *b.* $\frac{2}{5}$ *c.* $\frac{3}{5}$ *d.* $\frac{4}{5}$ *e.* $\frac{3}{5}$ *f.* $\frac{4}{5}$ *g.* $\frac{3}{5}$ *h.* $\frac{3}{5}$
2. *a.* $\frac{1}{6}$ *b.* $\frac{2}{6} = \frac{1}{3}$ *c.* $\frac{3}{6} = \frac{1}{2}$ *d.* $\frac{4}{6} = \frac{2}{3}$ *e.* $\frac{3}{6} = \frac{1}{2}$
f. $\frac{4}{6} = \frac{2}{3}$ *g.* $\frac{3}{6} = \frac{1}{2}$ *h.* $\frac{3}{6} = \frac{1}{2}$ *i.* $\frac{2}{6} = \frac{1}{3}$ *j.* 1
3. *a.* $\frac{8}{52} = \frac{2}{13}$ *b.* $\frac{8}{52} = \frac{2}{13}$ *c.* $\frac{26}{52} = \frac{1}{2}$ *d.* $\frac{16}{52} = \frac{4}{13}$
e. $\frac{28}{52} = \frac{7}{13}$ *f.* $\frac{12}{52} = \frac{3}{13}$ *g.* $\frac{16}{52} = \frac{4}{13}$ *h.* $\frac{39}{52} = \frac{3}{4}$
i. $\frac{16}{52} = \frac{4}{13}$
4. *a.* $\frac{2}{16} = \frac{1}{8}$ *b.* $\frac{8}{16} = \frac{1}{2}$ *c.* $\frac{9}{16}$ *d.* $\frac{6}{16} = \frac{3}{8}$
e. $\frac{2}{16} = \frac{1}{8}$ *f.* $\frac{14}{16} = \frac{7}{8}$ *g.* 1 *h.* $\frac{11}{16}$ *i.* $\frac{10}{16} = \frac{5}{8}$
5. (2) 6. (2) 7. (1)
8. (2) 9. (2) 10. (3)

15-6 The Probability of *Not A*; Probability as a Sum: *pages 497–498*

1. *a.* $\frac{1}{6}$ *b.* $\frac{5}{6}$ *c.* $\frac{3}{6} = \frac{1}{2}$ *d.* $\frac{3}{6} = \frac{1}{2}$ *e.* $\frac{2}{6} = \frac{1}{3}$
f. $\frac{4}{6} = \frac{2}{3}$ *g.* 1 *h.* 0
2. *a.* $\frac{3}{10}$ *b.* $\frac{7}{10}$
3. *a.* $\frac{13}{52} = \frac{1}{4}$ *b.* $\frac{39}{52} = \frac{3}{4}$ *c.* $\frac{12}{52} = \frac{3}{13}$ *d.* $\frac{40}{52} = \frac{10}{13}$
e. $\frac{48}{52} = \frac{12}{13}$ *f.* $\frac{50}{52} = \frac{25}{26}$ *g.* $\frac{51}{52}$
4. *a.* (1) $\frac{3}{12} = \frac{1}{4}$ (2) $\frac{4}{12} = \frac{1}{3}$ (3) $\frac{5}{12}$
b. $\frac{3}{12} + \frac{4}{12} + \frac{5}{12} = \frac{12}{12} = 1$
5. *a.* $P(P) = \frac{1}{10}$
$P(I) = \frac{3}{10}$
$P(C) = \frac{2}{10} = \frac{1}{5}$
$P(N) = \frac{2}{10} = \frac{1}{5}$
$P(K) = \frac{1}{10}$
$P(G) = \frac{1}{10}$
b. $\frac{1}{10} + \frac{3}{10} + \frac{2}{10} + \frac{2}{10} + \frac{1}{10} + \frac{1}{10} = \frac{10}{10} = 1$

6. $\frac{6}{7}$ 7. .907   8. $\frac{8}{9}$
9. *a.* $\frac{3}{7}$ *b.* $\frac{4}{7}$ *c.* $\frac{4}{7}$ *d.* 1 *e.* 0
10. *a.* $\frac{3}{4}$ *b.* $\frac{1}{4}$ *c.* $\frac{1}{4}$ *d.* 1 *e.* $\frac{3}{4}$
11. *a.* .2 *b.* .3 *c.* .5 *d.* .7 *e.* .8 *f.* .7
g. .5 *h.* 0
12. *a.* $\frac{1}{11}$ *b.* $\frac{2}{11}$ *c.* 0 *d.* $\frac{3}{11}$ *e.* $\frac{3}{11}$ *f.* $\frac{4}{11}$
g. $\frac{7}{11}$ *h.* $\frac{4}{11}$ *i.* 1
13. *a.* $\frac{4}{52} = \frac{1}{13}$ *b.* $\frac{13}{52} = \frac{1}{4}$ *c.* $\frac{1}{52}$ *d.* $\frac{16}{52} = \frac{4}{13}$
e. $\frac{39}{52} = \frac{3}{4}$ *f.* $\frac{48}{52} = \frac{12}{13}$ *g.* $\frac{8}{52} = \frac{2}{13}$ *h.* $\frac{51}{52}$
i. 0 *j.* $\frac{2}{52} = \frac{1}{26}$ *k.* $\frac{28}{52} = \frac{7}{13}$
14. *a.* $\frac{1}{10}$ *b.* $\frac{4}{10} = \frac{2}{5}$ *c.* $\frac{6}{10} = \frac{3}{5}$ *d.* $\frac{6}{10} = \frac{3}{5}$
e. $\frac{7}{10}$ *f.* $\frac{9}{10}$ *g.* 0 *h.* $\frac{7}{10}$ *i.* 0 *j.* $\frac{5}{10} = \frac{1}{2}$
k. $\frac{3}{10}$ *l.* 1

15-7 The Counting Principle and Sample Spaces: *pages 502–503*

1. *a.* 10 *b.* 40 *c.* 36
2. 80   3. 56   4. 42   5. 12
6. *a.* 40 *b.* 24 *c.* 12
7. *a.* $\{(T, H), (T, T), (H, H), (H, T)\}$ *b.* $2 \cdot 2 = 4$
c. 1 *d.* 2

8. *a.*

b. $\{(T, T), (T, F), (F, T), (F, F)\}$
c. This set is the same as the set of all possible truth values for two statements.

9. *a.* 8   *b.*

c. $\{(T, T, T), (T, T, F), (T, F, T), (T, F, F),$
$(F, T, T), (F, T, F), (F, F, T), (F, F, F)\}$

10. *a.*

b. $\{(A, X), (A, Y), (A, Z), (B, X), (B, Y), (B, Z)\}$

11. *a.* 4 *b.* 64 *c.* 4^n
12. 180

13. *a.* 36

b.
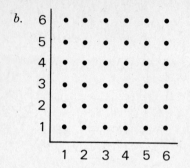

14. *a.* $26^2 \cdot 10^3 = 676,000$
  b. $10^3 \cdot 26^3 = 17,576,000$
  c. $10^4 \cdot 26^2 = 6,760,000$
15. *a.* $31 \cdot 30 = 930$ *b.* 31 *c.* $31 \cdot 31 = 961$

15-8 Probabilities and the Counting Principle; Predicting Outcomes: *pages 506–507*

1. *a.* $\frac{1}{2}$ *b.* $\frac{1}{6}$ *c.* $\frac{1}{12}$
2. *a.* $\frac{1}{12}$ *b.* $\frac{1}{4}$ *c.* $\frac{1}{3}$ *d.* $\frac{1}{6}$
3. $\frac{1}{4}$ **4.** $\frac{1}{4}$ **5.** $\frac{2}{15}$
6. *a.* $\frac{1}{2}$ *b.* $\frac{1}{16}$ *c.* $(\frac{1}{2})^n$ or $\frac{1}{2^n}$
7. *a.* $\frac{1}{6}$ *b.* $\frac{1}{4}$ **8.** *a.* $\frac{1}{8}$ *b.* $\frac{1}{8}$
9. *a.* $\frac{1}{64}$ *b.* $\frac{49}{64}$
10. *a.* .49 *b.* .21 *c.* .09 *d.* .21 *e.* .42 *f.* .58
11. 25 **12.** 4 **13.** 20
14. 175 **15.** 50 **16.** 17

15-9 Probabilities With Two or More Activities: *pages 511–512*

1. *a.* {(H, H), (H, T), (T, H), (T, T)} *b.* $\frac{1}{4}$ *c.* $\frac{1}{4}$
  d. $\frac{3}{4}$
2. *a.* $\frac{1}{4}$ *b.* $\frac{1}{4}$ *c.* $\frac{2}{4} = \frac{1}{2}$ *d.* $\frac{2}{4} = \frac{1}{2}$ *e.* $\frac{3}{4}$ *f.* $\frac{1}{2}$
  g. $\frac{1}{4}$
3. *a.* $\frac{1}{8}$ *b.* $\frac{1}{8}$ *c.* $\frac{2}{8} = \frac{1}{4}$ *d.* $\frac{3}{8}$ *e.* $\frac{1}{2}$ *f.* $\frac{7}{8}$ *g.* $\frac{1}{4}$
4. {(B, B, B, B), (B, B, B, G), (B, B, G, B),
  (B, B, G, G), (B, G, B, B), (B, G, B, G),
  (B, G, G, B), (B, G, G, G), (G, B, B, B),
  (G, B, B, G), (G, B, G, B), (G, B, G, G),
  (G, G, B, B), (G, G, B, G), (G, G, G, B),
  (G, G, G, G)}
  a. $\frac{1}{16}$ *b.* $\frac{1}{16}$ *c.* $\frac{2}{16} = \frac{1}{8}$ *d.* $\frac{6}{16} = \frac{3}{8}$ *e.* $\frac{1}{2}$ *f.* $\frac{15}{16}$
  g. $\frac{1}{4}$
5. *a.* {(H, H, H), (H, H, T), (H, T, H), (H, T, T),
  (T, H, H), (T, H, T), (T, T, H), (T, T, T)}
  b. $\frac{1}{8}$ *c.* $\frac{3}{8}$ *d.* $\frac{4}{8} = \frac{1}{2}$
6. *a.* {(1, M), (1, A), (1, T), (1, H), (2, M), (2, A),
  (2, T), (2, H), (3, M), (3, A), (3, T), (3, H)}
  b. $\frac{1}{12}$ *c.* $\frac{1}{12}$ *d.* $\frac{2}{12} = \frac{1}{6}$ *e.* $\frac{1}{12}$ *f.* 0 *g.* $\frac{6}{12} = \frac{1}{2}$

7. *a.*
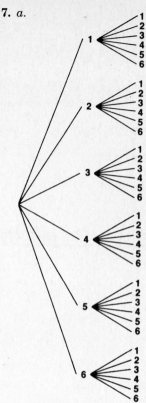

b.
(1, 1)	(2, 1)	(3, 1)	(4, 1)	(5, 1)	(6, 1)
(1, 2)	(2, 2)	(3, 2)	(4, 2)	(5, 2)	(6, 2)
(1, 3)	(2, 3)	(3, 3)	(4, 3)	(5, 3)	(6, 3)
(1, 4)	(2, 4)	(3, 4)	(4, 4)	(5, 4)	(6, 4)
(1, 5)	(2, 5)	(3, 5)	(4, 5)	(5, 5)	(6, 5)
(1, 6)	(2, 6)	(3, 6)	(4, 6)	(5, 6)	(6, 6)

8. *a.* $\frac{1}{36}$ *b.* $\frac{2}{36} = \frac{1}{18}$ *c.* $\frac{3}{36} = \frac{1}{12}$ *d.* $\frac{4}{36} = \frac{1}{9}$
  e. $\frac{5}{36}$ *f.* $\frac{6}{36} = \frac{1}{6}$ *g.* $\frac{5}{36}$ *h.* $\frac{4}{36} = \frac{1}{9}$ *i.* $\frac{3}{36} = \frac{1}{12}$
  j. $\frac{2}{36} = \frac{1}{18}$ *k.* $\frac{1}{36}$
9. $\frac{36}{36}$ or 1
10. The result will be the same as in Exercise 7.
11. *a.* $\frac{1}{36}$
  b. $\frac{1}{36}$ (the 5 must appear first, then the 2)
  c. 0 *d.* $\frac{3}{36} = \frac{1}{12}$ *e.* $\frac{3}{36} = \frac{1}{12}$ *f.* $\frac{18}{36} = \frac{1}{2}$
  g. $\frac{18}{36} = \frac{1}{2}$ *h.* $\frac{6}{36} = \frac{1}{6}$ *i.* 1
12. (3) **13.** (4) **14.** (2)

15-10 Permutations: *pages 515–516*

1. *a.* 2 *b.* 24 *c.* 720 *d.* 5,040 *e.* 8 *f.* 120
  g. 6 *h.* 40,320 *i.* 120 *j.* 336 *k.* 1 *l.* 144
2. *a.* 24
  b. EMIT, EMTI, EIMT, EITM, ETIM, ETMI,
  MITE, MIET, MTIE, MTEI, MEIT, METI,
  ITEM, ITME, IMET, IMTE, IETM, IEMT,
  TEIM, TEMI, TIEM, TIME, TMEI, TMIE
3. 120   **4.** 6   **5.** 24   **6.** 24
7. 40,320 **8.** 60! **9.** 26! **10.** 35!

15-11 More About Permutations: *pages 518–519*

1. $a.$ 120 $b.$ 90 $c.$ 600 $d.$ 24 $e.$ 380 $f.$ 7,920
$g.$ 9,240 $h.$ 5,040 $i.$ 5,040 $j.$ 999,900
$k.$ 6,720 $l.$ 720
2. $a.$ 24 $b.$ 60 $c.$ 120 $d.$ 210 $e.$ 6
3. $a.$ 30 $b.$ 870 $c.$ 24,360
4. $a.$ 210 $b.$ 504 $c.$ 990 $d.$ $n(n-1)(n-2)$
5. $a.$ 6 $b.$ 15,600 **6.** $31 \cdot 30 \cdot 29 \cdot 28$
7. $a.$ 650 $b.$ 676

15-12 Probability Without Replacement; Probability With Replacement: *pages 524–526*

1. $a.$ $\frac{2}{7}$ $b.$ $\frac{5}{7}$
2. $a.$ $\frac{4}{49}$ $b.$ $\frac{25}{49}$ $c.$ $\frac{29}{49}$ $d.$ $\frac{20}{49}$
3. $a.$ $\frac{2}{42} = \frac{1}{21}$ $b.$ $\frac{20}{42} = \frac{10}{21}$ $c.$ $\frac{22}{42} = \frac{11}{21}$ $d.$ $\frac{20}{42} = \frac{10}{21}$
4. $a.$ $\{(1, 1), (1, 2), (1, 3), (1, 4), (2, 1), (2, 2), (2, 3),$
$(2, 4), (3, 1), (3, 2), (3, 3), (3, 4), (4, 1), (4, 2),$
$(4, 3), (4, 4)\}$
$b.$ $\frac{1}{16}$ $c.$ $\frac{4}{16} = \frac{1}{4}$ $d.$ $\frac{6}{16} = \frac{3}{8}$
5. $a.$ $\{(l_1, l_2), (l_1, l_3), (l_1, g_1), (l_1, g_2), (l_2, l_1), (l_2, l_3),$
$(l_2, g_1), (l_2, g_2), (l_3, l_1), (l_3, l_2), (l_3, g_1), (l_3, g_2),$
$(g_1, l_1), (g_1, l_2), (g_1, l_3), (g_1, g_2), (g_2, l_1), (g_2, l_2),$
$(g_2, l_3), (g_2, g_1)\}$
$b.$ (1) $\frac{6}{20} = \frac{3}{10}$ (2) $\frac{2}{20} = \frac{1}{10}$ (3) $\frac{8}{20} = \frac{2}{5}$
(4) $\frac{18}{20} = \frac{9}{10}$
6. $a.$ $\{(g_1, g_1), (g_1, g_2), (g_1, g_3), (g_1, b_1), (g_1, b_2),$
$(g_2, g_1), (g_2, g_2), (g_2, g_3), (g_2, b_1), (g_2, b_2),$
$(g_3, g_1), (g_3, g_2), (g_3, g_3), (g_3, b_1), (g_3, b_2),$
$(b_1, g_1), (b_1, g_2), (b_1, g_3), (b_1, b_1), (b_1, b_2),$
$(b_2, g_1), (b_2, g_2), (b_2, g_3), (b_2, b_1), (b_2, b_2)\}$
$b.$ (1) $\frac{9}{25}$ (2) $\frac{4}{25}$ (3) $\frac{5}{25} = \frac{1}{5}$ (4) $\frac{16}{25}$
7. $a.$ $\frac{12}{2,652} = \frac{1}{221}$ $b.$ $\frac{156}{2,652} = \frac{1}{17}$ $c.$ $\frac{650}{2,652} = \frac{25}{102}$
$d.$ $\frac{132}{2,652} = \frac{11}{221}$ $e.$ $\frac{16}{2,652} = \frac{4}{663}$ $f.$ $\frac{169}{2,652} = \frac{13}{204}$
$g.$ $\frac{2,496}{2,652} = \frac{16}{17}$ $h.$ $\frac{2}{2,652} = \frac{1}{1,326}$
8. $a.$ $\{(H, Q), (H, D), (H, N), (Q, H), (Q, D), (Q, N),$
$(D, H), (D, Q), (D, N), (N, H), (N, Q), (N, D)\}$
$b.$ (1) $\frac{2}{12} = \frac{1}{6}$ (2) $\frac{4}{12} = \frac{1}{3}$ (3) $\frac{6}{12} = \frac{1}{2}$
(4) $\frac{2}{12} = \frac{1}{6}$

9. $a.$ (1) $\frac{56}{182} = \frac{4}{13}$ (2) $\frac{30}{182} = \frac{15}{91}$ (3) $\frac{86}{182} = \frac{43}{91}$
$b.$ 3
10. $a.$ $\frac{9}{49}$ $b.$ $\frac{16}{49}$ $c.$ $\frac{24}{49}$ $d.$ $\frac{7}{49} = \frac{1}{7}$
$e.$ $\frac{40}{49}$ $f.$ 0 $g.$ $\frac{33}{49}$
11. $a.$ (1) $\frac{72}{132} = \frac{6}{11}$ (2) $\frac{27}{132} = \frac{9}{44}$ (3) $\frac{27}{132} = \frac{9}{44}$
(4) $\frac{6}{132} = \frac{1}{22}$
$b.$ (1) $\frac{6}{132} = \frac{1}{22}$ (2) $\frac{54}{132} = \frac{9}{22}$ (3) $\frac{126}{132} = \frac{21}{22}$
(4) $\frac{78}{132} = \frac{13}{22}$ (5) $\frac{60}{132} = \frac{5}{11}$ (6) 0

15-13 Review Exercises: *pages 526–528*

1. 8 **2.** 25 **3.** 65%
4. $a.$ $\frac{2}{3}$ $b.$ $\frac{1}{3}$ $c.$ 0 $d.$ 0
5. $a.$ $\frac{2}{9}$ $b.$ $\frac{7}{9}$ $c.$ $\frac{6}{9}$ $d.$ 0
6. $a.$ $\frac{26}{52}$ $b.$ $\frac{4}{52}$ $c.$ $\frac{2}{52}$ $d.$ $\frac{13}{52}$
$e.$ $\frac{16}{52}$ $f.$ $\frac{28}{52}$ $g.$ $\frac{39}{52}$
7. 12
8. $a.$ $\frac{5}{36}$ $b.$ $\frac{6}{36}$ $c.$ $\frac{18}{36}$ $d.$ 1
9. $\frac{2}{8}$
10. $a.$ 120 $b.$ 90 $c.$ 24 $d.$ 870 $e.$ 210
11. (3) **12.** (3) **13.** (4)
14. $a.$ (1, 1) (1, 2) (1, 3) (1, 4) (1, 5)
(2, 1) (2, 2) (2, 3) (2, 4) (2, 5)
(3, 1) (3, 2) (3, 3) (3, 4) (3, 5)
(4, 1) (4, 2) (4, 3) (4, 4) (4, 5)
(5, 1) (5, 2) (5, 3) (5, 4) (5, 5)
$b.$ $\frac{5}{25}$ $c.$ $\frac{9}{25}$ $d.$ $\frac{9}{25}$ $e.$ $\frac{12}{25}$

15. $a.$

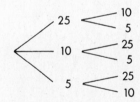

$b.$ 1. $\frac{2}{6}$ 2. 0 3. $\frac{4}{6}$ 4. 1 5. $\frac{4}{6}$
$c.$ $\frac{2}{6}$ $d.$ $\frac{2}{6}$
16. 25 **17.** 10
18. 8 girls, 16 boys

Chapter 16. Statistics

16-1 The Collection of Data: *page 532*

1. $a.$ unfair
$b.$ basketball players are taller than average
2. $a.$ unfair
$b.$ seniors would be taller than underclassmen
3. $a.$ unfair
$b.$ fourteen-year-old students would be shorter than older students
4. $a.$ unfair
$b.$ girls are usually shorter than boys

5. $a.$ fair
6. $a.$ unfair
$b.$ boys are usually taller than girls
7. $a.$ unfair
$b.$ three is too small a sample
8. $a.$ fair **9.** no **10.** no **11.** yes
12. no **13.** no **14.** yes **15.** b, c, e
16. collection of data, organization of data, drawing of conclusions

16-2 The Organization of Data Into Tables: *pages 535–537*

1. *a.*

Interval	Tallies	Frequency
180–189	‖‖ |	6
170–179	‖‖ ‖‖	10
160–169	‖‖ ‖‖ ||	12
150–159	‖‖ |	6
140–149	||	2

b. 1. 8 2. 28 3. 160–169 4. 140–149

2. *a.*

Interval	Tallies	Frequency
50–59	‖‖	5
60–69	|||	3
70–79	‖‖ ‖‖ ||	12
80–89	‖‖ ‖‖ ||||	14
90–99	‖‖ ||	7
100–109	‖‖ ||||	9

b. 1. 30 2. 20 3. 80–89 4. 60–69

3. *a.*

Interval	Frequency
91–100	7
81–90	10
71–80	7
61–70	2
51–60	2
41–50	2

b.

Interval	Frequency
89–100	8
77–88	9
65–76	8
53–64	3
41–52	2

c. 81–90 *d.* 77–88
e. yes; the scores from 81 to 88 are common to both intervals

4. *a.*

Interval	Frequency
35–39	1
30–34	2
25–29	5
20–24	5
15–19	10
10–14	4
5–9	6
0–4	5

b.

Interval	Frequency
32–39	2
24–31	6
16–23	14
8–15	7
0–7	9

5. *a.* too few intervals
b. not equal in size
c. some scores fall in two intervals
d. 0 is not included in an interval

16-3 Using Graphs to Present Organized Data: *pages 541–544*

1. *a.* Standard Oil, 1,150; John Hancock, 1,100; Sears Tower, 1,450; Empire State, 1,250; World Trade, 1,350; Chrysler, 1,050
b. Sears Tower *c.* 100 ft. *d.* John Hancock
e. 350 ft. *f.* none of these
2. *a.* Calcot, 55,000; Parr City, 25,000; Sampler, 25,000; Tyne, 5,000
b. Parr City and Sampler *c.* 5
d. 5:1 *e.* equal, 1:1
3. *a.* 20 *b.* lettuce *c.* 80 *d.* 25%
e. 15:10 or 3:2
4. *a.* 2 cm *b.* 10 cm *c.* .5 cm or 5 mm
d. 2.5 cm or 25 mm
5. *a.* $\frac{1}{2}$ in. *b.* 1 in. *c.* 5 in. *d.* $1\frac{1}{4}$ in. *e.* $3\frac{3}{4}$ in.
f. $\frac{1}{8}$ in.
6. *a.* $.30 *b.* 2nd *c.* 9th and 10th
d. 5th and 6th *e.* 8th and 11th *f.* $.40
7. *a.* 1940–1950 *b.* 1960–1970 *c.* 61 *d.* 65
e. (2) *f.* (4) *g.* (2)
8. *a.* graph
b. A line graph is used to show how a particular item changed.
9. *a.* graph
b. The line graph shows how the rate changed.
c. graph

16-4 The Histogram: *pages 547–548*

1.

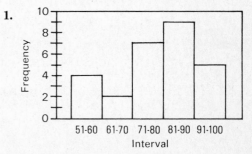

2.

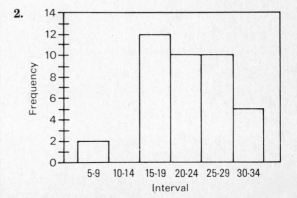

252

3.

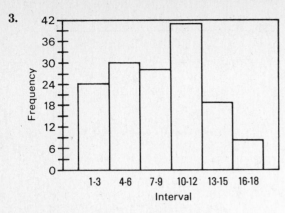

4. *a.* 150 *b.* 10–12 *c.* 20% *d.* 68

5. *a.*

Interval	Tallies	Number
35–37	||||	4
32–34	⊬|	6
29–31	⊬||	7
26–28	|	1
23–25	||	2

b.

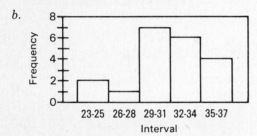

c. 1. 29–31 2. 10 3. 10%

6. *a.*

Interval	Tallies	Number
37.0-40.9	⊬|||	8
33.0-36.9	⊬||||	9
29.0-32.9	⊬|||	8
25.0-28.9	||||	4
21.0-24.9	|	1

b.

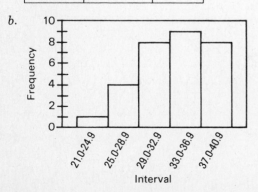

c. 5

16-5 The Mean, the Median, and the Mode: *pages 553–556*

1. 82 **2.** 86 **3.** $\dfrac{2x + 3y}{5}$ **4.** 95 **5.** 100

6. *a.* 82 *b.* 100 *c.* 63
  d. not possible; he would need a test score of 115

7. 34 **8.** 75 kg **9.** 18, 20, 22 **10.** 16, 33, 44
11. *a.* 10 *b.* 10 *c.* 8 *d.* 30.4 *e.* 4 *f.* 1.105
12. 174 cm
13. *a.* 7 *b.* 10 *c.* 4.1 *d.* 7.5 *e.* 9.5 *f.* 4.05
14. *a.* 3 *b.* 7 *c.* 4 *d.* 80 *e.* 3.2 *f.* 2 *g.* 6
  h. 22.5
15. 13.5 **16.** 15 **17.** \$1
18. 70 **19.** 5 **20.** 50.5
21. *a.* 2 *b.* 2, 8 *c.* 8 *d.* no mode *e.* 2, 8, 9
  f. 1 *g.* 2 *h.* no mode *i.* 2, 7 *j.* 19
22. *a.* 9 *b.* 8 *c.* no mode *d.* 8, 9
23. *a.* 2 *b.* 4 or 5
  c. 3 (or any number except 2, 4, and 5)
24. *a.* 1. mean is 7 2. median is 7
    3. no mode
  b. 1. mean is 24 2. median is 22
    3. mode is 22
  c. 1. mean is 5 2. median is $5\frac{1}{2}$
    3. no mode
  d. 1. mean is .71 2. median is 1
    3. mode is 1
25. (3) **26.** (2) **27.** (4)
28. (3) **29.** (3) **30.** (3)
31. (2)
32. *a.* 1. mean is \$375 2. median is \$347.50
    3. modes are \$345, \$350
  b. mean; it makes "average" salary appear higher
  c. median or mode; it makes "average" salary appear lower
33. *a.* 1. mean is 2 2. median is 1 3. mode is 1
  b. 2
  c. it is higher than all but two of the distances
34. *a.* 1. mean is 1 2. median is $\frac{3}{4}$ 3. mode is $\frac{3}{4}$
  b. $\frac{3}{4}$ (the mode) is the best average; it describes the nail the carpenter uses most

---

16-6 Measures of Central Tendency and Grouped Data: *pages 562–564*

1. *a.* 15 *b.* 7 *c.* 7 *d.* 6
2. *a.* 21 *b.* 18 *c.* 19 *d.* 20
3. *a.* 20 *b.* 21.75 *c.* 21 *d.* 20

4. *a.*

Grade	Frequency
20	0
19	1
18	2
17	4
16	3
15	2
14	1
13	1
12	1

b. 16   *c.* 17   *d.* 16

5. *a.* 1. mean, 4   2. median, 4   3. mode, 4
   b. median, mean and mode are equal
6. *a.* 1. total frequency, 25   2. mean, 40
      3. median, 40   4. mode, 38
   b. median or mean best describes the "average" suit
7. *a.* 26   *b.* 35–44   *c.* 45–54
8. *a.* 71   *b.* 22–27   *c.* 28–33
9. *a.* 28   *b.* 76–100   *c.* 26–50

10. *a.*

Test Scores	Frequency
91–100	9
81–90	6
71–80	3
61–70	0
51–60	2

b. 91–100   *c.* 81–90

11. *a.*

Interval	Frequency
180–199	4
160–179	10
140–159	7
120–139	9
100–119	5

b. graph   *c.* 140–159
d. 160–179

**16-7 Cumulative Frequency Histograms
and Percentiles:** *pages 569–572*

1. *a.*

Height	Frequency	Cumulative Frequency
77	2	20
76	1	18
75	7	17
74	5	10
73	2	5
72	2	3
71	1	1

b.

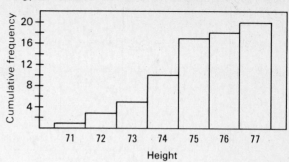

c. 5   *d.* 18

2. *a.*

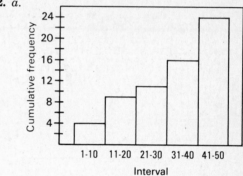

b. 11–20   *c.* 31–40   *d.* 41–50

3. *a.*

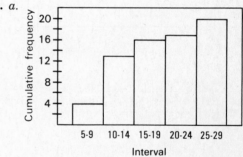

b. 10–14   *c.* 10–14   *d.* 15–19

4. *a.*

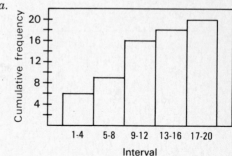

b. 1–4   *c.* 9–12   *d.* 9–12

5. *a.* histogram

b.
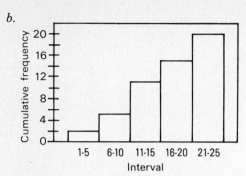

c. 11–15   *d.* 10

6. *a.* 26–50   *b.* 25   *c.* 75   *d.* 60%   *e.* 100%

7. *a.*
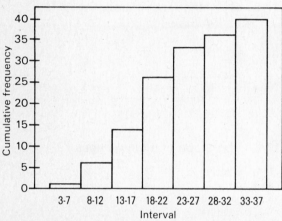

b. 18–22   *c.* 23–27   *d.* 35%   *e.* 13–17   *f.* 32

8. *a.* 60   *b.* 70%   *c.* 280   *d.* 91–120   *e.* 1–30
f. 35%

9. 188   **10.** 510   **11.** (4)   **12.** (1)

16-8   Review Exercises: *pages 572–573*

1. *a.* 67   *b.* 70   *c.* 72   **2.** 93
3. 5y + 8   **4.** *a.* 80°   *b.* 81°   *c.* 83°
5. (4)   **6.** (3)   **7.** (2)

8. *a.*

Interval	Frequency
24–29	2
18–23	0
12–17	6
6–11	9
0–5	3

b.
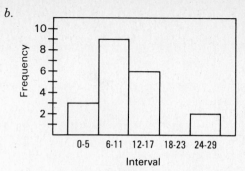

c. 6–11   *d.* 6–11

9. *a.* 80   *b.* 80   *c.* 70

d.

Scores	Frequency	Cumulative Frequency
60	1	1
70	9	10
80	8	18
90	1	19
100	5	24

e.
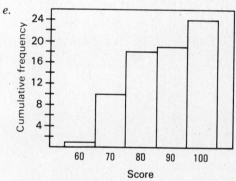

f. 80   *g.* $\frac{8}{24}$ or $\frac{1}{3}$

10. 7

Chapter 17.   The Coordinate Plane

17-1   Ordered Number Pairs and Points in a Plane: *pages 575–576*

1. $A(1, 2)$; $B(-2, 1)$; $C(-2, -1)$; $D(2, -2)$; $E(2, 0)$; $F(0, 1)$; $G(-1, 0)$; $H(0, -2)$; $O(0, 0)$
2–21. graphs
22. I   23. III   24. II   25. IV
26. I   27. 0   28. 0   29. (0, 0)
30. *a.* I *b.* IV *c.* II *d.* III
31. *a.* I *b.* I *c.* I *d.* I

17-2   Graphing Polygons and Finding Areas: *page 578*

1*a*–10*a*. graphs
1. *b.* triangle *c.* 14
2. *b.* rectangle *c.* 20
3. *b.* parallelogram *c.* 20
4. *b.* square *c.* 16
5. *b.* triangle *c.* 21
6. *b.* trapezoid *c.* 24
7. *b.* square *c.* 16
8. *b.* parallelogram *c.* 6
9. *b.* triangle *c.* 10
10. *b.* square *c.* 16
11. graph; (1, 4)
12. graph; $R(2, 0)$, $S(-2, 0)$ or $R(2, -8)$, $S(-2, -8)$
13. *a.* graph *b.* 24
14. *a.* graph *b.* 6

17-3   Finding Solution Sets of Open Sentences in Two Variables: *pages 580–581*

1. 6   2. 0   3. -4 4. 5.5
5. -4 6. 9   7. $4\frac{1}{2}$ 8. 4
9. $5\frac{1}{4}$ 10. -12 11. yes   12. no
13. yes   14. no   15. yes   16. yes
17. no   18. yes   19. no   20. yes
21. no   22. yes   23. yes   24. no
25. yes   26. yes   27. $(8, -2)$ 28. $(-2, -\frac{1}{4})$
29. (1, 8)   30. { }
31. $\{(-3, -10), (-1, -4), (2, 5)\}$
32. $\{(5, 8), (6, 8), (6, 9), (6, 10)\}$
33. $\{(10, 2), (10, 6), (10, 10), (12, 2), (12, 6), (12, 10)\}$
34. $\{(x, y)|y = 6x\}$ 35. $\{(x, y)|y = x + 9\}$
36. $\{(x, y)|y = -3x + 11\}$ 37. $\{(x, y)|y > 10x\}$
38. $\{(x, y)|y < 3x - 1\}$ 39. $\{(x, y)|y \geq x + 4\}$

17-4   Graphing a Linear Equation in Two Variables by Means of Its Solutions: *pages 584–585*

1. *a.* yes *b.* no *c.* no   2. yes   3. yes
4. no   5. yes   6. 1   7. 4
8. -1 9. any number   10. 7
11. 8   12. -1 13. 0
14. $y = -3x - 1$ 15. $y = 4x - 6$

16. $y = 3x$ 17. $y = 8x$ 18. $y = -2x + 4$
19. $y = 2x - \frac{5}{3}$
20-50. graphs

20.
x	y
0	0
1	4
2	8

21.
x	y
-1	-2
0	1
1	4

22.
x	y
-1	2
2	$\frac{1}{2}$
5	-1

46. *a.* $y = 2x$ 47. *a.* $y = x + 2$
48. *a.* $x + y = 6$ 49. *a.* $y - x = 1$
50. *a.* $2y - 3x = 6$

17-5   Graphing Lines Parallel to the *X*-Axis or *Y*-Axis: *page 587*

1–14. graphs
15. *a.* $y = 1$ *b.* $y = 5$ *c.* $y = -4$ *d.* $y = -8$
    e. $y = -2.5$
16. *a.* $x = 3$ *b.* $x = 10$ *c.* $x = 4\frac{1}{2}$ *d.* $x = -6$
    e. $x = -10$
17. (2)   18. (3)   19. (4)

17-6   The Slope of a Line: *pages 592–593*

1. *a.* positive *b.* $\frac{3}{2}$ 2. *a.* no slope   *b.* no slope
3. *a.* zero   *b.* 0   4. *a.* negative *b.* -2
5. *a.* positive *b.* 2   6. *a.* negative *b.* -1
7–24. graphs
7. 1   8. 2   9. -2 10. 2   11. $\frac{2}{3}$
12. -1 13. -3 14. 0   15. 0
25. slope of $\overline{AB} = 0$; slope of $\overline{BC} = 1$;
    slope of $\overline{AC} = -1$
26. *a.* graph *b.* parallelogram
    c. slope of $\overline{BC}$ = slope of $\overline{AD}$ = -3
    d. slopes are equal   *e.* slopes are equal
    f. slopes are equal
    g. slope of $\overline{AB}$ = slope of $\overline{CD}$ = 0   *h.* yes

17-7   Graphing Direct Variation: *page 596*

1*c.*–10*c.* graphs
1. *a.* 4   *b.* $y = 4x$ *d.* 4
2. *a.* 45   *b.* $y = 45x$ *d.* 45
3. *a.* 16   *b.* $y = 16x$ *d.* 16
4. *a.* $\frac{4}{3}$ *b.* $y = \frac{4}{3}x$ *d.* $\frac{4}{3}$
5. *a.* 10   *b.* $y = 10x$ *d.* 10
6. *a.* $\frac{5}{3}$ *b.* $y = \frac{5}{3}x$ *d.* $\frac{5}{3}$
7. *a.* $\frac{1}{5}$ *b.* $y = \frac{1}{5}x$ *d.* $\frac{1}{5}$
8. *a.* $\frac{3}{2}$ *b.* $y = \frac{3}{2}x$ *d.* $\frac{3}{2}$
9. *a.* $\frac{1}{4}$ *b.* $y = \frac{1}{4}x$ *d.* $\frac{1}{4}$
10. *a.* $\frac{20}{3}$ *b.* $y = \frac{20}{3}x$ *d.* $\frac{20}{3}$
11. *a.* 30   *b.* 44

17-8 The Slope and Y-Intercept of a Line: pages 598–599

1. $m = 3, b = 1$ **2.** $m = 1, b = -3$
3. $m = 2, b = 0$ **4.** $m = 1, b = 0$
5. $m = \frac{1}{2}, b = 5$ **6.** $m = -2, b = 3$
7. $m = -3, b = 0$ **8.** $m = 0, b = -2$
9. $m = -\frac{2}{3}, b = 4$ **10.** $m = 3, b = 7$
11. $m = -2, b = 5$ **12.** $m = 2, b = 3$
13. $m = \frac{5}{2}, b = -2$ **14.** $m = \frac{3}{2}, b = \frac{9}{4}$
15. $m = \frac{4}{3}, b = 0$ **16.** $y = 2x + 7$
17. $y = -x - 3$ **18.** $y = -5$
19. $y = -3x$ **20.** $y = \frac{2}{3}x + 1$
21. $y = \frac{1}{2}x$ **22.** $y = -\frac{1}{3}x + 2$
23. $y = -\frac{3}{2}x$
24. $y = 2x; \quad y = 2x + 1; \quad y = 2x - 5$
($y = 2x + b$, where b is any real number)
25. $y = x - 4; \quad y = 2x - 4; \quad y = -5x - 4$
($y = mx - 4$, where m is any real number)
26. same slope; graphs will be parallel
27. lines are parallel; will have different y-intercepts
28. same y-intercept, 1
29. graphs intersect y-axis at the same point, (0, 6)
30. equal   **31.** parallel   **32.** yes
33. no   **34.** yes   **35.** yes
36. (3)   **37.** (1)

17-9 Graphing a Linear Equation in Two Variables by the Slope-Intercept Method: pages 600–601

1–24. graphs. Exercises 16–24 follow in slope-intercept form.
16. $y = 2x + 8$ **17.** $y = -3x + 4$
18. $y = 2x + 3$ **19.** $y = \frac{4}{3}x + 3$
20. $y = 4x - 3$ **21.** $y = -\frac{3}{4}x + 3$
22. $y = \frac{2}{3}x - 2$ **23.** $y = -\frac{4}{3}x$
24. $y = \frac{2}{3}x - 2$

17-10 Writing an Equation for a Line: pages 602–603

1. $y = 2x + 2$ **2.** $y = 2x + 10$
3. $y = -3x - 7$ **4.** $y = \frac{1}{2}x$
5. $y = -\frac{3}{4}x$ **6.** $y = -\frac{5}{3}x - 5$
7. $y = 2x + 2$ **8.** $y = x - 2$
9. $y = \frac{4}{3}x + \frac{2}{3}$ **10.** $y = \frac{3}{2}x - 1$
11. $y = 3x + 1$ **12.** $y = -\frac{5}{3}x$
13. *a.* $y = 2x + 7$ *b.* $y = 3x - 2$
    c. $y = -\frac{2}{3}x$ or $2x + 3y = 0$
14. *a.* $y = 4x - 5$ *b.* $y = 3x + 7$
    c. $y = 4x - 3$ *d.* $y = -\frac{1}{2}x + 3$

15. *a.* $y = -\frac{1}{3}x + 6$ *b.* $y = x - 2$
    c. $y = 3x - 4$

17-11 Graphing a Linear Inequality in Two Variables: page 607

1. $y > 2x$ **2.** $y < \frac{5}{2}x$ **3.** $y \geq x + 3$
4. $y \leq -2x$ **5.** $y \leq 3x - 4$ **6.** $y \leq \frac{3}{4}x + 3$
7–30. graphs. Exercises 17–30 follow in slope-intercept form.
17. $y < -x + 4$ **18.** $y \geq -x + 4$
19. $y \leq -x - 3$ **20.** $y \geq x + 5$
21. $y \geq x + 1$ **22.** $y \geq \frac{1}{2}x - 2$
23. $y \leq -2x + 4$ **24.** $y > x - 6$
25. $y > 3x$ **26.** $y \leq -\frac{3}{4}x$
27. $y \leq \frac{2}{3}x - 2$ **28.** $y \leq 3x$
29. $y \geq -x + 4$ **30.** $y \geq \frac{1}{2}x - 2$
31. *a.* $y \geq x + 3$ *b.* graph
32. *a.* $x + y \leq 5$ or $y \leq -x + 5$ *b.* graph
33. *a.* $y - 3x \geq 2$ or $y \geq 3x + 2$ *b.* graph

17-12 Coordinates and Transformations: pages 610–611

1–15. graphs
1. $(-3, 5)$ **2.** $(-1, 4)$ **3.** $(-2, -3)$ **4.** $(2, 3)$
5. $(1, 0)$ **6.** $(2, -5)$ **7.** $(1, -3)$ **8.** $(-2, -3)$
9. $(2, 4)$ **10.** $(0, -2)$ **11.** $(4, 8)$ **12.** $(3, 6)$
13. $(0, 6)$ **14.** $(4, -1)$ **15.** $(2, 5)$
16a–20a. graphs
16. *b.* $x = 0$ (the y-axis) and $y = 0$ (the x-axis)
17. *b.* $x = 3$ and $y = \frac{5}{2}$ **18.** *b.* $x = 3$
19. *b.* $x = -\frac{3}{2}$ and $y = -2$ *c.* $(-\frac{3}{2}, -2)$
20. *b.* no   *c.* yes, (4, 2)

17-13 Graphs Involving Absolute Value: page 613

1–9. graphs
10. *a.* graph   *b.* $x = 0; y = 0$

17-14 Review Exercises: pages 613–614

1. -2 **2.** $y = \frac{3}{2}x - 6$ **3.** $y = -x + 7$
4. $\frac{-2}{1}$, or -2 **5–10.** graphs
11. $\frac{2}{1}$, or 2   **12.** -2 **13.** $x = 3$
14. $y = 2x$ **15.** 4   **16.** (2)
17. (1)   **18.** (2)   **19.** (4)
20. (2)   **21.** (4)
22. *a-b* graph   *c.* trapezoid
    d. $DA = 10, BC = 6$ *e.* 5   *f.* 40   *g.* $x = 0$
23–25. graphs

Chapter 18. Systems of Linear Open Sentences in Two Variables

18-1 Graphic Solution of a System of Linear Equations in Two Variables: *pages 618–620*

1. (3, 6)
2. (−1, 3)
3. (0, 3)
4. (4, 3)
5. (2, 2)
6. (1, −5)
7. (−3, 4)
8. (1, 3)
9. (6, 2)
10. (3, 7)
11. (2, 6)
12. (3, 2)
13. (0, −2)
14. (1, 3)
15. ($\frac{7}{2}$, 5)
16. (1, 6)
17. (−2, 5)
18. (−5, −3)
19. (−2, −3)
20. (−2, −3)
21. (3, 4)
22. (3, −2)
23. (5, −2)
24. (0, −5)
25. ($\frac{7}{2}$, −2)
26. (3, 2)
27. (0, 0)
28. (−5, 3)
29. (−$\frac{3}{2}$, −3)
30. (−1, 0)
31. inconsistent
32. dependent
33. consistent
34. dependent
35. inconsistent
36. consistent
37. no
38. no
39. a. $x + y = 8$
    $x - y = 2$
    b. (5, 3)
40. a. $x + y = 3$
    $y = x + 5$
    b. (−1, 4)
41. a. $2x + 2y = 12$
    $y = 2x$
    b. (2, 4)
42. a. $2x + 2y = 14$
    $y = x + 3$
    b. (2, 5)

18-2 Algebraic Solution of a System of Simultaneous Linear Equations by Using Addition: *pages 624–625*

1. (2, 3)
2. (2, 1)
3. (8, 4)
4. (9, 4)
5. (−8, 2)
6. (5, 1)
7. (12, −1)
8. (5, 5)
9. (8, 4)
10. (6, 1)
11. ($\frac{1}{2}$, 1)
12. (2, 3)
13. (−$\frac{1}{2}$, 3)
14. (2, 3)
15. (1, 3)
16. (3, 2)
17. (4, −2)
18. (2, 5)
19. (5, 2)
20. (4, 5)
21. (1, 1)
22. (6, 2)
23. (−3, 2)
24. (5, 6)
25. (3, 6)
26. (6, 5)
27. (10, −6)
28. (−15, 12)
29. (2, 1)
30. (−3, 1)
31. (−7, 9)
32. (0, −$\frac{5}{2}$)
33. (7, −3)
34. (2, 2)
35. (6, 5)
36. (6, 0)
37. (2, 12)
38. (7, 2)
39. (6, 4)
40. (−8, 3)
41. (24, 8)
42. (8, 12)
43. (9, 4)
44. (6, 4)
45. (200, 300)
46. (150, 250)
47. (500, 100)

18-3 Algebraic Solution of a System of Simultaneous Linear Equations by Using Substitution: *page 627*

1. (7, 7)
2. (−2, −2)
3. (7, 14)
4. (8, 2)
5. (2, −1)
6. (−6, 2)
7. (4, 5)
8. (8, 10)
9. (4, 7)
10. (2, 5)
11. (−8, −3)
12. (6, 5)
13. (5, 2)
14. (4, 3)
15. (5, 4)
16. (6, 4)
17. (−4, 3)
18. (5, −1)
19. (9, 27)
20. (3, −3)
21. (5, 2)
22. (6, 4)
23. (2, 2)
24. (7, 5)
25. (3, −6)
26. (4, $\frac{1}{2}$)
27. (6, 18)

28. (10, 9)
29. (−3, 4)
30. (60, 240)
31. (5, 1)
32. (4, 3)
33. (3, 9)

18-4 Solving Verbal Problems by Using Two Variables

Number Problems: *page 629*

1. 30, 6
2. 37, 40
3. 35, 69
4. 49, 15
5. 33, 10
6. 30, 45
7. 500, 400

Business Problems: *pages 630–631*

1. pretzel, $.75; soda, $.50
2. gardener, $60; helper, $30
3. bat, $9.00; ball, $4.50
4. veal, $6.25; pork, $2.50
5. brown rice, $2.50; white rice, $2.90

Geometry Problems: *page 631*

1. 17 cm, 8 cm
2. 14 ft. by 5 ft.
3. 30°, 150°
4. 65°, 115°
5. 60°, 30°
6. 32°, 58°
7. 40°, 70°, 70°

Miscellaneous Problems: *pages 631–632*

1. 60 in advance, 40 at the door
2. 120
3. 4 twenties, 2 tens
4. eight 30-cent stamps, six 20-cent stamps
5. 64 pounds at $2/lb., 16 pounds at $3/lb.
6. squash, $.49; eggplant, $.69
7. Roger, $25,500; Wilma, $21,500
8. $400 at 5%, $1,000 at 8%
9. $2,600 at 4%, $1,400 at 6%
10. $9,000 at 8%, $12,000 at 6%

18-5 Graphing Solution Sets of Systems of Inequalities: *pages 634–635*

1–34. graphs

18-6 Review Exercises: *pages 635–636*

1. 4
2. (4, 2)
3. (3, −3)
4. (−4, 0)
5. (7, −4)
6. (−1, $\frac{1}{2}$)
7. (4, −12)
8. (−3, 5)
9. (10, −5)
10. (0, 7)
11. (5, −5)
12. (4, −1)
13. (3, 9)
14. (8, 6)
15. (400, 600)
16. (2, 4)
17. 41 and 23
18. notebook, $.80; pencil, $.20
19. 35 and 55
20. a. {(4$\frac{1}{2}$, 1$\frac{1}{2}$)} b. graph
21–23. graphs
24. (−4, 4); many answers are possible
25. 30 regular and 70 student tickets

Chapter 19.   The Real Numbers

19-1   The Set of Rational Numbers:
pages 642–643

1. $\frac{7}{2}$
2. $\frac{-9}{3}$
3. $\frac{5}{6}$
4. $-\frac{1}{5}$
5. $\frac{5}{2}$
6. $\frac{-13}{6}$
7. $\frac{13}{6}$
8. $\frac{-5}{12}$
9. $1\frac{3}{5}$
10. $-3\frac{1}{3}$
11. $\frac{1}{6}$
12. $\frac{-11}{15}$
13. $5\frac{1}{2}$
14. $-3\frac{1}{2}$
15. $-\frac{1}{2}$
16. $\frac{3}{8}$
17. $\frac{11}{16}$
18. $-\frac{17}{24}$
19. -2.15
20. $2\frac{9}{16}$
21. $-1\frac{7}{24}$
22. $3.07\overline{5}$
23. $.625\overline{0}$
24. $2.25\overline{0}$
25. $-5.5\overline{0}$
26. $1.625\overline{0}$
27. $-.58\overline{3}$
28. $1.\overline{6}$
29. $.\overline{7}$
30. $\frac{1}{2}$
31. $\frac{5}{9}$
32. $-\frac{2}{9}$
33. $\frac{1}{8}$
34. $\frac{25}{99}$
35. $\frac{7}{90}$

19-2   The Set of Irrational Numbers:
page 644

1. rational
2. rational
3. irrational
4. rational
5. rational
6. irrational
7. rational
8. irrational
9. rational
10. irrational
11. irrational
12. irrational
13. rational
14. rational
15. irrational
16. irrational

Note: In 17–20, other answers are possible.
17. .8 or .78 or .79
18. .155 or .16 or .161
19. 3.5 or 3.4 or 3.3
20. 2.35 or 2.4

19-3   The Set of Real Numbers:
pages 646–647

1. 2.5
2. -5.7
3. .535353
4. $.\overline{7}$
5. $-.53$
6. .2121 . . .
7. false
8. true
9. true
10. false
11. true
12. false
13. true
14. false
15. false
16. true
17. (3)
18. (4)
19. (2)
20. $-n$
21. $\frac{1}{n}$
22. 0
23. 1

19-4   Finding a Rational Root of a Number:
pages 650–651

1. index 2, radicand 36
2. index 3, radicand 125
3. index 4, radicand 81
4. index 5, radicand 32
5. index n, radicand 1
6. 9
7. 1
8. 11
9. 15
10. 30
11. $\frac{1}{3}$
12. $\frac{2}{5}$
13. .7
14. 1.2

15. .2
16. 4
17. 9
18. 11
19. -8
20. -12
21. 0
22. ± 10
23. ± 13
24. 20
25. -25
26. $\frac{1}{2}$
27. $-\frac{3}{4}$
28. $\pm\frac{5}{9}$
29. $\frac{7}{10}$
30. $\pm\frac{12}{13}$
31. .8
32. -1.2
33. $\pm .3$
34. $-.1$
35. $\pm .02$
36. 1
37. 3
38. 2
39. -2
40. 5
41. 8
42. $\frac{1}{2}$
43. .7
44. 3 or $\frac{9}{3}$
45. $\frac{9}{5}$
46. 4
47. 36
48. 11
49. 39
50. 97
51. 13
52. 5
53. 24
54. -74
55. a. $\frac{1}{2} > \frac{1}{4}$ b. $\frac{3}{4} > \frac{9}{16}$ c. $1 = 1$
    d. $\frac{3}{2} < \frac{9}{4}$ e. $4 < 16$ f. $100 < 10,000$
56. a. $n > n^2$ b. $n = n^2$ c. $n < n^2$
57. a. $\frac{1}{3} > \frac{1}{9}$ b. $\frac{2}{5} > \frac{4}{25}$ c. $1 = 1$
    d. $\frac{7}{5} < \frac{49}{25}$ e. $2 < 4$ f. $3 < 9$
58. a. $\sqrt{m} > m$ b. $\sqrt{m} = m$ c. $\sqrt{m} < m$
59. $\{2, -2\}$
60. $\{10, -10\}$
61. $\{\frac{2}{9}, -\frac{2}{9}\}$
62. $\{.7, -.7\}$
63. $\{4, -4\}$
64. $\{6, -6\}$
65. $\{5, -5\}$
66. $\{3, -3\}$
67. $\{2\}$
68. $\{1\}$
69. $\{3, -3\}$
70. $\{2\}$
71. a. 6 ft.   b. 24 ft.
72. a. 14 yd.   b. 56 yd.
73. a. 11 cm   b. 44 cm
74. a. 15 m   b. 60 m
75. $4x, x > 0$
76. Some solutions are shown; others are possible
    $101 = 10^2 + 1^2$
    $102 = 10^2 + 1^2 + 1^2$ or $7^2 + 7^2 + 2^2$
    $103 = 9^2 + 3^2 + 3^2 + 2^2$ or $7^2 + 7^2 + 2^2 + 1^2$
        or $10^2 + 1^2 + 1^2 + 1^2$
    $104 = 10^2 + 2^2$
    $105 = 8^2 + 5^2 + 4^2$ or $10^2 + 2^2 + 1^2$
    $106 = 9^2 + 5^2$
    $107 = 9^2 + 5^2 + 1^2$ or $7^2 + 7^2 + 3^2$
    $108 = 10^2 + 2^2 + 2^2$ or $6^2 + 6^2 + 6^2$
    $109 = 10^2 + 3^2$
    $110 = 7^2 + 6^2 + 5^2$ or $10^2 + 3^2 + 1^2$

19-5   Square Roots That Are Irrational
Numbers: *page 653*

1. 2, 3
2. 3, 4
3. 6, 7
4. $-2, -1$
5. $-4, -3$
6. 7, 8
7. 8, 9
8. $-12, -11$
9. 11, 12
10. $-13, -12$
11. $-1, \sqrt{3}, 2$
12. $3, 4, \sqrt{17}$
13. $-4, -\sqrt{15}, -3$
14. $-\sqrt{7}, 0, \sqrt{7}$
15. $\sqrt{21}, 5, \sqrt{30}$
16. $-\sqrt{23}, -\sqrt{19}, -\sqrt{11}$
17. rational
18. irrational
19. rational
20. irrational
21. irrational
22. rational
23. irrational
24. rational
25. rational
26. irrational

19-6 Using a Table to Find Squares and Square Roots: *pages 653–654*

1. 729 **2.** 4,624 **3.** 8,836
4. 14,161 **5.** 17,424 **6.** 21,609
7. *a.* 3.6 *b.* 3.61 **8.** *a.* 7.3 *b.* 7.28
9. *a.* −7.9 *b.* −7.94 **10.** *a.* 11.6 *b.* 11.62
11. *a.* −9.3 *b.* −9.33 **12.** *a.* 2.2 *b.* 2.24
13. *a.* 9.5 *b.* 9.54 **14.** *a.* 9.2 *b.* 9.22
15. *a.* −10.5 *b.* −10.54 **16.** *a.* 11.9 *b.* 11.87
17. *a.* 3.7 *b.* 3.73 **18.** *a.* 4.9 *b.* 4.88
19. *a.* 14.4 *b.* 14.42 **20.** *a.* 7.0 *b.* 6.95
21. *a.* −5.6 *b.* −5.61
22. 10 **23.** 13 **24.** 25 **25.** 39
26. 13.8 **27.** 8.8 **28.** 8.9 **29.** 38.7

19-7 Using Divison to Find Approximate Square Roots: *page 656*

1. *a.* 1 *b.* 1.4 *c.* 1.41
2. *a.* 2 *b.* 1.7 *c.* 1.73
3. *a.* 5 *b.* 4.6 *c.* 4.58
4. *a.* 6 *b.* 6.2 *c.* 6.24
5. *a.* 9 *b.* 8.9 *c.* 8.94
6. *a.* 9 *b.* 9.5 *c.* 9.49
7. *a.* 10 *b.* 10.4 *c.* 10.39
8. *a.* 5 *b.* 4.8 *c.* 4.85
9. *a.* 9 *b.* 9.4 *c.* 9.39
10. *a.* −11 *b.* −10.7 *c.* −10.73
11. *a.* 5 *b.* 5.3 *c.* 5.34
12. *a.* 8 *b.* 8.2 *c.* 8.20
13. *a.* 66 *b.* 66.2 *c.* 66.25
14. *a.* 11 *b.* 11.1 *c.* 11.12
15. *a.* 12 *b.* 11.6 *c.* 11.60
16. 2.8 cm **17.** 5.4 cm **18.** 9.8 cm
19. 11.8 cm **20.** 14.1 cm

19-8 Finding the Principal Square Root of a Monomial: *page 657*

1. $2a$ **2.** $4d$ **3.** $7z$ **4.** $\frac{4}{5}r$
5. $.9w$ **6.** $3c$ **7.** $6y^2$ **8.** cd
9. x^2y **10.** r^4s^3 **11.** $2xy$ **12.** $6a^3b^2$
13. $12a^2b$ **14.** $13x^2y$ **15.** $.6m$ **16.** $.7ab$
17. $.2y$ **18.** $.1x^2y$
19. *a.* $7c\ (c > 0)$ *b.* $28c$
20. *a.* $8x\ (x > 0)$ *b.* $32x$
21. *a.* $10xy\ (x, y > 0)$ *b.* $40xy$
22. *a.* $12ab\ (a, b > 0)$ *b.* $48ab$

19-9 Simplifying a Square-Root Radical: *pages 659–660*

1. $2\sqrt{2}$ **2.** $2\sqrt{3}$ **3.** $2\sqrt{5}$
4. $2\sqrt{7}$ **5.** $2\sqrt{10}$ **6.** $3\sqrt{3}$
7. $3\sqrt{6}$ **8.** $3\sqrt{7}$ **9.** $3\sqrt{10}$
10. $7\sqrt{2}$ **11.** $3\sqrt{11}$ **12.** $6\sqrt{3}$
13. $9\sqrt{2}$ **14.** $5\sqrt{7}$ **15.** $10\sqrt{3}$
16. $6\sqrt{2}$ **17.** $8\sqrt{3}$ **18.** $4\sqrt{5}$

19. $12\sqrt{10}$ **20.** $6\sqrt{5}$ **21.** $30\sqrt{2}$
22. $3\sqrt{2}$ **23.** $\sqrt{3}$ **24.** $3\sqrt{6}$
25. $2\sqrt{7}$ **26.** $10\sqrt{6}$ **27.** $8\sqrt{5}$
28. $21\sqrt{5}$ **29.** $24\sqrt{x}$ **30.** $x\sqrt{3x}$
31. $7x^2\sqrt{x}$ **32.** $6r\sqrt{s}$ **33.** (3)
34. (3) **35.** (3) **36.** (4)
37. 17.3 **38.** 13.4 **39.** 33.9
40. 5.3
41. *a.* no; $\sqrt{25} \neq 3 + 4$ *b.* no
42. *a.* no; $\sqrt{16} \neq 5 - 3$ *b.* no

19-10 Adding and Subtracting Radicals: *pages 661–662*

1. $15\sqrt{2}$ **2.** $9\sqrt{5}$ **3.** $15\sqrt{3}$
4. $12\sqrt{6}$ **5.** $6\sqrt{2}$ **6.** 0
7. $4\sqrt{3}$ **8.** $-2\sqrt{7}$
9. $4\sqrt{5} + 3\sqrt{2}$ **10.** $12\sqrt{x}\ (x \geq 0)$
11. $8\sqrt{y}\ (y \geq 0)$ **12.** $6\sqrt{2}$
13. $8\sqrt{3}$ **14.** $3\sqrt{5}$ **15.** $\sqrt{2}$
16. $-\sqrt{3}$ **17.** 0 **18.** $19\sqrt{3}$
19. $5\sqrt{2}$ **20.** $\sqrt{2} + \sqrt{3}$ **21.** 0
22. $23\sqrt{2}$ **23.** $-4\sqrt{2}$
24. $3\sqrt{7a}\ (a \geq 0)$ **25.** $14\sqrt{x}\ (x \geq 0)$
26. $5\sqrt{b}\ (b \geq 0)$ **27.** $\sqrt{3x}\ (x \geq 0)$
28. $3a\sqrt{3}\ (a \geq 0)$
29. *a.* $10\sqrt{2}$ *b.* $8\sqrt{3}$ *c.* $24\sqrt{3}$
30. *a.* $\sqrt{2}$ *b.* $3\sqrt{3}$ *c.* 0
31. (1) **32.** (4) **33.** (4)
34. *a.* $12\sqrt{5}$ *b.* 26.8 **35.** *a.* $10\sqrt{3}$ *b.* 17.3

19-11 Multiplying Square-Root Radicals: *pages 663–664*

1. 3 **2.** 7 **3.** $a\ (a \geq 0)$
4. $2x\ (x \geq 0)$ **5.** 6 **6.** 72
7. $2\sqrt{7}$ **8.** $10\sqrt{3}$ **9.** $9\sqrt{2}$
10. $70\sqrt{6}$ **11.** $36\sqrt{2}$ **12.** $10\sqrt{10}$
13. $-12a$ **14.** $3y$ **15.** 2
16. y **17.** t **18.** 54
19. $10x$ **20.** $9a$ **21.** $3x\sqrt{5}$
22. $3a\sqrt{b}$ **23.** $5x$ **24.** $4t$
25. *a.* 120 *b.* rational
26. *a.* 48 *b.* rational
27. *a.* $108\sqrt{2}$ *b.* irrational
28. *a.* $20\sqrt{2}$ *b.* irrational
29. *a.* $\frac{20}{9}$ *b.* rational
30. *a.* 1 *b.* rational
31. 2 **32.** 12 **33.** 72 **34.** 75
35. *a.* $2\sqrt{6}$ *b.* 4.9 **36.** *a.* 12

19-12 Dividing Square-Root Radicals: *pages 665–666*

1. 6 **2.** 5 **3.** $\sqrt{7}$ **4.** $\sqrt{7}$
5. 16 **6.** $2\sqrt{3}$ **7.** $5\sqrt{2}$ **8.** $42\sqrt{2}$
9. 3 **10.** $\frac{7}{3}$ **11.** $\frac{1}{4}$ **12.** 3
13. 8 **14.** 25 **15.** $10\sqrt{3}$ **16.** $\frac{3}{2}\sqrt{2}$

17. irrational   18. rational   19. irrational
20. irrational   21. rational   22. irrational

23. $\frac{6}{7}$ 24. $\frac{\sqrt{3}}{2}$ 25. $\sqrt{5}$

26. $\frac{2\sqrt{2}}{7}$ 27. $4\sqrt{2}$ 28. 1

29. *a.* $\frac{2}{5}$ *b.* $\frac{3}{5}$ *c.* $\frac{1}{5}$ *d.* 0   *e.* $\frac{2}{5}$ *f.* 1

19-13   The Geometry of the Circle: *pages 669–671*

1. *a.* 4 in.   *b.* 26 ft.   *c.* $4\frac{1}{4}$ in.   *d.* .7 m   *e.* 5.5 cm
2. *a.* 2 ft.   *b.* $3\frac{1}{2}$ in.   *c.* $1\frac{3}{4}$ in.   *d.* .7 m   *e.* 1.95 cm
3. 1:2   4. 2:1
5. *a.* 10π *b.* 16π *c.* 4.7π *d.* $\frac{1}{3}\pi$ *e.* $.08\pi$ *f.* $\frac{11}{8}\pi$
6. *a.* 8π *b.* 18π *c.* 7.6π *d.* $\frac{2}{5}\pi$ *e.* $.12\pi$ *f.* $\frac{7}{2}\pi$
7. *a.* 10π cm   *b.* 9π ft.   *c.* 4.8π mm   *d.* $\frac{1}{3}\pi$ in.
8. *a.* 50.24 cm   *b.* 25.12 in.   *c.* 15.7 mm   *d.* 10.99 in.
9. *a.* 88 cm   *b.* 22 ft.   *c.* 22 mm   *d.* 33 in.
10. 88 in.   11. 13.2 m
12. *a.* 30   *b.* 15   13. *a.* 25   *b.* 12.5
14. *a.* 1   *b.* $\frac{1}{2}$ 15. *a.* 4.2   *b.* 2.1
16. *a.* $\frac{1}{3}$ *b.* $\frac{1}{6}$
17. 140 yd.   18. (3)   19. (3)   20. (1)
21. (2)   22. (3)   23. doubled   24. 4
25. divided by 2   26. 5π 27. $r = \frac{C}{2\pi}$
28. $d = \frac{C}{\pi}$ 29. $\pi = \frac{C}{d}$

19-14   Area and Volume Related to the Circle: *pages 675–677*

1. *a.* 16π *b.* 81π *c.* $.64\pi$ *d.* $.09\pi$ *e.* $\frac{1}{9}\pi$ *f.* $\frac{9}{4}\pi$
2. *a.* 36π *b.* π *c.* 1.44π *d.* $.04\pi$ *e.* $\frac{1}{25}\pi$ *f.* $\frac{25}{16}\pi$
3. *a.* 64π sq. in.   *b.* 81π cm^2 *c.* $\frac{1}{16}\pi$ sq. in.   *d.* $.09\pi$ m^2 *e.* 2.25π m^2 *f.* $\frac{4}{9}\pi$
4. *a.* 314 cm^2 *b.* 314 sq. ft.   *c.* .50 mm^2 *d.* 7.07 sq. in.   *e.* .03 m^2 *f.* 1.77 cm^2
5. *a.* 154 sq. ft.   *b.* 15,400 mm^2 *c.* 1,386 cm^2 *d.* 38.5 sq. in.   *e.* .786 sq. in. or $\frac{11}{14}$ sq. in.   *f.* 1.77 mm^2
6. *a.* 4,410π cu. in.   *b.* 13,860 cu. in.
7. *a.* 588π cu. ft.   *b.* 1,848 cu. ft.
8. *a.* 420π cm^3 *b.* 1,320 cm^3
9. *a.* 11.76π m^3 *b.* 36.96 m^3
10. *a.* 400π cu. in.   *b.* 1,256 cu. in.
11. *a.* 4π cu. ft.   *b.* 12.56 cu. ft.

12. *a.* π mm^3 *b.* 3.14 mm^3
13. *a.* $.032\pi$ cm^3 *b.* 0.10048 cm^3
14. *a.* $\frac{4,000}{3}\pi$ or $1333.\overline{3}\pi$ *b.* 4,186.67 (nearest hundredth)
15. *a.* $\frac{343}{6}\pi$ or $57.1\overline{6}\pi$ *b.* 179.67 (nearest hundredth)
16. *a.* 4   *b.* 9   *c.* 15   *d.* $\frac{1}{8}$ *e.* 1.4
17. *a.* 10   *b.* 20   *c.* 20π
18. *a.* 16   *b.* 8   *c.* 64π
19. *a.* 12.25π m^2 *b.* 38.5 m^2
20. 254.34 sq. in.   21. 11,880 gal.
22. *a.* multiplied by 9   *b.* multiplied by 3
23. (3)   24. (3)   25. (2)   26. (4)
27. (4)   28. (3)   29. (4)   30. (1)   31. (3)
32. *a.* 12   *b.* 6   *c.* 144   *d.* 36π *e.* $144 - 36\pi$
33. *a.* 5   *b.* 10π *c.* 28   *d.* 25π *e.* 48   *f.* $25\pi - 48$
34. *a.* girl; each boy's share was $\frac{16\pi}{2} = 8\pi$ while each girl's share was $\frac{36\pi}{4} = 9\pi$
    b. \$1.60
    c. \$1.35
    d. 12-inch pizza, since it is more pie for less money

19-15   Review Exercises: *pages 678–679*

1. *a.* rational   *b.* rational   *c.* irrational   *d.* rational   *e.* rational   *f.* irrational   *g.* irrational   *h.* irrational
2. *a.* $-r$ *b.* $\frac{1}{r}$
3. $\frac{3}{5}$ 4. -7 5. -3
6. ± 1.1 7. ± 9 8. $\pm .3$
9. ± 10 10. ± 12 11. 6.5
12. $20x$ 13. $2y^2$ 14. c^5d
15. $.1m^8$ 16. $6\sqrt{5}$ 17. $9\sqrt{2}$
18. $\sqrt{7}$ 19. $4\sqrt{3b}$ 20. $\sqrt{2}$
21. 0   22. $6\sqrt{2}$ 23. $-\sqrt{3}$
24. 32   25. 45   26. $14\sqrt{10}$
27. 7   28. $8\sqrt{3}$ 29. 1
30. (3)   31. (2)
32. *a.* $\overline{OF}, \overline{OG}, \overline{OH}$ *b.* $\overline{FG}$ *c.* $\overline{FG}, \overline{GH}$
33. 14   34. 225π 35. 28.26 sq. in.
36. *a.* 40π *b.* 400π *c.* $1,600 - 400\pi$
37. *a.* 4   *b.* $h = \frac{V}{\pi r^2}$ *c.* V is multiplied by 4
38. (2)   39. (1)
40. $\frac{3}{4}\pi (6)^2 = 27\pi$ or 84.8 sq. ft.

Chapter 20   Quadratic Equations

20-1   The Standard Form of a Quadratic Equation: *page 681*

1. $x^2 + 9x - 10 = 0$ **2.** $2x^2 + 4x = 0$
3. $x^2 - 3x + 8 = 0$ **4.** $x^2 - 4x - 3 = 0$
5. $3x^2 - 27x = 0$ **6.** $x^2 - 3x - 10 = 0$
7. $x^2 - 5x - 20 = 0$ **8.** $\dfrac{x^2}{2} - \dfrac{x}{4} + 3 = 0$

9. $x^2 + \dfrac{x}{2} - 6 = 0$

20-2   Using Factoring to Solve a Quadratic Equation: *pages 684–685*

1. $x = 2$ or $x = 1$ **2.** $x = 4$ or $x = 1$
3. $x = 4$ or $x = 4$ **4.** $r = 7$ or $r = 5$
5. $c = -5$ or $c = -1$ **6.** $m = -9$ or $m = -1$
7. $x = -1$ or $x = -1$ **8.** $y = -8$ or $y = -3$
9. $x = 5$ or $x = -1$ **10.** $x = 6$ or $x = -1$
11. $x = -3$ or $x = 2$ **12.** $x = -5$ or $x = 3$
13. $r = 9$ or $r = -8$ **14.** $x = 4$ or $x = -3$
15. $x = 7$ or $x = -7$ **16.** $z = 2$ or $z = -2$
17. $m = 8$ or $m = -8$ **18.** $x = 2$ or $x = -2$
19. $d = 2$ or $d = 0$ **20.** $s = 1$ or $s = 0$
21. $x = -3$ or $x = 0$ **22.** $z = -8$ or $z = 0$
23. $x = 2$ or $x = \frac{1}{2}$ **24.** $x = 3$ or $x = \frac{1}{3}$
25. $x = 2$ or $x = \frac{2}{3}$ **26.** $x = -2$ or $x = -\frac{1}{5}$
27. $x = 3$ or $x = -2$ **28.** $y = 7$ or $y = -4$
29. $c = 5$ or $c = 3$ **30.** $m = -\frac{3}{2}$ or $m = -2$
31. $r = 2$ or $r = -2$ **32.** $x = 11$ or $x = -11$
33. $y = 6$ or $y = 0$ **34.** $s = -4$ or $s = 0$
35. $y = 10$ or $y = -2$ **36.** $x = -\frac{5}{2}$ or $x = 3$
37. $x = 5$ or $x = 4$ **38.** $x = 6$ or $x = -5$
39. $x = -9$ or $x = 6$ **40.** $x = -\frac{1}{2}$ or $x = -2$
41. $x = -3$ or $x = -1$ **42.** $x = -\frac{2}{3}$ or $x = 3$
43. $x = 7$ or $x = -5$ **44.** $y = 4$ or $y = -1$
45. $x = 5$ or $x = -8$ **46.** $x = 4$ or $x = -6$
47. $y = 3$ or $y = -6$ **48.** $x = 6$ or $x = -6$
49. 12 cm   **50.** 12

20-3   Solving Incomplete Quadratic Equations: *pages 687–688*

1. $x = \pm 2$ **2.** $a = \pm 6$ **3.** $x = \pm 10$
4. $y = \pm 3$ **5.** $k = \pm 7$ **6.** $x = \pm 2$
7. $r = \pm 9$ **8.** $x = \pm 2$ **9.** $x = \pm 5$
10. $x = \pm 3$ **11.** $x = \pm 7$ **12.** $y = \pm 3$
13. $y = \pm 6$ **14.** $x = \pm 6$ **15.** $x = \pm 5$
16. $x = \pm\sqrt{10}$ **17.** $x = \pm 3\sqrt{3}$ **18.** $x = \pm\sqrt{2}$
19. $x = \pm 2\sqrt{2}$ **20.** $x = \pm 5\sqrt{3}$ **21.** $x = \pm 2\sqrt{2}$
22. $x = \pm 3\sqrt{3}$ **23.** $x = \pm\sqrt{61}$ **24.** $x = \pm 3\sqrt{3}$
25. $x = 4.9$ **26.** $x = 6.3$ **27.** $x = 5.7$

28. $x = \pm b$ **29.** $x = \pm 5a$ **30.** $x = \pm\dfrac{r}{3}$

31. $x = \pm\dfrac{a}{2}$ **32.** $x = \pm\sqrt{c^2 - a^2}$ ($|c| \geq |a|$)

33. $x = \pm\sqrt{c^2 - b^2}$ ($|c| \geq |b|$)
34. $s = \pm\sqrt{A}$ ($A \geq 0$)

35. $r = \pm\sqrt{\dfrac{A}{\pi}}$ ($A \geq 0$)

36. $r = \pm\sqrt{\dfrac{S}{4\pi}}$ or $\pm\dfrac{1}{2}\sqrt{\dfrac{S}{\pi}}$ ($S \geq 0$)

37. $r = \pm\sqrt{\dfrac{V}{\pi h}}$ ($V \geq 0, h > 0$)

38. $t = \pm\sqrt{\dfrac{2s}{g}}$ $\left(\dfrac{s}{g} \geq 0\right)$

39. $v = \pm\sqrt{\dfrac{Fgr}{m}}$ $\left(\dfrac{Fgr}{m} \geq 0\right)$

40. 24 sq. ft.   **41.** 6 m by 18 m
42. $2\sqrt{10}$ in.

20-4   The Quadratic Formula: *page 691*

1. $x = 1$ or $x = 6$ **2.** $x = 1$ or $x = -5$
3. $x = -1$ or $x = -2$ **4.** $x = \frac{1}{2}$ or $x = -1$
5. $x = \frac{1}{3}$ or $x = -2$ **6.** $x = -\frac{2}{3}$ or $x = -1$
7. $x = -3$ **8.** $x = \frac{1}{2}$
9. $x = -5$ **10.** $x = -4$ or $x = 3$
11. $x = -6$ or $x = 4$ **12.** $x = -1$ or $x = 2$
13. $x = 2$ or $x = 4$ **14.** $x = \frac{5}{2}$ or $x = -2$
15. $x = \pm 3$ **16.** $x = \pm 2$
17. $x = 0$ or $x = 3$ **18.** $x = 0$ or $x = 5$
19. $x = 1 \pm \sqrt{3}$ **20.** $x = 5 \pm \sqrt{21}$
21. $x = -1 \pm \sqrt{5}$ **22.** $x = 2 \pm \sqrt{6}$

23. $x = \dfrac{4 \pm \sqrt{2}}{2}$ **24.** $x = \dfrac{1 \pm \sqrt{5}}{4}$

25. $x = \dfrac{2 \pm \sqrt{3}}{3}$ **26.** $x = \pm 2\sqrt{5}$

27. $x = \pm\sqrt{\dfrac{5}{2}}$

20-5   Using the Theorem of Pythagoras: *pages 695–697*

1. $c = 5$ **2.** $c = 17$ **3.** $b = 8$
4. $b = 5$ **5.** $a = 8$ **6.** $a = 15$
7. $c = 2$ **8.** $c = 8$ **9.** $b = 5$
10. a. $c = \sqrt{13}$ b. $c = 3.6$
11. a. $c = 3\sqrt{2}$ b. $c = 4.2$
12. a. $b = 4\sqrt{3}$ b. $b = 6.9$

13. *a.* $c = 5\sqrt{2}$ *b.* $c = 7.1$
14. *a.* $a = 2\sqrt{3}$ *b.* $a = 3.5$
15. *a.* $b = 4\sqrt{2}$ *b.* $b = 5.7$
16. $x = 4\sqrt{2}$ **17.** $x = 3\sqrt{3}$ **18.** $x = 4\sqrt{3}$
19. $x = 2\sqrt{2}$ **20.** 36 ft.   **21.** 15.8 ft.
22. 26 km   **23.** 40 yd.   **24.** 17 in.
25. 25 cm   **26.** 26 ft.   **27.** 50 m
28. *a.* 5 cm   *b.* 60 cm^2
29. 240   **30.** 17 in.   **31.** 2.8 m
32. 5.7 m   **33.** 7.1 m   **34.** 8.5 m
35. 9.9 m   **36.** 127.3 ft.
37. *a.* 24 cm   *b.* 240 cm^2
38. *a.* 40 in.   *b.* 300 sq. in.
39. $2\sqrt{3}$ cm   **40.** $3\sqrt{3}$ cm   **41.** $4\sqrt{3}$ cm
42. $5\sqrt{3}$ cm   **43.** $\dfrac{5\sqrt{3}}{2}$ cm or $\frac{5}{2}\sqrt{3}$ cm
44. *a.* graph   *b.* $AB = 4, BC = 4, AC = 4\sqrt{2}$
   c. 8
45. $d^2 = s^2 + s^2$
   $d^2 = 2s^2$
   $d = \sqrt{2} \cdot \sqrt{s^2}$
   $d = s\sqrt{2}$
46. yes   **47.** no   **48.** yes   **49.** no

20-6 Using Quadratic Equations to Solve Problems

Number Problems: *pages 698–699*

1. 4   **2.** 12   **3.** 5 or -6
4. 9 or -8 **5.** 5   **6.** 4
7. 5 or -3 **8.** 20, 30   **9.** 11, 6
10. 7, 2 or $-2, -7$ **11.** 4, -2 or 2, -4
12. 5, -2 or 2, -5 **13.** 7, 8 or $-8, -7$
14. 9, 11 or $-11, -9$ **15.** 6, 7
16. 7, 8   **17.** 3, 4, 5   **18.** 9, 11, 13
19. 5, 6 or $-6, -5$ **20.** 7
21. 5 or $-\frac{1}{2}$ **22.** 4, 6   **23.** 2 or $\frac{1}{2}$
24. 3   **25.** 6 or -7

Geometric Problems: *pages 700–702*

1. 6 cm by 12 cm   **2.** 30 cm, 40 cm
3. 6 m by 10 m   **4.** 16 cm, 5 cm
5. 8 in. by 2 in.   **6.** 6 cm
7. 5 m by 15 m   **8.** 3 ft.
9. 2 m   **10.** 10 cm, 5 cm
11. 12 cm, 7 cm
12. 66.8 ft. (to the nearest tenth)
13. 3 cm, 4 cm   **14.** 5 m, 12 m
15. 6 cm, 8 cm, 10 cm
16. *a.* 15 cm, 20 cm   *b.* 150 cm^2
17. *a.* (a) legs are 6 cm, 8 cm
       (b) area = 24 cm^2
   b. (a) legs are 12 cm, 16 cm
       (b) area = 96 cm^2
   c. (a) legs are 15 cm, 20 cm
       (b) area = 150 cm^2
   d. (a) legs are 60 cm, 80 cm
       (b) area = 2400 cm^2
18. *a.* legs are 5 cm 12 cm   *b.* area = 30 cm^2
19. 2 hr.

20-7 Graphing $y = ax^2 + bx + c$: *pages 703–704*

1–20. graphs

20-8 Review Exercises: *pages 704–705*

1. $x = 9$ or $x = 2$ **2.** $y = 6$ or $y = -6$
3. $x = 5$ or $x = -3$ **4.** $k = 0$ or $k = -2\frac{1}{2}$
5. $w = 2$ or $w = -9$ **6.** $t = 4$ or $t = -3$
7. $m = 2$ **8.** $x = \pm 3\sqrt{2}$
9. $c = 13$ **10.** $a = 9$
11. $c = 6$ **12.** $\sqrt{40}$ or $2\sqrt{10}$
13. 30
14. *a.* 8   *b.* 4   *c.* 11   *d.* 6   *e.* 38
15. 6   **16.** 5 and 14
17. 6 and 7   **18.** graph
19. 8 ft. by 17 ft.   **20.** $x = 1 \pm \sqrt{3}$